KT-153-353

Three Great War Stories

In the same series

THREE GREAT ANIMAL STORIES

Return to the Wild
The New Noah
Sauce for the Mongoose

THREE GREAT ESCAPE STORIES

The Wooden Horse
Escape Alone
Return Ticket

THREE GREAT SEA STORIES

Malta Convoy
Tinkerbelle
Unbroken

THREE GREAT ADVENTURE STORIES

One More River
Airline Detective
The Tartan Pimpernell

THREE GREAT AIR STORIES

Reach for the Sky
Skymen
The Man in the Hot Seat

THREE GREAT PONY STORIES

The Midnight Horse
They Bought her a Pony
Ponies for Hire

THREE GREAT ROMANTIC STORIES

Bride of Pendorric
The Heir of Garlands
Home at Sundown

THREE GREAT WESTERNS

North Against the Sioux
The Longhorn Trail
Custer's Gold

Three Great War Stories

The Tunnel

The Man Who Saved London

Carve Her Name with Pride

Illustrated

Collins
St James's Place
London

Three Great War Stories was first published 1967
Second Impression 1969
Third Impression 1971

The Tunnel was first published 1957
A junior edition was first published 1959

The Man Who Saved London was first published 1960 under the title of *Agent Extraordinary*

A junior edition was first published 1964

Carve Her Name with Pride was first published 1956
A junior edition was first published 1964

ISBN 0 00 192326 9

Reprinted 1972
Reprinted 1973
Printed in Great Britain
Collins Clear-Type Press
London and Glasgow

Contents

The Tunnel

by

ERIC WILLIAMS

TO MY WIFE

Contents

PART ONE

CHAPTER I

AT LARGE IN GERMANY

PETER HOWARD lay quietly in the thick undergrowth of the German forest and listened to the aircraft engines droning away into the darkness overhead. Still slightly dazed by his fall, he was conscious only of the silence, the resinous smell of pine trees, and that he was somehow safe from the flame and noise that had filled the last twenty minutes.

At length, with great effort, he raised his head. Everything on the ground was silent, but he realised that before long the woods would echo with the shouts of German soldiers searching for the airmen, whose parachutes they must have seen descending from the blazing aircraft. Searchlights had held him until the last minute, isolating the white swinging parachute, blinding him and indicating his path of descent.

Rising unsteadily to his feet he pressed the quick-release fastener of the parachute harness, which fell clear of his legs. He tore open the front of his inflated Mae West and struggled free. Looking round him in the wood for somewhere to hide the parachute he saw a thick clump of undergrowth and, gathering the billowing silk in his arms, he quickly stuffed it beneath the brambles. On top of the white silk he put his Mae West and the heavy padded harness, covering them with the loose moss that grew like a carpet on the forest floor. He worked fast, stopping only to listen for the sound of movement in the wood. Drops of sweat gathered in his hair and ran down his nose as he worked, although it was December and the night was cold. His limbs were trembling, and he panted with the urgency of his movements. The Germans would soon be here, and he must get away.

He looked up at the sky. Checking himself by Polaris, as he had done so often in the air, he started off at a steady walk through the forest, keeping the North Star on his right hand and walking as silently as his heavy flying boots would allow. Soon he came to a narrow path and, turning south, he continued down this until he reached a wide grass fire-lane which ran straight as a ruled line through the quiet woods.

He stopped at the junction, afraid to take to the open but aware that he would walk more easily on the soft grass of the ride. The silence was unnerving. It reminded him of when, as a boy, he had climbed into the local park to poach pheasant. Then, too, it had been the silence that had frightened him—the silence that had been so essential to his purpose and yet had been so much his enemy. Silence that could so easily be broken by a careless foot and which, when so broken, would fly to pieces at the angry shout and trampling footsteps of the gamekeeper. Now, in Germany, it seemed to him that the whole forest was waiting for him to move, listening for the noise made by his feet in their clumsy flying boots.

At first, remembering only the fire and the need to hide his parachute and get away, he had acted without deliberation; but now he began to plan ahead, to wonder where he would go from here. He knew that somewhere round him in the forest the rest of his crew would be hiding their parachutes and making their plans to evade capture. He thought for a moment of trying to find them but, still impelled by the urgent desire to get away, he came out into the open and started to jogtrot down the ride. Apart from a few bruises he was unhurt and he felt certain that given a fair chance he could reach Holland. He had obtained a "fix" just before they were attacked and he knew that he had landed somewhere north of Osnabrück—say, forty or fifty miles from the Dutch border. Once in Holland he might get food and clothes and perhaps money from a friendly farmer. The fire-lane would lead him in the right direction and would get him quickly away from the spot where he had fallen.

As he jogged along he felt, inside him, a slight loosening of the tightness, the stiffness that had seized his limbs when first the cannon shells had torn through the fuselage and the red tongues of fire had filled the blacked-out cabin with their hungry glow. He remembered the petrol saved for Christmas, and that this was to have been the last trip over Germany before his leave. It was an easy target, a " piece of cake "—and they had to go and get shot down by a nightfighter. Yet he could not help feeling glad that he was out of it, out of the swaying aircraft and the sick fear of the searchlights and the flak.

To-night, he felt, they'd had bad luck from the start.

On the way out over the North Sea they'd had trouble with one of the engines. The oil pressure had been reading low and the engineer, nervous, had advised them to turn back. Then the oil had regained its normal pressure and they had carried on. They had been hit by flak over the French coast on the way in; not badly, but enough to frighten them and make the inferno above the target look angrier than it usually did. That was the worst part of any bombing trip, he thought, the waiting for the target to grow near. That last half-hour, with the target in full view all the time, the cones of searchlights and the wicked, beautiful display of flak winking and flashing and changing colour, with the tracer floating up slowly like sparks from a garden fire.

They had flown into it this time, right into it. And they had flown out of it again with one engine on fire, skimming the tops of the houses as they came, nearly out of control, but clear; clear and miraculously unwounded. Once away from the bump and growl of flak and the probing beams of searchlights the pilot had extinguished the burning engine, decided to make for base at a thousand feet; and they had settled down for the long cold trip home. They had been congratulating themselves on getting out safely when the night-fighter came in to attack.

Peter did not remember much of what had happened after the rear-gunner had given the warning. The pilot, handicapped by the dead engine, had done all he knew to lose the fighter.

Peter could hear his heavy breathing over the intercomm as he threw the sluggish bomber about the sky. He heard the rear-gunner giving directions to the pilot, who was doing everything he could to avoid the fighter and yet maintain his height. Several times they thought they had given him the slip, only to hear the rear-gunner say, " He's coming in again, skipper, he's coming in from the port quarter ! Turn to port . . . Now . . . *Dive !* " And they heard the sudden clatter of his guns as he fired a long burst at the fighter breaking away.

For the navigator, the engineer and the wireless operator, the whole fight had been in the heavy breathing of the pilot, the voice of the rear-gunner and the clatter of his guns ; in the sudden lurching of the aircraft. Sitting in the blacked-out cabin they could see nothing. The rear-gunner in his turret could see the red-hot exhaust cowling of the attacking fighter, while the pilot and the front-gunner could see the long, graceful trajectory of his tracer bullets as they sped past and over their heads. But for the three men sitting in the half-light of their cabin, the fight had come mainly through their earphones. Whenever they heard the excited voice of the rear-gunner and the clatter of his guns the wireless operator raised his fist, thumb extended upwards, and thrust out his lower lip in a gesture of supreme confidence. " Good old Mac," he seemed to be saying, " we're O.K. now —that's fixed the blighter." And Peter, huddled over his chart-table, grinned back and nodded his head.

The fighter had made several attacks and at last driven them, jinking wildly, to within a few hundred feet of the ground. A burst of machine-gun bullets, raking them from nose to tail, had set them on fire and torn great holes in the perspex cockpit cover. Inside the aircraft it had been light as day, and reeking of cordite from their own machine-guns. Everything was light and noise and the sickening smell of burnt cordite.

The pilot, realising that it was impossible to save the aircraft, had given the order to bale out.

Peter remembered taking the pilot's parachute from its rack and placing it on the seat beside him, knowing as he did it the futility of his action. The pilot, acknowledging it, had raised a hand in salute and returned to his task of holding the aircraft steady while the rest of the crew baled out.

When Peter reached the escape hatch it was open, the wind tearing and howling and blowing away the smoke from the burning wing. He found his own parachute and clipped it on to the harness at his chest. With the fuselage burning fiercely behind him and the earth a few hundred feet below, he thrust his legs through the escape hatch and was dragged out by the force of the slipstream. He must have pulled the ripcord, he did not remember doing so, because the parachute opened with a stinging crack. Something hit him on the side of the head, something kicked him between the legs, and he found himself hanging uncomfortably, swinging sickeningly from side to side.

Gradually the pendulum movement had lessened, and he was able to look around him. Away in the distance he could see several more white parachutes floating slowly down. He had tried to count them, hoping that all the crew were there, but he could not concentrate. He was turning now, twisting at the end of the shroud lines, and the discomfort of the harness between his legs was becoming a pain.

Now, on foot in the forest, he tried to shut the memory of those last few minutes from his mind. To forget the flames, the noise and the fear. To lose the vision of his pilot quietly holding the aircraft in the air while the rest of the crew leaped to safety. Wally was now probably lying dead in the charred wreckage of his aircraft. The others, if they had landed safely, were somewhere round him in the forest. He regretted that he had not tried to make contact with them, but consoled himself with the thought that, alone, he would stand a better chance of hiding up.

After running and walking for several miles he came to a place where the earth road which he was now following crossed a narrow winding stream. Ahead and to his left, reflecting the moonlight, he could see a pond encircled by tall rushes and beyond this the vague outlines of a farm.

He climbed down beside the simple wooden bridge and drank from the stream, feeling the earth bank damp beneath his knees. The water, black as ink in the darkness, was soft and tasted brackish, and Peter remembered the water-purifying tablets in the escape tin in his battledress pocket. The tin box was difficult to open and he swore softly as he wrestled with the lid. He had taken a similar tin over Germany for so long that he had almost forgotten its purpose, and had collected it automatically with his navigation chart and radio instructions. He thought of Pop Dawson, the Intelligence Officer, and his vague lectures on evasion. He would have liked Pop to be with him now. He had been very good on what to do if you came down in France or Belgium, but Peter could not remember him saying very much about coming down in Germany. He himself had never thought about being shot down and getting out unhurt. Death was the ever-present possibility but the other, the half-way house of being at large or in a prison camp in Germany, he had never really considered.

At last he got the escape kit open and examined its contents: a water-bottle of thin rubber, shaped like an old-fashioned purse; a bar of chocolate, stale and already covered with whitish powder; a small brass compass; a book of matches; Horlicks tablets and some cakes of concentrated food. Incongruously among this workmanlike assortment was a packet of chewing-gum. He unwrapped the water-bottle, filled it from the stream and added two of the purifying tablets. He tied the string tightly round the nect of the bottle, fastened it to his belt and climbed back on to the earthen road.

The farm when he passed it was quiet; not even a dog barked, and Peter imagined the farmer and his family sleeping again after the bombers had gone. He walked carefully past the out-buildings, round several fields of ploughed sandy soil, and once more into the forest which stretched ahead.

He was almost enjoying himself now, his first panic resolving into a firm determination to avoid capture—to get back, somehow, to England. It was good to walk alone in the forest, alone with a single clearly defined objective. A quiet, slow, lonely campaign after the noise, urgency and clamour of the last few months. He began to walk more slowly, savouring the silence of the woods.

Another wave of bombers droned their way towards England, thousands of feet above his head. He looked up, but they were too high for him to see. His young brother Roy had been flying to-night. How strange if it should be he who flew, like a homing pigeon, so far above. He imagined the crew immobile at their stations. Soon they would be crossing the Dutch coast. They would lose height over the North Sea, and as they drank the last of their coffee, would make the jokes that are always made as a bomber nears its base. Family jokes, no longer funny, but made because they expressed the solidarity of the family. His own crew had acquired that solidarity flying for hours through the darkness of the sky. Seven men enclosed in a shell of battering roaring noise, invisible to each other but joined into intimacy by the microphones of the intercomm.

He imagined the front-gunner slowly rotating his turret as he quarters the sky for enemy aircraft. Alone in the clouds, alone with his guns and the stars and the queer thoughts that enter a man's head thousands of feet above the earth. It is cold in the turret. The gunner is unable to see the bulk of the aircraft behind him. Only when he listens for it is he conscious of the sound of the engines. Suddenly there is a click in his earphones, and softly and casually, as though the man's hand were resting on his shoulder, he hears the voice of the rear-gunner talking to the navigator. Above the roar and batter of sound in the lonely turret he hears the voice as though it were his own inner self speaking, more intimate even than his own voice which, if he were to speak outside the microphone, would vanish with the whistle of the wind. The voice, disembodied, speaks softly in his ear. It says, " Where are we, Joe—astronomically speaking I mean ? " and the crew laugh. And then the pilot's voice, " Shut up, rear-gunner, we're not clear yet. Get back to your job." And the rear-gunner's reply, " O.K., skipper—just waking up the navigator." And the earphones click again, and all is silent.

The crew in the aircraft overhead would be thinking of the flarepath and boundary lights of their own aerodrome, and all the well-worn routine of the homing bomber. The final circuit before landing. The friendly W.A.A.F. driver on the dispersal truck. The sleepy ground staff waiting to bed the aircraft down for the rest of the night. Then the interrogation, and eggs and bacon in the mess.

Whatever they were thinking they were going home; while he was alone in the middle of a pine forest in Germany, slow and earthbound, ill-equipped for a journey that would last at best for several days.

The forest appeared to be endless. During the past few hours he had crossed several roads, lying for minutes listening before daring to cross; but always the forest lay ahead, silent, vast and uninhabited.

He was feeling tired now, and the heavy fleece-lined flying boots were chafing his heels. He had formed some sort of plan for the journey westward and had decided on a twenty-mile walk every night, with a good rest during the day. He must walk only at night. He remembered Pop Dawson at the end of one of his lectures: "I can't tell you much about Germany—except that you won't get help there. Walk by night and lie up somewhere during the day. Try to reach an occupied country as quickly as you can."

Until now Germany had existed for Peter only as an area on the map, its towns targets and its rivers navigational aids. It had been a vast sea of blackness to be crossed as secretly as possible, a sea patrolled by night-fighters and erupting sudden bursts of flak and blinding violet light. He had known there were towns and cities there, women and children, villages and farms. But to the bomber crew Germany was primarily a chart, their target a pinpoint to be found and bombed impersonally as one would bomb a target on the bombing range at home.

He kept going until morning, walking and running alternately and making long detours across farmland to circumvent villages. At first, in the wooded country, the soil had been dry and sandy, but later he came to a more open plain, flatter and with much water. The villages were larger and more spread out, and it took longer to get round them. Once he took the risk of following

the road over a level-crossing. As he ducked under the second bar he heard a voice shouting at him from a signal box which stood at the side of the track. The German words came unexpectedly out of the night, and in his panic he could not remember a word of the language. He hurried on without speaking and, once out of sight of the railway, ran for nearly a mile in his panic to get away.

When he could run and walk no longer he settled down under some bushes on the bank of a stream, to lie up until the next evening. It was not an ideal hiding-place but dawn had come suddenly. The eastern sky was already pale, and he was afraid he would not find a better place before full daylight.

At first he had been able to sleep, his head on the warm collar of his sheepskin flying jacket. Later, wakened by the cold, he had been unable to keep his legs warm. It was damp under the bushes, a dampness that seemed to strike upwards through his battledress trousers and eat into his hip-bone as he lay on his side on the sloping ground. He took off the short Irvin jacket and lay on this, cold everywhere now but protected from the damp. By his watch it was nine-thirty, the day was grey and overcast, and he wondered how he would spend the hours until darkness.

His hiding-place, concealed from the road by the thick bushes, seemed quiet enough, but he decided that the next day would be spent well away from the road. He would light a fire and boil some water. He lay for some time thinking of hot water; in bottles, in baths, in a central heating plant. No man could live without a fire, he decided. It would have to be a thick wood, well away from the road, and a fire made of dry twigs so that there should be no smoke.

At lunchtime he ate one of the cakes of concentrated food, and sucked two of the Horlicks tablets. He refilled the water-bottle from the stream and again disinfected the water. He spent the next half-hour in removing the flying brevet and flight lieutenant's ranking tapes from his uniform, putting them in his pocket to prove his identity if he were captured.

Once during the afternoon he was nearly discovered by some boys who were playing along the banks of the stream. They were playing soldiers, but he could not make out whether the enemy were the English or the Russians. In his day it had always been the Germans. The leader of the band, a tall fair youth in abbreviated shorts—who, anachronistically, carried a sword although all his followers made the popping noise of tommy-guns or the bang of hand-grenades—had disposed his men, the Germans, among the bushes on Peter's bank of the stream, while the enemy were forced to occupy the bare sloping banks on the other side. At first there was much scouting and manœuvring for position during which Peter, pressed close to the ground in his hiding-place, prayed that they would not find him. Later, when the two armies engaged, he was able, from his vantage point under the bushes, to see most of the action. The troops were throwing clay pellets now and the British—or the Russians—were in full retreat. Half-way up the slope the fair-haired boy caught one of the enemy, a small dark child, and began to belabour him with the sword. At first Peter thought it all part of the game, but the beating was real, and the captured member finally departed for home blubbering, with blood from his nose streaming down the front of his woollen jersey. There was something frightening in the child's crying, a knowledge of persecution deeper than that of English boys, and Peter, crouching in his hiding-place, renewed his determination to stay there until it was fully dark.

As soon as darkness fell he came out of his hiding-place and hobbled up to the road. He was so stiff that he could hardly walk, but he soon got into his stride and set out strongly, glad to be on the move again.

In making a wide detour to avoid the first village he stumbled into some barbed wire and tore his trousers from the thigh to below the knee. His first reaction was one of unreasonable anger, followed quickly by an excess of misery quite out of proportion to the damage done. He hastily tied the corners of the tear together with a piece of string that he found in his pocket, and slogged on once more, seething with a bitter hatred for the German farmer who had filled his ditches with barbed wire.

He stopped later by the bank of another stream, and bathed his feet in the cold water while he laced together the edges of his torn trousers. His feet were blistered now and he had worn a large hole in the heel of each of his socks.

Just before midnight he was surprised on the road by some soldiers and girls on bicycles, but he was able to dive into a ditch without being seen. They sounded happy and warm, laughing and talking as they passed him, and he decided to steal a bicycle as soon as he could. With this in mind he explored the barns and outhouses of the next farm he came to, but he was heard by a dog which began to bark. Fearing discovery he slipped away, and took once more to the road.

As he walked the country became more and more waterlogged, and whenever he had to make a detour round a village he found himself floundering, often waist-deep, in dykes and water-meadows. By now he was plastered from head to foot with mud. His flying boots were filled with water and flapped soggily round his feet.

He tried to travel as nearly due west as he could, but the road was erratic, running straight for miles and then stopping suddenly at a farm where he would be forced to take to the fields and blunder on until he found another road. He did not take to the country more than was necessary because of the waterlogged nature of the ground. Ten minutes on the road were worth hours of crawling in and out of ditches, and he sometimes walked for miles north or south in order to keep to the road.

He hummed to keep his spirits up, and tried to remember what he could of the German language. He had not learned German at school; French and Latin had been considered sufficient. He got as far as "*Gute Nacht*" and rehearsed this in case anyone spoke to him. He was lonely now, and wished that he had met another member of his crew. Even after a day and a night he was lonely, with a nagging feeling that he should declare himself to the Germans—that it was dangerous for him to live and move in the country unrecognised. It was almost as though he needed contact with another human being to prove to himself that he had in fact come out of the aircraft alive.

He did not walk so far to-night. His feet were sore, and his right shoulder and hip were stiff from the fall he had taken on landing. He was hungry, too, with a hunger that was almost a pain. He had abandoned his plans for the fire in the depths of the wood—the flat plain on which he now walked was treeless—

and he settled down for the day in the loft of a barn behind a farmhouse.

The barn was better than the bushes, it was dry. He made himself a bed in the soft clover-scented hay and soon fell asleep. Later in the morning he was awakened by hunger and the sound of a horse and cart in the yard outside the barn. He lay still, listening to the rough German voices, until the cart was driven away and there was no longer any sound of life from the yard outside. It was not until the cart had gone that he realised that he had been lying stiff with fear, and that his knees were fluttering uncontrollably.

As quietly as possible he got to his feet and crept across the half-empty loft towards the square hole in the floor through which he had entered. It was an old barn, the broken wood floor roughly patched with sheets of tin, and it was difficult to move without making a noise. He lay for a time on the dry powdery wood, looking down into the barn below. Everything was quiet. There were two stalls in the barn, one obviously used for the horse, the other as a store, with piles of fodder and a heap of roots. Carefully he climbed down the ladder and searched the barn for oats ; but there was nothing but hay and the roots. They were swedes, yellow and unhealthy-looking. He chose two of the smallest and took them back with him to the loft. When he tried to eat them they were coarse and hot and fibrous, and caused a thirst that made him curse himself for not filling his water-bottle the night before. He felt tempted to forage round the farmyard for water, but he forced himself to stay where he was.

Several times during the day a man wearing khaki breeches and a short black coat came into the barn. To Peter, peering through a hole in the floor, he looked as though he might be a French prisoner of war. Each time the man came to the barn he seemed more French, but Peter resisted the impulse to reveal his presence and waited impatiently for the evening.

As the day passed he began to feel the cold, even in the hay. He searched the barn thoroughly for old clothes but could not find even a sack. He stuffed some of the hay inside his battle-dress blouse, and fell asleep again.

Soon after dark he started on his third night's walk. His feet were badly blistered and his calf muscles had set, so that he had difficulty in walking. His tongue was like leather and he was sick several times—a thin bile that made him feel as though he had a hangover. He drank some water from a ditch by the side of the road, and thought bitterly of the chocolate he had left uneaten in the aircraft.

As he loosened up he walked more easily, but he was light-headed and careless. More than once he passed people on the road, not being quick enough to dive into the ditch before they saw him. Must pull myself together, he thought, mustn't get caught. He ducked his head in a stream and felt refreshed.

This night he walked straight through villages. He was too tired to go round them. I'll rest up on the border, he decided, and stalk the last mile or so. For the present he felt impelled to move forward as fast as he could, his mind already grappling with the problem of crossing into Holland—an unknown country occupied by the Germans, yet holding out some hope of help from a friendly people. He tried to remember what he had been told of this border, whether it was guarded or merely submerged into the giant stronghold of Occupied Europe, but his memory told him nothing. He slogged on, driven westward by the compulsion that had driven him ever since he had landed.

In the early morning he came across some mounds in a field. In the frightening half-light of the lonely plain he thought that they were air-raid shelters, that he had stumbled on to a shadow factory or a barracks. He paused for a time, looking at them, and discovered that they were only potato clamps. He dug some potatoes out with his hands and ate them. They were old and nearly as hard to stomach as the swedes.

In his determination to reach the Dutch border as soon as possible he did not choose a hiding-place until it was too late. Dawn caught him unprepared in a bleak and empty countryside.

All around him, as far as he could see, there was nothing but an unending expanse of flat marshy ground, almost colourless in the early morning twilight. Now and again a patch of water caught the light, reflecting it back, cold and metallic-looking, against the murkiness of the ground. As colour swiftly hardened from the softness of the early dawn a chill wind came from the north-east, ruffling the water in the meadows, pressing the damp serge of his battledress trousers against his legs. He walked on in the ever-increasing light, until he came to a thin hedge which grew at the lip of a wide ditch. He followed this away from the road, and crawled beneath some brambles into the most uncomfortable hide-out he had yet chosen ; damp, cold and only partially hidden from the road.

He slept fitfully for about an hour-and-a-half and then, wakened as usual by the cold, he lay shivering and muttering to himself. He tried to control the violent trembling of his limbs, but it was beyond control. It came in spasms like an ague, racking him from head to foot until his limbs ached with the violence of his shivering. He wriggled his body round inside his vest, rubbing his skin against the rough wool, hoping to create some warmth from the friction. He was not hungry now. His stomach was empty, aching high up behind the diaphragm, but the thought of food made him feel sick.

He lay there until early afternoon, never fully unconscious but numb and deadened by the cold and lack of sleep. At last he could stand it no longer. He had to move. Crawling out from under the bushes he limped towards a covert that he could see on the other side of some fields. Once in the wood he felt, he would be able to last out until darkness. It was not far and he was so covered with mud that his uniform would not be recognised. He looked round him cautiously, but he could see no sign of life. The keen wind that blew across the flat expanse of grey and brown countryside drove before it a thin drizzle of fine rain. He walked on, his head bent against the wind.

He did not see the girls and the man until he was almost on top of them. Then he looked up and saw them, a knot of drab figures, their heads covered in sacks, loading some sort of root crop on to a cart. Although the path that he was following would take him within hailing distance of them, he was afraid to turn back. It would look suspicious. He plodded on towards them, head lowered, conscious of their inquiring gaze, and cursing himself for a reckless fool.

As he drew abreast of them he looked up. The man was middle-aged and wore a black cap with earflaps; his face was dark and hard, and he had a hostile look. The girls had stopped working and were all facing him like a herd of cattle.

"*Heil Hitler!*" Peter said. He waved his right arm in a vague salute. The man did not reply, and he could feel his suspicious gaze all the way across the fields to the woods. He had pulled his trousers down over his flying boots, but the leather jacket was too obvious. Once under cover of the trees he began to run, knowing in his heart that he had thrown the game away. He knew it as certainly as if the man had voiced his obvious suspicion.

On the far side of the covert were more ploughed fields, and he skirted these at a shambling trot. There were flocks of great black crows here, sleek and bloated, walking clumsily and beating themselves slowly into the air as he approached. He was exhausted by the time he reached a small thicket beyond the ploughland and he threw himself down, too spent to worry about camouflage.

When he had regained his breath he got to his feet and pushed on towards the west. He must be nearly in Holland now. Behind him, he felt, the peasant would already have given the alarm. The whole countryside would be aroused. He must get across the border. It seemed to him, numbed as he was with cold and fatigue, that once in Holland he would be safe. With any luck he could cross the border that evening and get help from a friendly farmer.

He walked on blindly, must have been walking half-asleep, because, suddenly he was in a marshy plain studded with clumps of thick bushes. In front of him was a broad river, the water

cold and deep, brimming to its earthen banks. This must be the Ems, the border could only be a few more miles from here. He thought of swimming, but could not face the dank yellowness of the water and the stark emptiness of the bank beyond. Turning to his right he walked downstream until he saw a concrete road bridge springing from earth ramparts on either side of the river. He worked away from the river bank and approached the bridge from the road. It was guarded by a soldier who was inspecting the papers of everyone who crossed. This was the first enemy soldier that Peter had seen after three years of war, and he lay for some time hidden among the bushes at the side of the road, watching the stream of peasants passing the barrier.

In spite of his exhaustion he found it exciting to watch the soldier on the bridge—the well-known silhouette with its scuttle-shaped helmet and long full-skirted greatcoat. He had seen it so often in illustrations and in films that now it seemed familiar. There was only one soldier, at this end of the bridge, and after watching for some time he came to the conclusion that this must be the border. The barrier was a temporary affair and by the attitude of the peasants it seemed that the soldier was not usually there.

He made up his mind to wait until nightfall and try to cross under cover of darkness. He studied the construction of the bridge, and decided that he would be able to climb it from the river bank and edge his way across outside the parapet. He crept back to a clump of bushes below the level of the road, and composed himself to wait.

He must have fallen asleep, for it was nearly dark and he could hear German voices around him in the bushes. There were shouts and the sound of men beating the dead grass aside with sticks. He looked carefully out from his hiding-place and saw a long line of men in green uniforms, armed with shotguns and rifles. They were about twelve feet apart and were beating steadily towards him.

Once again he knew the fear that he had known as a child, a

fear that he had forgotten until he started flying over Germany. The rising of the stomach, the dizziness, the nausea. Then came the sudden calmness, the desire to laugh, the joy when he had overcome the fear.

He must get out of this. He was nearly home. To get caught now would be stupid. One more effort and he would be over the border. The Germans were beating towards the river, hemming him in between themselves and the water. If he could slip quietly into the river and swim across . . . Cautiously he rose to his feet, turned round, and found himself face to face with the policeman.

He was a wizened little man in a bottle-green uniform with breeches and jackboots. Under the narrow-brimmed helmet his face was stern, his jaw set beneath a straggling grey moustache. In his hand the old-fashioned revolver, pointing uncertainly at Peter's stomach, looked incongruously lethal. He stood, a yard between them, dangerous in the very strangeness of his unaccustomed role.

Peter hesitated. There was only the old man between him and the river, but behind him were the foresters with their guns. Slowly he raised his hands above his head.

CHAPTER II

ON THE RUN

Now THAT the hunt was over he could not help thinking how theatrical the whole thing seemed. He stood self-consciously with his hands above his head, while the policeman prodded him nervously in the stomach with the revolver. The foresters, guns levelled, stood in a solemn half-circle behind him. No one appeared to know what to do next. He half-lowered his hands, but a sharp jab with the revolver reminded him that, to his captors at least, he was an object of considerable menace.

The policeman held out his left hand. " *Papiere !* "

Peter did not understand.

" *Papiere !* " the policeman repeated, and impatiently rubbed his thumb and forefingers together.

" I have no papers," Peter said.

" *Papiere, papiere !* " The policeman was getting angry.

Peter lowered his arms, this time with the policeman's consent and made the motions of tearing paper and throwing away the pieces.

" *Jude !* " The policeman spat the word, his old face screwed into an expression of distaste.

Yuda, thought Peter, what the hell's *Yuda*? . . . *Jude !* He thinks I'm a Jew. " *Nicht Jude !* " he said and shook his head.

The policeman seemed to be forcing himself into some kind of rage. He scowled again. " *Roosevelt Jude.*"

" *Roosevelt nicht Jude,*" Peter said.

" *Churchill Jude.*"

Peter looked round at the foresters. He was tired and he did not feel up to a political argument. He did not feel up to any sort of argument. Racial hatred had always frightened him. He was frightened now that they might take him for Jew and shoot him out of hand.

"*Churchill nicht Jude,*" he said.

The policeman's attention was distracted by some small boys who had been following up the beaters and were now crowding in, peering with interest at the ragged and mudcaked figure of the quarry. The policeman moved them back and, remembering his drill, handed the revolver to one of the foresters while he searched Peter's clothes for firearms or a knife. He patted the pockets, under the armpits and down the sides of the trouser legs. He found the escape kit, looked at it and handed it back. Now that he was certain that his captive was unarmed he relaxed, took out a battered metal case and offered Peter a cigarette. He took one himself and lit them both with an old-fashioned cigarette-lighter, which he had great difficulty in working. It was like a day's rough shooting at home. The foresters, leaning on their guns, had retired into private daydreams of their own. Tobacco smoke curled lazily into the winter air. Even the small boys were quiet.

The policeman finished his cigarette, spat and wiped his mouth with the back of his hand. It was time to move. He motioned Peter to raise his hands above his head again and walk towards the road.

He was marched, at the end of the revolver, out of the bushes and down the road towards a level-crossing. It was nearly dark, and the lighted windows of the village looked warm and comforting. He was almost glad that they had caught him. Now perhaps they would give him something to eat. The thought of food made him suddenly ill, and he was afraid that he would vomit in the street.

By now the villagers were beginning to gather, and the policeman formed his company into some semblance of order. First walked two foresters dressed in green knickerbockers and carrying shotguns at the shoulder; then Peter, wearing mud-covered battledress, sodden flying boots and a brightly-spotted silk handkerchief round his neck. With four days' growth of beard and hands held at shoulder height, he felt like the villain in a Wild West film. During his early operational days he had always flown with a revolver in its holster at his waist. If he had this now, he thought, the picture would be complete. After him came the policeman, gently prodding his prisoner in the small of the back with the revolver. Behind them marched a solid phalanx of foresters, followed at a respectful distance by an ever-increasing crowd of curious villagers.

Half-way down the village street they were met by an Army officer. He was wearing tight-fitting olive-green uniform and badly-cut breeches whose seat was one enormous leather patch. He carried an ornamental dagger slung from his belt by silver chains and in jackboots he looked out of place on his decrepit bicycle. He dismounted when he saw the procession and stood, holding the bicycle, waiting for them to draw near.

The policeman stopped in front of the officer, bringing the procession to an abrupt halt. He raised his arm in an exaggerated Nazi salute and said, "*Heil Hitler!*"

The officer replied with a military salute. He was young, fair and pink. His blue eyes looked at Peter for a moment, but flickered away again. He spoke to the policeman in German; he seemed to be asking a question.

The policeman made a long statement. Peter lowered his arms, but raised them again when he felt the muzzle of a shotgun in the small of his back.

The officer spoke again. He ignored the prisoner, carefully not looking in his direction. Peter stood listening to the strange tongue, not understanding it, knowing that they were talking about him, and feeling acutely conscious of his beard and the jagged rent in his trouser leg. He wished that they would let him lower his arms. He was cold again now, trembling, and he was worried in case the officer should think that he was frightened.

The officer and the policeman exchanged salutes, and the

procession continued its triumphal march down the village street to a small hotel by the railway station.

They had allowed him to wash and now he sat in the small private room, with its stiff ancestral photographs and lace curtains, trying to appear at ease. The policeman was explaining something to him in German, but he did not even begin to understand what it was all about. At times one or other of the foresters would say something to him, apparently speaking a dialect because he could not pick out a single familiar word. The policeman had a notebook in which he had so far written nothing but the date.

When the naval officer arrived they all stood up. He was young and his face was tanned by the weather. As he held out his hand to Peter he made it an act of friendliness. " My name is Friedrichs," he said. " I have come because I speak English."

" How d'you do." Peter shook his hand.

" The policeman would like some information from you." There was the common disregard for the non-fighting services in his manner.

" I would prefer to wait until I am in a prison camp."

The officer smiled. " You are right," he said. " I would have said the same in your place." He spoke to the policeman in German.

The policeman looked disappointed. He fingered the notebook, and said something emphatically in the same language.

" He wants your name and details for his report," the officer explained. He took out a cigarette-case and handed Peter a cigarette. " I am here unofficially. I live here in the village. If there is anything I can do for you . . ."

" Where shall I be taken ? " Peter asked.

The officer spoke again to the policeman. " An escort is on its way to fetch you. You will be taken to a prison camp, probably Frankfurt." He smiled. " It is not too bad. You are alive at least."

Peter did not answer.

The officer emptied his cigarette-case. "I will leave you these. You need not tell the policeman anything." He looked suddenly young and shy. "Good luck. It is all the fortune of war. You were only a few kilometres from the Dutch border."

Peter's barriers were nearly down, the dammed-up words of days of loneliness were waiting to be released to this man who spoke to him in English. But he held himself in check. They stood for a moment in silence, awkwardly, before the German, after shaking hands again, saluted and left the room.

When he had gone a girl brought sandwiches of black bread and a cup of *ersatz* coffee. She was young and dark, and when she put them on the table in front of Peter she smiled.

"*Essen*," the policeman said, and pointed to his mouth.

Peter handed the sandwiches round the table but the foresters would not eat them, urging him to go ahead. They left him alone at one end of the table while they engaged in low-voiced discussion at the other end.

He tried to eat, but could not swallow. He tried to drink the coffee but it was too hot. Once he started eating, the sandwiches vanished quickly and when he had finished he drank the coffee, feeling its bitter warmth restore his spirits. He lit one of the naval officer's cigarettes and wondered how long his escort would be.

Apparently the policeman and the foresters had reached a decision for, rising to their feet, they made signs for him to accompany them to the bar. They made him sit on a chair in the middle of the room, and opened the door to allow in a long queue of curious villagers. At first he was irritated by this, but the policeman's pride was so naïve that he could not be angry. He supposed that he was the first Englishman they had seen; so he sat there, patient but embarrassed, hoping that the naval officer would return and rescue him.

After the last civilian had left, the policeman made Peter remove his flying boots which he took and placed behind the bar. The foresters then drew chairs around the central stove and invited their prisoner to drink. *Schnapps* was poured from a large wicker-covered bottle behind the bar. They drank *schnapps* and beer, and one of the foresters smoked a pipe. Peter had a pipe in his pocket and the forester gave him some tobacco. It was light and dry and burned his tongue.

It was warm in the bar and the faint odour of stale food and beer was soon drowned in the pungent smell of German tobacco. Peter, his feet on the rail that enclosed the nearly red-hot stove, felt warm and almost happy. There was a glass of *schnapps* in his hand—six of its predecessors were already making the blood course warmly through his veins. He was happier than he had been for a long time.

The policeman was feeling good, too. It had obviously been a great day for him, a day that he would talk of here in this same bar for years to come. He meant to make it an evening worth remembering.

As he drank with them Peter wondered why they did not lock him up. Was it because they hadn't a spare room, or did they think he had shot his bolt? Or were they being courteous? He remembered wryly what the people of his village had threatened to do to any German airman that they found. Pitchforks, carving knives and horsewhips flashed through his memory. Would they really have done it? These people gave him food and cigarettes and *schnapps*. Did the people at home do the same for a German airman?

The policeman had opened his wallet and was showing him pictures of his infantry platoon in the 1914 War. He was bigger then, and had a big, serious-looking moustache. All the men were serious-looking, as though war were a serious thing in those days. Then he remembered the ancestral pictures on the wall. No, it was not war that had been serious in those days, but photography. He giggled inwardly at the silly joke.

The policeman also had an Iron Cross in his wallet; he wore the ribbon on his tunic. He was growing maudlin, and repeated over and over again a long explanation. It had something to do with the war. Peter gathered that he considered that the war had been a mistake.

One by one the foresters said "*Heil Hitler!*" took up their shotguns and departed, until there were only the policeman and two of the foresters left with Peter in the bar. One of the foresters was already drunk. He wore a shapeless hat with a tuft of boar bristles pinned to the side, and the buttons of his short green tunic were carved from horn. The other, not so drunk, smoked a pipe with a carved soft bowl which had been burned down at one side by constant lighting. It was past midnight and they had nearly finished the crock of *schnapps*.

Through a haze of fatigue and alcohol Peter saw the face of the policeman pressing close to his. The old man's tunic was unbuttoned showing a grey collarless flannel shirt and braces underneath. In his hand was the notebook. He pointed to the swastika on his tunic, and grabbed Peter by the arm. "*Nicht hier*," he said, pointing to the badge, "*hier!*" and he tapped a forefinger on his chest beneath the tunic. Obviously he was trying to say that it was not the official who wanted the information, but the man. He had written his own name and address at the top of the page, and indicated that he wanted Peter to sign below.

Peter took the notebook. All that he was allowed to give were his rank, name and number. He thought of Pop Dawson as he wrote: *Flight Lieutenant Peter Howard*, 1174667, *R.A.F.*, *Captured by the above*, 20.12.42.

He remembered Pop Dawson and was overcome with shame. Here he was sitting with the enemy, drinking *schnapps* with them. He wasn't really captured yet. He might still get away. When the escort arrived he would be taken to Frankfurt—the naval type had told him that, also that they were almost on the Dutch border. He would never be nearer England than he was now. He glanced at the policeman who was putting the Iron Cross back into his wallet, at the foresters engaged in fuddled conversation. If he managed to give these chaps the slip, would there be a guard in the street, outside the door? The lavatory was useless as an avenue of escape. He had been there several times during the evening—the window was barred. There were two other doors to the bar, one leading to the private room where he had eaten and the other to the street outside. The policeman, with the flap of his revolver holster unbuttoned, sat between him and the door. Behind him was the staircase up which the girl had gone to bed; but even if he managed to reach the top without being hit, there was still the possibility of a guard outside the house. He must find out.

He would sing. He would get the others to join in, and they would make so much noise that if there were a man outside he would look in to see what all the row was about. But it must look natural. He was not the singing type; organised singsongs usually filled him with embarrassment. And it must be a song in which the others would join. It would have to be a song of the last war . . . Simulating drunkenness, he caught the policeman by the arm and began a personal, almost tuneless version of *Pack Up Your Troubles In Your Old Kitbag.*

At first the policeman looked at him with owlish astonishment. Then, surprisingly, he recognised the tune. (It was not until some time later that Peter learned that the Germans had their own marching song to the same tune.) The policeman sang with him in German. The foresters joined in. Peter's tuneless voice was drowned in a roar of Teutonic fervour. It was magnificent. It was just what he wanted. He beat time with his mug on the table, shouting at the top of his voice, while the policeman, the present forgotten, sang in an older war; a war in which he too had fought as a soldier.

Surely enough the door opened and a forester armed with a rifle looked in. He shouted something in German, pointed up the stairs, and withdrew.

Then the policeman passed out. Without any warning he fell flat across the table, his hands sprawling out in front of him, his absurd helmet rolling across the floor and coming to rest against the bar. Suddenly he seemed pitiful to Peter—an old man in his cups, his scanty hair lying in the spilt beer on the table top.

The foresters would have left him there—continued with their song—but Peter lifted the old man's head from the table and leaned him back in the chair. His head fell forward with a loose heaviness, his whole body limp and sagging.

"Water!" Peter said, and made the motion of throwing water in the policeman's face.

The foresters grinned. The one with the pipe took the old man's head, the other his knees, and they carried him across the room and into the lavatory at the back. For a moment Peter sat alone in the smoke-filled room. This was his chance and he must take it now. He crossed the floor silently in his socks, retrieved his boots from behind the bar and quickly climbed the stairs to the floor above. Which was the girl's room? He knew that if he went in there her screams would attract the attention of the man outside. Would there be a bathroom? If so, it was probably immediately above the lavatory.

Quietly he opened the door on the far side of the landing. This must be the back of the house; he knew that there was a guard on the front. The room was a bedroom. Inside, he could see a gigantic wardrobe and a high bed heaped with eiderdowns. There was a figure in the bed and he hesitated in the doorway for a moment listening to the heavy breathing and wondering what to do. He thought how terrified the sleeper would be, should he or she awake—and how harmless he actually was.

The window was open, its lace curtains blowing into the room, and he decided to climb through. There was no time to waste. He went in, carefully closing the door behind him. The figure in the bed was moving restlessly. He paused by a bundle of clothes lying on a chair by the bed, hoping that their owner was a man. They were women's clothes. He thought of changing into them, but the awful possibility of being caught half-dressed in this woman's room made him dismiss the idea.

He climbed out of the window, dropped on to the roof of a lean-to shed, and down into the yard below. So far there had been no alarm. He crossed the yard, clambered over the fence and landed heavily on the ground outside.

Swiftly he made for the bridge near which he had been caught earlier in the afternoon. After a brief reconnaissance, he found that it was not guarded. The barrier had obviously been for him.

He ran as fast as he could for about a mile, keeping dangerously to the road but wanting to get as far into Holland as he could before daybreak. The countryside on both sides of the road was the same flat waterlogged marshland that he had crossed the night before, now intersected by wide dykes; and he knew that he could not travel fast away from the road. He knew also that the Germans would be out in full force by the following morning, and he decided to declare himself to a Dutch farmer and ask to be hidden for the next few days.

The rest and the food had done him good, but his energy was short-lived. When he could run no more he lurched on painfully, his only desire to flop into a hollow in the ground and sleep.

Now that he was in Holland he could not help feeling that he had played the policeman a dirty trick. It was stupid to think this way, he knew, but his conscience troubled him. He had been drinking with them all night and had not paid for a single round. He must have become light-headed again, because he kept seeing the policeman's face. The old man seemed to be looking at him reproachfully. They could have locked him up, but they had given him *schnapps*. He was worried that the old man might be shot for letting him get away.

Just before dawn he came to a small farm behind a windbreak of trees about a mile from the main road. He hid among the trees and watched the farm for signs of German occupation. He saw two young girls of about eight or nine years old, and a woman with a shawl over her head. There were no signs of men about the place. Once, as he lay there, a German Army lorry passed swiftly along the main road, but apart from that there was no activity.

He knew that he must take the risk. Travelling like this would get him nowhere. He must get civilian clothes and, if possible, papers. His boots were soft and shapeless, useless for walking, and he did not feel capable of another night on the road.

Before approaching the farm he examined the surrounding country in all directions. With his heart beating high inside his chest he came out from under the trees, walked to the back of the farmhouse, and knocked on the door.

The door was opened by one of the small girls. He could see the fear plainly in her face as she looked at him.

"R.A.F.," Peter said, and made signs of a parachute falling.

The child ran back into the house and he followed her quickly into a large stone-flagged kitchen. Standing in the centre of the room was the woman he had seen earlier in the day. She too seemed frightened and looked at him without speaking.

"R.A.F.," he said. "British—*Englander*."

Still the woman did not speak. It seemed to him that she did not want him there—that she was trying to will him out of the house again.

He smiled a reassurance. "Peter Howard!" He pointed to his chest, "*Englander—Flieger*. Parachute." And made signs as he had done for the girl.

There was a slight loosening of the woman's stricken immobility.

"Food," he said, and pointed to his mouth.

She crossed to a cupboard and brought out some cheese, butter, black bread and a large bowl of pickled cabbage, which she put on the table. He sat down and began to eat. He heard her talking to the girl, who presently ran down the path and across the field towards the wood where he had hidden. He wondered whether she had gone for the police. There was nothing that he could do about it now.

The woman had come back into the kitchen and was watching him eat, watching him and glancing nervously out of the window in the direction the little girl had gone. He desperately wanted to make some sort of contact, to find out what her sympathies were.

"Thank you," he said. "Good!" And he patted his stomach. He was rewarded with the ghost of a smile, that made him wonder whether he had eaten their evening meal.

He finished the food and rose to his feet. The woman backed towards the door. He noticed that she was younger than he had

thought, but pale and very thin. When she smiled she was almost beautiful. He wanted to make her smile again. The only way to make contact was to ask for something.

" Shave," he said, " Razor," and went through the pantomime of shaving the five days' stubble from his face. The act must have been good, for she smiled again and ran to the inner room. She came back carrying an old-fashioned cut-throat razor, a shaving brush and a cake of soap. She put these down on the table and brought a bowl of hot water, a mirror and a towel.

He looked at his face in the mirror. His dark hair was thickly matted, and the lower part of his face was covered in black stubble. There were pouches under his eyes, and the eyes themselves were bloodshot. No wonder the child had been afraid. He grinned a reassurance into the mirror and was surprised to see how white his teeth appeared against the darkness of his face.

He had not removed his clothes since the night before he had been shot down and, stripping to the waist, he washed thoroughly and began to shave. The cut-throat razor was difficult to handle, but the half-unconscious routine of scraping the familiar jaw was comforting.

He wiped the residue of soap from his chin and tried to ask the woman for civilian clothes. When he pointed to his uniform and made what he thought were the appropriate signs she merely nodded and smiled, as though he had asked her to admire his appearance. He gave it up and decided to ask the farmer when he arrived home—if indeed it were the farmer and not the police the girl had gone to fetch.

In the meantime he sat on a stiff wooden chair by the peat fire drying the legs of his trousers. His battledress blouse was steaming on the hearth. I've ruined my boots, he thought. Most of the polish had been washed off, leaving the leather white and dry-looking. Moved by some impulse of caution he took the small brass compass belonging to the escape kit from his pocket, and slitting the sheepskin lining of the left boot with a penknife he slipped the compass between the sheepskin and the outside leather. It would be safer there.

He sat in the warmth and security of the kitchen, conscious of the busy movements of the woman in the next room, wondering whom the girl had gone to fetch. The woman had seemed friendly enough, but had she really understood? Was it possible that she thought that he was German? He made a movement as though to call to her, but the language difficulty was too great. His head fell forward on to his chest and he slumped down into the chair, too tired to worry any more.

When he awoke there was a man in the kitchen; a middle-aged man who stood in front of his chair, holding a grey felt hat in his hands and peering at him through steel-rimmed spectacles. "I am the schoolmaster," the man said, "I speak a little English."

Peter stood up, and they shook hands.

"Where have you come from?" the schoolmaster asked.

"My aircraft was shot down in Germany. I have walked from there."

" Has anyone seen you ? "

" The Germans caught me on the border, but I got away."

" No one saw you come here ? "

" No."

" When were you shot down ? "

" Last Friday night." He thought, as he said it, how long ago it seemed.

" Ah, that was the big raid." The schoolmaster looked relieved. " An aircraft crashed not many miles from here. It was burning in the air, I saw it come down like a burning torch."

" What time was that ? "

" A few minutes after midnight."

It may have been ours, Peter thought. " What sort of aircraft was it ? "

The schoolmaster was vague. " A bomber," he said. " A big aircraft. The pilot was most fortunate. He was alone in the aircraft when it landed in a great lake not far from here. He was not hurt at all. He was taken by the Germans—they arrived before I could get there."

It must have have been ours, Peter thought. Good old Wally. And this chap had tried to help him, too. " Have you helped many airmen ? " he asked.

The schoolmaster smiled and lifted his hand in a typical classroom gesture. " No—it is better that you should not ask me questions."

" The Germans will guess that I have crossed into Holland," Peter said.

The man moved to the fireplace and stood looking into the fire. " I will move you as soon as it is dark. For the time it is best that you should sleep. The woman will dry your clothes and this evening, when it is dark, I will come for you." He spoke to the woman in their own tongue, giving her instructions ; then he turned to Peter again and held out his hand. He had an odd, professional manner—more like a doctor than a schoolmaster. He bowed from the waist, said something to the child and took her mother with him out into the yard.

When the woman came back into the kitchen she motioned Peter to follow her, and took him to a small bedroom at the top of the house, a room whose sloping ceiling reminded him of his bedroom at home. She said something in Dutch and he understood that she would return in a few minutes for his clothes. At first he felt reluctant to let them out of his sight, particularly the boots, knowing that he would be helpless without them; but he realised that he could not go on alone, that he was warm and dry, and that he could sleep now while plans were being made.

He undressed completely and as he climbed into the high bed with its soft feather mattress and bulky eiderdown, he felt ridiculously safe. It was as though he had come home again.

He was asleep before the woman came to take his clothes away.

Then it was night and the woman held a candle in her hand. "*Kommen Sie!*" She was shaking him by the shoulder. "*Kommen Sie! Schnell, schnell!*" She left the candle on the chest by the bed, and he could tell by the way she ran down the stairs that he must hurry. His clothes, dry and neatly folded, were on the chair by the bed. The woman had even mended the tear in his trousers.

As he dressed he felt that everything was going well. He was convinced that it was Wally who had escaped from the crashed aircraft, and he was glad that he was safe. For himself, he was as good as home again. The schoolmaster had seemed to know what he was about. Quietly confident. Peter grinned as he dressed. He and his brother had never been "absolutely certain," but always "quietly confident." It had been part of their private language.

When he got downstairs the schoolmaster was not there. Instead, he saw a young woman dressed in a blue-belted raincoat with a dark scarf round her head. The scarf and the hair that escaped from under it were covered with fine raindrops that glittered in the light of the candle. She seemed excited and spoke to him in English.

"My husband has been arrested. He was stealing a car. They must not know that it was for you, or they will shoot him. You must go."

"Who are you?" he asked, losing in that instant all his former confidence, feeling that he had made a mistake in coming here.

"I have come to tell you that you leave the house." She turned to the woman and spoke to her in Dutch, and then to Peter in English. "This woman is already a widow and if they find you here she will be shot—and the children will be orphans. The farm will be burned. My husband . . . If they know that he was helping you . . . Please go!"

She began to gather his things together, the boots from the fireplace, the Irvin jacket from the chair. "They may be coming soon," she said. "Keep away from the roads and when you get far from here ask at another farm—perhaps they will help you. But here it is too dangerous." She pushed the flying jacket at him and compelled him towards the door.

Outside in the darkness and the driving rain he stood for several seconds without a plan. The stars that had guided him fitfully throughout his journey were hidden behind the clouds. But he had little need of their guidance now, being no longer driven towards the west. He had crossed the border but was still without the warmth of friendliness.

He followed the lane to the main road and walked farther into Holland. Perhaps once out of the border country he would get more help. His trousers were already wet again and rain dripped down his nose and into the collar of his Irvin jacket.

He walked all that night, more lonely and cold now that he had known the comfort that lay beyond the shuttered windows that he passed.

By daylight he was still on the road, but managed to find a hiding-place between two haystacks near a farm. He lay there as long as he could but towards midday, impelled by hunger and loneliness, he decided to seek help at the farm. Looking carefully up and down the road he set out for the buildings that he could see a quarter of a mile away. Just as he was rehearsing what he would say to the farmer, he was overtaken swiftly and silently by two policemen on bicycles. It was useless to resist. He had lost the spirit to resist. They walked the few miles to the village without speaking.

CHAPTER III

JOURNEY TO DULAG-LUFT

He lay on his back in the narrow cell, trying to make maps and faces out of the damp patches which stained its lime-washed walls. He was so disgusted at having been captured that he refused to think of it. He lay on a wooden plank, and the thin grey blanket that covered him smelled abominably of ancient vomit. They had taken his flying boots and his sheepskin jacket, and he was cold. He had not eaten since early that morning and now it was late in the afternoon. The pale watery light creeping in through the small heavily-barred window fell obliquely on the bucket with its rough wooden seat, which stood in one corner of the cell. He could smell it from where he lay.

He felt sick with remorse and self-disgust. It had been too silly. A long, straight, open road; the two policemen on bicycles. He had not even tried to run for it.

There had been no cigarettes and *schnapps* this time. The cold dislike of the young policemen had been frightening. They had been, to him, indistinguishable from Germans—they may have been Germans. Anyway, their behaviour had been very different from that of the old policeman of two nights ago, and he had been glad when the door of the cell had closed behind them.

He felt no bitterness against the Dutch. The interpreter had told him that for every airman discovered in hiding the *Gestapo* would shoot ten Dutchmen. For him, as the man had pointed out, it would only mean a slim chance to avoid eventual capture; for the Dutch it would mean much more.

He sighed and stretched himself uncomfortably on his wooden

bed. There would be no escape from this place, he was certain of that. Solid concrete, with a door that was inches thick. Even the bread and *ersatz* coffee that he had been given for breakfast had been pushed through a trap in the door. He would rest until they moved him again, and try to get away during the journey. He turned his face to the wall and presently he fell asleep.

He was being shaken gently by the shoulder. He had been dreaming again, at first he thought it was his batman. Then he heard a voice calling, " *'Raus, 'raus !* " and became conscious of the scent. It was like the perfume they sprayed in cheap old-fashioned cinemas. He opened his eyes. A German soldier was bending over him, dragging him from the forgetfulness of sleep to the bleak reality of his cell. He sat up and pushed the hair back from his face. There were two soldiers, both armed with automatic pistols. One carried a black imitation-leather brief-case.

Peter swung his legs over the side of the bed and looked at them. They were most unmilitary-looking soldiers. The one who had been shaking him was young and dark, with an unhappy full-lipped face. He wore a collar and tie with his *Luftwaffe* uniform, and the long dark hair under his forage cap was slightly waved. The silver chevrons on his sleeve gave him a theatrical, musical-comedy appearance, but the automatic pistol in his hand looked real enough.

" You can put that thing away," Peter told him.

" So long as we understand one another." The corporal spoke surprisingly good English. He straightened himself up and put the pistol back in its holster.

The older man, who was not an N.C.O., handed Peter his flying boots.

" You must come now," the corporal said.

Peter pulled on the still-damp flying boots and followed the two soldiers out into the corridor. " Where are we going ? " he asked.

The corporal grinned knowingly. " You will find out in good

time. For you the war is over. You do not ask questions—you do not think any more. You do as you are told, no ?"

"No." Peter said it flatly.

"So ? Then you will find life very difficult. You will find here the German discipline."

"I should like my Irvin jacket, please." He felt that in making the demand he was making one last bid for self-respect.

"Your jacket ?"

"My sheepskin flying jacket. The policeman took it from me last night with the boots."

"I know nothing of such a jacket."

"Let me see the policeman."

"I have not come here to talk about flying jackets. I have come to take you away. Now we have wasted enough time. Come !"

"I demand my flying jacket !" Peter was suddenly overcome with fury, more annoyed about the possible loss of the jacket than he had been about tearing his trousers on the barbed-wire. Normally an even-tempered man, he was perturbed by these sudden irrational fits of rage. He managed to control his voice. "It is military equipment and you have no right to take it."

"I have not taken the jacket."

"Then I demand to see the policeman."

"You are a prisoner. You cannot demand any longer." The corporal was getting excited, shouting and waving his arms in emphasis.

Peter raised his voice in reply. "I am an officer and I demand to see an officer of my own rank before I leave this building." It sounded silly to him as he said it, but its effect on the corporal was surprising. He turned abruptly and led the way back into the cell.

"Wait here, please. I will bring the police officer."

Peter and the other soldier stood in the cell and listened to the footsteps of the corporal receding down the corridor. The soldier looked at Peter and smiled in conciliation. Peter scowled.

The police officer, when he came, was indignant. He was a big man with closely-cropped dark hair and a heavy-jowled coarse, unshaven face. There was a mark round his head where the cap had been, and his small pig-like eyes were shot with red. There had been no such jacket, he said. The prisoner had been captured as he was standing now. If there had been such a jacket it would naturally have been returned to the prisoner. Peter saw that it was hopeless. Choking with rage, he was marched down the corridor and out into the cold early morning air.

They walked to the railway station in silence, and found that the train would not arrive for another hour. Leaving the older man to guard the prisoner, the corporal went to the waiting-room and turned everyone out on to the platform, shouting at them as though they were half-witted recruits on the barrack square. As the passengers filed out, Peter could see anger and hatred for the invader written on their faces. Some of them smiled when they recognised his uniform, and several raised their fingers in the victory sign. The corporal must have noticed this, but he said nothing. He motioned Peter into the waiting-room and stood inside with his back against the door. "The flying jacket will probably go to the troops on the East Front."

"Then you know that I had a jacket?"

"You say so." He had adopted the tone of an unintelligent mother humouring a wayward child.

Peter did not reply.

"Listen," the corporal said. "We have to travel all day together. Why cannot we be friendly and talk to one another? I would like to practise my English."

"In case we win the war?"

"*Ach*, you will not win the war. The *Führer* cannot afford to lose the war."

"It isn't entirely up to the *Führer*," Peter said.

"You should not have fought against us in the first place," the corporal told him. "The *Führer* has said many times that we had no quarrel with England."

Peter did not reply.

"We are only doing now what England has done in the past."

"It's no use talking about it," Peter said. He remembered Pop Dawson and his security lectures. They will try to get you into conversation, he had said. The only way to avoid giving information is to refuse to talk. The corporal seemed a bit phoney, anyway, his English was too good.

The other soldier came in with three cups of soup. He was rather like the old policeman in that he seemed too tired for this war; too tired and not caring enough what it was all about. He put the soup on the table, smiled nervously, and relapsed into a sort of coma.

The corporal took three slices of black bread from his brief-case and gave one to Peter. "You have not much bread in England," he said.

"We have plenty of bread," Peter told him.

"*Ach*, for the rich."

"For everyone."

"*Ach*, that is what you say." He smiled his disbelief, and bit hungrily at the bread.

When the train steamed in the corporal turned all the passengers out of the nearest compartment and shut the door leading on to the corridor. He made the other soldier sit next to the window while he sat in the corner next to the corridor. Peter sat between them. The corporal unbuttoned the flap of his holster and loosened the automatic pistol. "If you attempt to escape I shall shoot," he said.

It took them all day to get to Cologne; a day in which the wooden seats became harder, and the air of the compartment more foul. At one stage Peter made signs for the older man to open the window and let in some fresh air but the corporal, obviously fearing an escape attempt, forbade him to do so. On most stations there was a Red Cross cuffet dispensing free soup, and while the older soldier went foraging, the corporal, growing more and more short-tempered, guarded the prisoner and prevented other passengers from entering the compartment. There was no heating in the carriage, and Peter sat and brooded over the loss of his flying jacket.

At midday the soldiers opened their briefcases, and took out bread and sausage which they shared equally with their prisoner. They drank hot *ersatz* coffee from vacuum flask water-bottles and smoked foul, loosely packed cigarettes.

Several times the corporal attempted to engage Peter in conversation, but his non-committal and conclusive replies dropped each topic still-born into the moist and smoke-filled atmosphere.

He sat, hunched up against the cold, on the wooden seat and wondered about the rest of his crew. Had they been captured or were they even now hiding up under hedges and waiting for darkness to fall? None of them spoke German; but Kim, the Canadian wireless operator, spoke French. Wally was in German hands, he knew that, but what about the others . . .

They had shared a car, the old Aston Martin without a silencer which had so often made the night hideous between Cambridge and the aerodrome. She had run on hundred-octane aviation spirit and, maintained by the aircraft's ground crew, had "gone like a bomb." What would happen to her now? He would write as soon as he could to his young brother Roy, telling him that he could have her. He felt sure that the rest of the crew would agree—that is, if none of them got back, of course. If one of them got back the car would belong to him. He imagined himself driving her again, the slim wheel in his hands and the crew piled in on top of him, the exhaust blaring defiance at the police as they roared into Cambridge . . .

He must get out of this. The thought of spending the rest of the war behind barbed-wire filled him with a sudden panic. If only he had made more of his chances while he was still free . . . He checked himself and tried to think constructively. The corporal had told him that they would change trains at Cologne and then travel eastward to Frankfurt-on-Main. He would try to give them the slip during the change of trains. In the meantime he must try to sleep and let them think that he had given up all hope of escape.

But he could not sleep and sat with his eyes closed trying to imagine what the station would be like and how he would make his getaway. He thought of Waterloo and Victoria stations with their many entrances and exits, and dreamed fantastic chases through the subways with the guards unable to shoot because of the crowds. He imagined himself out in the busy streets, dodging through the traffic and burying himself down narrow alleys between tall houses. It was a fine dream while it lasted but in the end he found himself still in the stuffy carriage with the corporal watching him and the soldier snoring in the opposite seat.

Later that evening they steamed into Cologne.

The platform was crowded, and the corporal made them remain in the compartment until all the passengers had left the train and the platform was clear. Then he drew his pistol and marched Peter down the deserted platform towards the booking hall. It was icy cold after the damp cold of the railway carriage, and Peter began to wonder whether it would be a better idea to wait until he reached the prison camp before he attempted to escape. He was very conscious of the muzzle of the automatic pistol a few inches from his back. After all, he would have time to prepare in the camp, make civilian clothes and collect food. If he got away now, in uniform, in the heart of Cologne, he would not last for long.

Again the corporal cleared all the passengers out of the waiting-room, and Peter noticed that they resented the bullying way in which they were ordered out. The corporal treated them exactly as he had treated the Dutch, shouting at them, ignoring their angry protestations.

An hour later they went out on to the platform to wait for the Frankfurt train. As they stood on the platform a train on the opposite track began to move out. It was a goods train. Peter glanced quickly around. Two steps would take him to the edge of the platform, four more across the track—and he could jump on to the couplings of the slowly-moving train. The corporal would not fire for fear of hitting the public—or would he?

While he hesitated, the older guard stepped between him and the edge of the platform, unconsciously thwarting his attempt. The goods train stopped again a few yards outside the station. Lucky I didn't dash for it, Peter thought, wouldn't have got very far if I had.

The Frankfurt train was crowded but this time the corporal got one of the girl porters to empty a compartment for them. She was a big girl, blondely bulging under her rough blue serge uniform. She wore jackboots with high heels, rather like the Russian boots that Peter could remember his mother wearing when he was a child.

After the train had left the station the girl came into the compartment and chatted with the corporal. She looked at Peter with obvious interest. He wondered if she would help him to escape, but dismissed the idea as fantastic. She seemed to be fascinated by his appearance and repeatedly urged the corporal to take some course of action which Peter could not understand. Finally the corporal agreed and, apologising in English, asked if the girl could have some sort of trinket to keep as a souvenir. Thinking that she might be helpful later in the journey he gave her a penny, a halfpenny and a sixpence; but shortly after this she left the compartment and did not return.

As the train covered mile after mile in an eastward direction, Peter felt that his chance of escape was growing more and more remote. His guards were less nervous now, and he decided to try to jump from the window of the lavatory at the end of the corridor. He had been there several times during the day and one or other of his escort had gone with him, insisting that the door should be left open so that they could watch him.

This time the corporal came and Peter, explaining that this was to be a more protracted visit, gained his permission to close the door.

As soon as he had locked the door he turned to the window. It was a rise-and-fall window and was not secured in any way. He lowered it and looked out. The train was moving quite slowly along a grass embankment. He looked towards the rear of the train. Leaning from the next window were the head and shoulders of the corporal, who smugly waved his automatic pistol in admonition. Peter grinned ruefully and joined him in the corridor. "I wanted to get a spot of fresh air," he explained.

CHAPTER IV

SOLITARY CONFINEMENT

WHEN THEY arrived at Frankfurt the corporal dismissed the other guard and took Peter into the busy street. They waited in a queue of patient civilians at a tram stop, and he wondered at the banality of his arrival. He had expected an armed escort and at least a truck, and here he was about to travel in a tramcar with a crowd of civilians going home from work.

The corporal did not speak as they stood in the queue, and Peter also thought it better not to advertise the fact that he was English.

They stood on the platform of the tramcar, well away from the step, and swayed for miles through the soft night air that was redolent with a strange perfume, almost of incense. Later he discovered that this was the odour of burning brown coal blocks. It was to be an odour that would for ever, for him, be associated with that crowded tramcar swaying through the heart of an enemy countryside.

The prison camp, as they approached it, walking silently down the soft earth road, looked stark and hard; an arpeggio of up-right posts and taut barbed-wire. There were shaded arc lamps suspended from gallows above the wire, and these cast a band of concentrated brilliance about thirty feet wide entirely round the camp. The small compound in which stood the long squat shapes of the blacked-out huts was in darkness, but searchlights stabbed and blazed across it, moving nervously in hesitant sweeps over the grey roofs of the huts, caressing the wire with their long probing fingers of light.

Sentries, muffled against the cold, stamped their feet and

scuffed the loose dust of the road outside the wire, their breath pluming like smoke in the light of the arc lamps. Outside, there was light and animation. Inside, everything was silent and in darkness.

The corporal showed his pass at the gate and they were allowed to enter—without ceremony, Peter thought, into a place with such a tenacious air.

He was left alone in a large room while the corporal went to report their arrival. It was obviously the dining-hall. He sat at one of the long tables and studied a portrait of Hitler which hung on the end wall. The *Führer* was wearing a khaki uniform that looked a size too large, but in this dim light his gaze appeared hypnotic. He became bored with looking at Hitler, and examined a notice-board which was fixed to the wall near the door. He could not read the notices, but they had a familiar look—daily routine orders.

He heard footsteps behind him and, glancing over his shoulder, saw a soldier in grey fatigue uniform, without a cap, standing in the doorway. The soldier, ignoring him, stood with eyes fixed on the portrait of his *Führer* and raised his arm in silent salute. Then he crossed to the notice-board and began to read the orders.

While Peter waited for the corporal several soldiers came to read the orders, and each of them stood with arm upraised before he entered the room. The gesture of the upraised arm, so amusing when burlesqued on the stage or screen, here had a servile, fanatical strength. It was not a formal salute, such as he himself gave the national flag when passing. It was homage to the man, febrile and frightening.

In the small grey-walled office, the corporal handed his prisoner over to a stout *Feldwebel* who sat, tunic unbuttoned, behind a wooden desk. The corporal produced a long envelope and obtained in return the *Feldwebel's* signature on a form. It was as though he had delivered a parcel.

The *Feldwebel* laid down his pen, and took his grey forage cap from one of the drawers in the desk. He led Peter down a long passage, the walls of which were composed of two rows of identical doors. The passage was grey and airless but clean, and their footsteps were loud on its wooden floor.

As they passed door after door, Peter noticed that each carried a number above a small grille, which could be concealed by a sliding panel. Some of the grilles were covered and some were not, and outside most of the doors were shoes or flying boots, put out as though for cleaning. He also noticed that from the wall by some of the doors a small red wooden arm projected like a railway signal

Then he heard the sound of cries from one of the cells and muffled thuds as though a man were beating the other side of the thick door with his fists; but the *Feldwebel* ignored this and continued to the end of the corridor where the gaoler sat on a wooden chair reading a magazine. He was an elderly man, bespectacled, and looked more like an attendant at a public lavatory than a soldier. He rose to his feet as the *Feldwebel* approached, and unlocked one of the doors.

" Here it is," the *Feldwebel* said. " Better get stripped down now."

"What for?"

The *Feldwebel* was patient. "I got to search you. It's my duty to see that you're not hiding arms or escape material—see?" He grinned, a mouth full of bad teeth. "Wouldn't get very far if you did escape because we take your boots at night—see?"

"I have the right to be searched by an officer of my own rank," Peter said.

"I know, I know, they all say that." For the *Feldwebel* it was obviously a well-worn routine. He was not aggressive, but Peter felt that he would not get very far with his objections. "Now be sensible," the *Feldwebel* said. "All the officers have gone home for the night. See? Besides the underclothing of the English is often so dirty that the officers don't like to search them."

As Peter undressed he had to admit to himself that there was something in what the fellow said. His underclothes were plastered with mud, his feet were filthy and his fingernails were rimmed with black. He thought of explaining that he was not always like this, that this was the result of days and nights in the country; but he thought that the *Feldwebel* would probably know about that too.

As he undressed the *Feldwebel* took the clothes one by one and dropped them in a dismal heap in the corner of the cell, to be taken away—he told Peter—for X-ray examination. The gaoler who collected the clothes left in their place a pile of khaki uniform that smelled strongly of disinfectant.

The noise made by the guard removing the black-out shutters from outside his window jerked Peter into wakefulness. It was morning, and the sunlight, filtering in through the obscured glass of the window, made a silhouette of iron bars and the guard's head and shoulders as he fastened back the wooden shutters.

He looked round him at the cell which he had been too tired to examine the night before. It was about ten feet long by five feet wide, and the walls were grey; plain, pale grey plaster dirtied above the wooden bunk by the heads and shoulders of earlier prisoners. On the narrow bunk was a sackful of wood shavings or straw, which had gone lumpy and crackled when he moved. He had slept well enough, but now he was stiff and raised himself painfully on his elbow. There was a table in one corner of the cell and a small four-legged stool. On the table were a metal jug and a thick glass tumbler, chipped at the edge. Underneath the table was a metal chamberpot. The cell seemed dry and clean enough, but frighteningly impersonal. It had the smell of an institution; the smell of dirt kept under by brute force and disinfectant. He felt more immured than he had felt since he had been captured. The place seemed too efficient.

He got off the bed, and gingerly pulled the rough khaki uniform over his filthy limbs. It was a French or Polish Army uniform, with full baggy breeches and a tight high-necked tunic. The sleeves were too short, and he was unable to button the breeches at the waist. They had taken his flying boots so he sat on the bed with his feet under the still-warm blankets. They had also taken his watch, and he had no idea of the time. He was hungry, and wanted to relieve himself, but he would not use the chamberpot.

The *Feldwebel* had told him that to call the guard he must turn the knob on the wall near the door. This would release the red signal arm outside in the corridor. He got up from the bed, turned the knob, and went back to the bed to wait. Nothing happened. Nothing happened for ten minutes. He realised that once the signal arm was down there was nothing he could do; the arm could only be put up again from outside the cell. Now he could only wait until the guard noticed it, or until he came to unlock the door if he had already seen it. He was suddenly angry again. He leapt from the bed and hammered on the door with his fists. All the frustration and anger of imprisonment were in the frantic beating on the door. He beat until his fists were sore and then, in the after silence, he heard footsteps outside in the corridor and someone shouting in German.

He hammered on the door again in a sudden renewal of blind rage. "Come on, you clot!" he shouted. "Open the door! Open this door, you clot!"

"You think I don't speak English." The German accent came thickly through the heavy door. "But I do speak English . . . You call me a clot—now I make you wait, see!" And he heard the footsteps recede firmly down the corridor.

He sat down on the bed again, trembling. He could wait. He wouldn't use the chamberpot for any German. Drawing his knees up to his chin he clasped his arms around his shins, and waited.

Some time later the door was opened by a soldier armed with an automatic pistol. He was a young man, with a white thick-skinned face which twitched nervously as he peered into the cell.

"Toilet," Peter said. "Wash!"

"*Toilette besetzt.*" The soldier said it impatiently.

"Breakfast," Peter said. "Food——" He pointed to his mouth.

The soldier showed his wristwatch and traced his forefinger round half the dial. "*Halbe stunde,*" he said.

"Toilet," Peter repeated.

"*Toilette besetzt,*" the soldier said, and locked the door.

Hours seemed to pass while he sat uncomfortably on the bed and tried to ignore his distended bladder. It had become a point of honour not to use the chamberpot. Eventually he heard the key turn in the lock and the soldier—angel of mercy now—filled the doorway. "*Toilette frei,*" he said, and handed Peter his flying boots.

Peter hobbled down the corridor. The soldier followed, and watched him through the doorless doorway. Peter did not care. The next few seconds were pure bliss.

Back in his cell he examined the flying boots. The compass was still where he had hidden it, under the sheepskin lining. He decided to leave it there for want of a better hiding-place.

He sat there waiting for his breakfast. The minutes dragged by. He heard footsteps in the corridor again and the sound of metal on metal. By the time the breakfast got half-way down the corridor he could hear the cell doors open and close. He waited in a fever of impatience. Then he thought that they had passed his door. Perhaps he was to get no breakfast. At last the key turned in the lock and the breakfast was pushed in—two very thin slices of black bread and a small glass of pale thin tea. He cupped his hands round the thick glass and sipped his "tea." It was made from some sort of herb and tasted faintly of mint. He ate the sour black bread as slowly as he could, making each mouthful last as long as possible.

Later in the morning the gaoler unlocked the door and handed him in a broom. Peter raised his eyebrows in interrogation. The man made signs that he was to sweep out the cell; but he shook his head in refusal. The gaoler took the broom and re-locked the door. The cell remained unswept.

He lay on his back on the bed, and waited for lunch. The fact that he had no watch worried him. He felt that it must be four o'clock a least. When the lunch did come, he asked the gaoler the time. It was half past one.

The lunch was a plate of boiled white cabbage and three potatoes cooked in their jackets.

He lay on his back on the bed and waited for dinner. When it got dark the lights were switched on from outside the cell and a guard came round outside the hut and put up the black-out shutters. With the shutters in place the room seemed smaller, and he had to fight down a moment's panic, hold back an impulse to hammer at the door and demand to be released.

Dinner was two thin slices of black bread and a cup of *ersatz* coffee.

After dinner the gaoler came in and asked him for his boots. As he watched him put them down outside the door, he laughed again at his original impression that they had been put out to be cleaned.

Shortly after this the light flickered twice. He thought that perhaps there had been a failure, or that they were changing over circuits; and he was unprepared when five minutes later the lights were extinguished for the night. He undressed in the darkness; but the next night, and for every night that he remained in the cell, he understood and obeyed the signal.

The next day, after breakfast, the gaoler again offered him th broom. Again he refused, and again the cell remained unswepte

One of the things about the cell that worried him most was. the obscured glass of the window. The light came through it satisfactorily, but the thought of what lay beyond it—country, town or further prison—tantalised him. He tried peering through the uneven surface from every angle, but could see nothing. The window had been locked with a square key and he could not unfasten it.

The long weary day was punctuated by the meals, which served only to exacerbate his hunger, and his periodic visits to the toilet. He was rested now, and the close confinement was getting on his nerves. He remembered Pop Dawson, knew that this was being done with a purpose; but still he could not prevent himself from getting rattled. If only he had something to read. If only his eyes could follow the printed lines. Anything, anything at all to take his mind outside this box of grey encroaching plaster.

So the long days dragged on. Restless days now, days in which he blamed himself for not escaping when he had the chance, days in which further escape seemed impossible, and the future stretched out as an infinity of similar days; enclosed by narrow walls, fed like an animal in a cage. As far as he could tell, no one but the *Feldwebel* and the gaoler seemed to know that he was there. Each time the gaoler brought him food he demanded to see the officer in charge, but the man merely looked at him blankly and shrugged his shoulders.

He awoke suddenly. It was night, the black-out shutters were still up, but the electric light was blazing in his face. The cell was very hot, and the light brighter than it had been in the evening, burning itself out as though with too much voltage. He lay wondering what had happened. There were voices in the corridor—then silence. Then, inexorably, the lights went out again. He tried to sleep, but could not settle down. The cell was so hot that he threw the blankets off and lay there in his underclothes.

He must have slept, because when he awoke the lights were on again. The cell was hotter than before. He was sweating. He lay and listened but he heard nothing. Suddenly, inexplicably, the lights went out again.

The following morning, after the black-out shutters had been taken down, he tried to rationalise the events of the previous night. Had he been dreaming, or had the light really been on and the cell heated almost beyond endurance? Perhaps there had been some new arrivals, which would account for the light, and he had imagined the heat. Perhaps there had been new arrivals, and the heat had been an accident. Perhaps the temperature and voltage always built up during the night . . . Perhaps they were trying to break down his morale.

At last, on the fourth day, as he was waiting for his lunch to arrive, the door was opened wide by the gaoler who then sprang stiffly to attention. After a dramatic pause a young, blond, very English-looking *Luftwaffe* officer entered the cell. He wore a pilot's badge on his tunic, and the Knight's Cross of the Iron Cross with bar. Peter, who had been sitting on the bed, rose to his feet feeling awkward in his ill-fitting khaki uniform. "Good morning," he said.

"Good morning." The German's accent was that of the West-End stage. "Thought I'd just pop in and say how do."

"Won't you sit down?" Peter said.

The German sat stiffly on the edge of the bed and produced a packet of cigarettes. He smelled strongly of shaving lotion but even this was refreshing after the smell of disinfectant. "You flew very well," he said.

"What?"

"I said that you flew very well. It was I who had the good fortune to shoot you down."

Peter felt more at ease. This was pure Pop Dawson. "Congratulations," he said.

"It was good luck. You put up a magnificent fight. It was just fortune of war, old boy."

Peter thought this was rather overdoing it.

"I would like to shake you by the hand," the German said.

Peter took his hand, wondering when he was going to get the cigarette. Surely the cigarette came next?

Yes, Pop had been right, the German offered him a cigarette. He noticed that it was an English one.

He sat on the edge of the bed and smoked the first cigarette for days. He would have preferred a pipe, but as he inhaled he felt the nicotine release the sugar in his blood, relieve the nagging hunger, soothe his nerves.

"The Wellington is not an easy aircraft to shoot down." The German's soft insistent voice dragged him back to the subject.

"No?"

"Not with the Merlin engines. Yours had the Merlin engines, I suppose?"

"I don't know."

"You don't know?" Then the pilot chuckled, the superior chuckle of pilots the world over. "Of course—you are the navigator. I have just been talking to your pilot. He tells me that you were lost."

So Wally was here, too. Peter felt an almost overpowering desire to ask about the rest of the crew, but realised that this was what the German was angling for. Perhaps it was a trap and they were still at large. He remained silent.

"A bit off course, weren't you, coming back from Hanover?" The German's soft, insistent voice was urging him to defend his skill in navigation. But he saw the trap. "I'm sorry, you know I can't talk about flying."

The German laughed, and Peter noticed his gold teeth. "Oh, I'm not an intelligence officer—I'm aircrew like yourself. I'm here on rest after my first tour of operations. I've been flying *Junkers 88s*. Have you tried your hand at flying?"

"I'm not allowed to discuss flying."

"Look here, old boy—I only came in for a chat. I'm not

interrogating you. Good Lord, I haven't sunk as low as that." He rose to his feet, offended. " However, if you're going to be stand-offish, I'll go and talk to someone else."

Peter did not want him to go. Dangerous as he was, he represented the outside world. " I'm sorry. Naturally I'm pleased to have someone to talk to. But I'm afraid I'm not allowed to discuss Service matters."

" Well, of course not, old boy! It was just that both being fliers . . ." He allowed himself to sit on the bed again. " Now what can I do for you? I'm only a visitor, don't forget . . ."

" Well—in the first place I'd like to shave. I've not been allowed to wash since I've been here. And then I'd like something to read. And to have the window of my cell open. It gets pretty stuffy in here."

" I'll do what I can about it "—then he forgot the part he was playing—" but I'm afraid that as you're not willing to co-operate with us you're going to find things a little hard at first. Life would be much easier for you, y'know, if you would decide to be sensible and tell us the little things we ask. They're not important things, you understand—we just want them for the records we make of all prisoners."

" I'm sorry, I'm afraid I can't discuss these things."

" Very well." He was on his feet again, and this time Peter did not try to stop him. " If you choose to be obstinate I'm afraid I can do nothing for you." He gathered up the cigarettes and matches from the bed and replaced his cap. " If you change your mind, tell the guard, and I will come and see you again."

During the days that followed Peter was allowed no exercise and his diet never varied. Since his first visitor he had heard nothing from Intelligence, but now he did not worry any more. The first interrogator had so closely followed the specification given by Pop Dawson that he ceased to dread the next. He spent most of his time lying on the sack of wood shavings, which he had pounded down to fit his shape, and dreaming up fantastic meals.

Every morning the gaoler brought the broom into the cell and every morning Peter refused to sweep, until at last the cell got so dirty that he had to sweep it in self-defence. Instead of being triumphant, the guard was quite pleasant about it, and in the afternoon he popped his head round the door in a conspiratorial way, a bakelite safety razor in his hand. " Wash ? Shave ? " he said.

He took Peter to the washroom half-way down the corridor. It was next door to the toilet, but he had never been allowed there before. He saw a row of basins along the wall and, opposite them, a shower bath. The guard gave him the razor, a piece of soap and a brush. " *Schnell, schnell,*" he said.

The blade was blunt, and shaving was a torture. He scraped off as much of the stubble as he could, and was washing the soap away as the gaoler returned. Peter pointed to the shower. " May I have a bath ? " he said.

The German shook his head. " *Nein, das ist kaputt. Kalt,*" he said. " Cold ! "

" Good ! " Peter said ; a cold bath was better than nothing. " *Kalt* good," he repeated.

The gaoler looked anxiously up and down the corridor, and nodded his head. " *Ja—schnell, schnell,*" he said.

Peter undressed as quickly as he could while the gaoler turned on the shower. The cold water was agonising, but glorious. He scrubbed his legs and feet, and managed to get off most of the dirt. The gaoler kept urging him to hurry, and did not seem happy until he was dressed again and on his way back to the cell.

After the bath he felt more energetic and began to explore the cell. He saw that if he could get some sort of lever he would be able to open the window. The electric light cable was secured to the wall by stout metal clips and after much hard pulling he was able to loosen one of these and prise up the window catch. The window opened inwards, and outside there were strong iron bars sunk deeply into the woodwork.

He leaned his elbows on the window frame, put his head between the bars, and breathed the cool damp air. There was a faint tang of pines and the elusive incense-like odour of burning brown coal blocks. Immediately in front of him was a football pitch, muddy and neglected, its goal posts standing at drunken angles ; while beyond this the pines, tall and pink, glowed warmly in the sun. He stood looking at them for a long time until the woods merged into dusk and he shivered by the open window.

From now on he opened the window whenever he was alone in the cell and, more than once, he was only just able to close it before the door opened to admit one or other of his interrogators.

The young German pilot had been back several times, but his visits had been short and unproductive. A more frequent visitor was a bespectacled *Feldwebel* with a clipped moustache, who said that he had been a waiter in London before the war. He spoke at length on social matters, on art, on national characteristics ; and of how Germany did not hate England, but was surprised and hurt when she declared war. All this again was pure Pop Dawson, and Peter was able to enjoy it without being trapped.

One day the *Feldwebel* brought him a small piece of sausage on a slice of bread. " It is time you were moved to the camp," he said. " You are losing your strength lying here."

" When will they move me ? " Peter asked.

" My friend," the *Feldwebel* said, looking at him through his heavy glasses. " My friend—it is all a matter of red tape. Of form-filling. All the officers here are professors from a university. They have narrow, one-track minds and cannot see things as men of the world. They have been instructed that they must get those forms filled in—but once the forms are completed they will be forgotten. Absolutely forgotten. They will be put on a file, and nobody will ever see them again. My friend—for your own sake I ask you to fill in these forms. And then you will be sent to the main camp, where you will meet your comrades. There is too much form-filling in Germany. One has to fill in forms to obtain anything. And if you do not comply, my friend, I can see that you will lie here and rot ! " There were tears in the large brown eyes behind the spectacles, and Peter had to think hard of Pop

Dawson to avoid giving in and completing the form, which he guessed the *Feldwebel* had in his inner pocket.

At intervals during his confinement the nocturnal heating and light-switching routine was carried out, but he never discovered whether this was a deliberate third-degree method or merely heralded the arrival of another prisoner.

He soon learned that it was advisable to save one of the three lunchtime potatoes to eat in the evening. He kept it warm by putting it on the top of the metal radiator at the end of the cell.

One day he found he had a neighbour—by his accent an American or a Canadian—and he obviously wanted to go to the toilet very badly indeed. Each time the red signal fell—Peter could hear it in his cell—he heard the man walk furiously up and down, cursing loudly, until the gaoler arrived with his customary, "*Toilette besetzt—Kamerad*," or literally, "Toilet occupied—friend." The fifth time that this occurred Peter heard the prisoner shout in exasperation, "Say, who is this guy Conrad? He seems to live in that place!"

His neighbour also had trouble with the interrogators, and once, at the height of an argument, Peter heard a loud thump that might have been caused by a man falling. Soon after this the American was moved away.

Every morning he piled the table and the stool on to the bed, stripped to the waist and carried out his own routine of physical training based on a combination of Yogi breathing exercises and Swedish drill. Once an interrogator came into the cell while he was in the middle of this solemn performance and, to his delight, called in the guard and had the cell thoroughly searched.

Lying on his bed one afternoon, he noticed the shadow cast by the centre bar of his window on the wall above his head. After idly watching it move along the wall as the sun moved round the sky, he thought of making a clock. When breakfast came the following morning, he made a mark on the wall under the shadow with the heel of his boot. He did the same for the midday and the evening meals. He subdivided the sections between these marks, and the clock was complete. Then he discovered that the meals did not always arrive at the same time; sometimes they were an hour early or an hour late. So he destroyed the clock.

He made a jigsaw puzzle by tearing a sheet of paper into small irregular pieces and trying to fit them together again; but this occupation was so pointless that he threw the paper away in disgust.

And at intervals the interrogators came and questioned him, or engaged him in apparently innocent conversation which always seemed at last to lead back to the forbidden topic.

On the tenth morning—he had counted them by scoring lines on the windowsill with the metal clip that he had torn from the wall—the gaoler brought him a book. It was a long book, and he began to read it carefully. He felt that he would be there for a long time, so he read every word, refusing to skip to get the sense as he usually did. He lingered over every line, seeking the author's intention, appreciating his choice of words, living intensely the lives of the characters in the book.

He had just finished the fourth chapter when a guard came to return his uniform and tell him to get ready to go across to the main camp, and he was surprised to find that he did not want to go. The cell had become a known, familiar place, had changed imperceptibly from a prison into a refuge. He asked if he could take the book with him, but was told that this was "*streng verboten.*"

Standing in the corridor, ready to go with him to the main camp, were some dozen other prisoners. He glanced swiftly at their faces, but saw none of his crew nor anyone he recognised. They were dressed in every sort of uniform from R.A.F. blue battledress to khaki bush-shirts and shorts, from flying boots to wooden clogs; but they were alike in their pallor and unkempt appearance.

After some shuffling about they were all assembled in a long straggling line and marched between armed guards out into the strong light of the open compound.

CHAPTER V

KINDRED SPIRITS

IT WAS exciting to be out in the open air again, after the close disinfected atmosphere of the cell. The air was hard and cool, strong with the scent of the pine forests which surrounded the camp. Surprisingly, the ground was covered with snow, and shouting children on skis swooped round them as they marched the few hundred yards down to the camp in the valley below. There was a lot of talking among the prisoners. Peter heard snatches of excuse and explanation. " So we just nipped across to look at Hamburg on the way back——" " ——pumped us full of lead——" " navigator took us smack over Cologne." " There we were, light as day——" " ——tried to fight our way out of it but——" " Absolutely useless——"

For himself, he did not want to talk. The spell of solitary confinement had dried his flow of speech instead of damming it. For the moment he did not care if he never spoke of flying again.

By his side a young Army officer, a captain in khaki battledress, wearing a fringe of soft dark beard, hummed quietly to himself, also withdrawn from the crossfire of verbal cannon shells.

Lining the road were wooden houses built like Swiss chalets, with balconies extending the whole length of the house. They were toylike with their high-pitched roofs and carved wooden gables, and Peter would have liked to stop and look inside. He imagined what the interior would be—the chequered linen and the honest wooden furniture.

The new arrivals were met at the gates of the compound by a small reception committee of older prisoners. There were three of them, three uncouth figures standing in the black slush of the compound waiting to welcome the new unfortunates. The first —he seemed to be in charge—was a portly middle-aged man wearing a round knitted hat, a khaki cloak fastened at the neck with a metal clip and wooden clogs. He introduced himself as

the British adjutant ; the other two, he said, were the doctor and the padre.

While the others were shaking hands Peter looked round him at the long green wooden huts, with their snow-covered roofs, the high double-fenced barbed-wire and the raised sentry boxes above the wire. As they stood there, a British soldier, brawny in his collarless khaki shirt, came from behind one of the huts, dragging a strange-looking wooden cart piled high with empty boxes. He spoke in German to the greatcoated guard at the gate. He spoke abruptly, obviously telling him to open the gate and to look sharp about it. The guard obeyed with surprising docility.

The padre led them into the nearest hut, which seemed to be the camp theatre. It had a raised stage at one end, but was now set out as a dining-room with forms and long trestle tables. They went through this to a smaller room, also a dining-room but with smaller tables and white tablecloths.

They each took a thick pottery mug from the table and drew tea from a large enamelled urn. The tea was strong and sweet.

"Good Lord, real tea," someone said.

"It comes in the Red Cross parcels," the adjutant explained. "Helps to keep the cold out. The grub's not bad really. We don't get enough of it, but what there is isn't bad. You'll be here for about ten days, then you'll be sent on to a permanent camp. This place is only a transit camp."

"What are the chances of escape from here?" It was the young Army officer.

"Not a hope, old boy. Even if you got out of the camp, this snow would give you away. You'd leave tracks wherever you went. No—I shouldn't think about it from here. Wait till you get to the permanent camp. Wait till summer—you'd not get far in this weather . . . What are things like in England? Where were you shot down?"

"Libya."

"What were you flying?"

There was a gleam of amusement in the dark eyes above the downy beard. "A B.S.A."

The adjutant looked nonplussed for a moment. He looked at the slim figure in khaki battledress, and slowly realised. "Oh—you're in the Army!"

When they had finished their tea, the adjutant took them to a locked room where military clothing was stacked on shelves from floor to ceiling. He gave them each a toothbrush, a cake of soap, a towel, some woollen underclothes, a pullover and an R.A.F. greatcoat. "They're sent out by the Red Cross," he explained. "I'll get you to sign for them, as I expect they'll be entered against your account at home. Now I expect you'd like a bath."

The water was hot. Peter stripped off his dirty underclothes and stood under the shower for about twenty minutes, soaping himself and letting the hot water run over his head and down his back. The room became full of steam from the dozen showers. Pink figures ran shouting across the slatted floor. The sound of falling water mingled with snatches of song. He felt happy again. If they could get a shower like this every day things wouldn't be too bad. He made the most of it, fearing that it would be a weekly affair. He stood under the hot water until he was thoroughly soaked and pink all over from the heat, then turned on the cold water until he was gasping and spluttering. He dried himself on his new towel, and went across to the washbasin standing against the wall and cleaned his teeth with the new toothbrush. He brushed for about ten minutes; and then he shaved, shaved as carefully as he would have done if he had been going to a dance in the Mess. It was grand, this shave with a new blade, grand to feel the stiff bristles melt into nothing before the razor. After shaving he dressed in the clean underclothes and went back to the room where, the adjutant had told him, he would find a bed.

There were six beds in the room, and on one of them the Army captain was sitting, drying his hair.

"Is there a spare bed?" Peter asked.

"They're all spare, I think." He stopped rubbing his head. "I thought I'd have this one. But I don't mind, if you'd rather be near the door."

"No, it's all right, thanks," Peter told him, "I'll take this." He put his clothes on one of the beds near the window. "My name's Howard, Peter Howard."

"I'm John Clinton. I say—what sort of dump is this?"

"In what way?"

"This 'permanent staff' business. I've been talking to one of the chaps who's been here a few days. He says that they feed in a mess of their own—special rations and everything. Permanent staff! They look it too, I must say. That adjutant was fairly dripping with fat." He sat, young and indignant, holding the towel between his slim brown hands. He seemed too warm, too vital to be kept for long in this sterile atmosphere.

At first Peter felt an impulse to defend his own service against this attack from the Army, but the captain's indignation was without rancour. He grinned instead. "I thought you didn't altogether approve."

"It's his precious defeatist attitude," Clinton said, "telling us not to escape from here, indeed. Frightened it'd upset his precious routine, I expect." He sat on the edge of the bed, his black hair standing on end, angrily tying the laces of his suède desert boots. "Permanent staff, indeed."

"He's right in a way, you know," Peter said. "We wouldn't get far with all this snow on the ground."

"That's just an excuse, but it becomes an attitude of mind if you're not careful." He rose to his feet and began to rearrange the blankets on his bed. "I'm getting out of this as soon as I get the chance."

"I wouldn't be too optimistic," Peter said.

As he walked along to the end hut where, the adjutant had told him, he would find his crew, Peter thought of John Clinton and his youthful indignation. He had been like that himself, once. But now, at thirty, he had grown more tolerant. He found it difficult enough to drive himself at times without the added task of driving others. Clinton could not be more than twenty-two or three, he decided. Straight from school into the Army, probably.

He found his crew crowded together into a small room with ten other sergeants. The place seemed full of two-tier metal bunks and had a fire burning fiercely in the cast-iron stove. It was unbearably hot and smelled of old socks, drying uniforms and closely-crowded humanity.

Mac, the New Zealand rear-gunner, was the first to see him. "Pete!" he said. "Hey chaps, look who's here!"

Peter went in. All his crew were there, and he was glad to be with them, but embarrassed because as an officer his living conditions were so much better than theirs. He had felt this embarrassment in England where—although they had shared the same crew-room and flown in the same aircraft—social distinctions had ordained that they should eat and sleep in different Messes. Here, surrounded by their enemies, it seemed even more absurd.

Wally made a place for him, near the stove. He was cooking something in a tin, which he stirred at intervals with a piece of wood. "We were just talking about you, Peter," he said. "We thought you must have made it." He turned back to the tin again; earnest, methodical Wally, as interested in the brew he was making as he would have been in flying his aircraft.

"Or bought it," the wireless operator said.

Peter felt their friendliness wash round him, stronger than any difference in living conditions or perquisites of rank. "I jolly nearly made it," he told them. "Got into Holland, but got nabbed by the police. It was my own fault for walking about in broad daylight. What happened to you chaps?"

"Junior didn't get far," Wally said, "did you, Junior?"

Junior grinned. He was a Canadian and the oldest member of the crew. He was lying on one of the lower bunks, both his feet swathed in bandages.

"His boots fell off," Wally explained. "His boots fell off as the parachute opened, and the silly clot walked for two nights in his socks."

"Shucks, I didn't walk very far."

"When they caught him they made him walk seven miles in his socks." Mac said it as a joke.

"The ground was pretty soft thought" Junior sighed and wriggled himself more comfortably into the mattress. "I did better than Mac anyway."

Mac had an ugly red cut on his forehead, and one of his eyes was turning yellow. It had obviously recently been black.

"What on earth happened to you?" Peter asked.

"It wasn't on the earth," Mac said. "I came down in a tree.

The 'chute got caught in the top branches and left me hanging about fifteen feet from the ground."

"What did you do, bang the quick-release?"

"My oath—then landed flat on me back."

"That's how you got the black eye!"

"No it wasn't. I cut my head open as I came down through the branches—but I got the black eye from a silly fool of a farmer . . . I thought I was in Holland . . ."

There was a hoot of laughter from the listening airmen. "Typical rear-gunner," one of them said. "It's a wonder he didn't think he was over England."

Mac ignored the interruption. "I thought I was in Holland, so I walked up to a farm and asked them for a meal." He looked resentfully at Peter. "What d'you think happened then? The silly fool hit me in the eye! I sort of realised that I wasn't wanted, and came to the conclusion that I wasn't in Holland after all. He started to scream at me in German so I scarpered off as hard as I could. I'm going back after the war though—I'll get that farmer . . ." Tenderly he stroked his swollen eye. "My oath . . . I got into the woods after that, and started to go west. I kept going for a couple of days, and then got picked up by some jokers in green plus fours. I made a dash for it, but they started popping off shotguns at me. Then I tripped over a root and thought I'd better stay where I was. How long've you been out of the cooler, Pete?"

"Came out to-day."

"I've got some tucker here." Mac ducked under the clothes-line heavy with damp washing, and crossed to a row of wooden lockers. He returned with a few biscuits and a piece of cheese. "Got these from an Aussie in the cookhouse." The biscuits looked dirty, and the cheese had a semi-circle bitten out of one end, but Peter took them gratefully.

Wally was still stirring his tin on the top of the stove. "Just a minute, Pete—we're making a brew here. Be something to drink with the cheese. Bring me a cup, Teddy."

The engineer handed him two of the large pottery beer mugs

from which they had drunk their tea earlier in the morning, and Wally poured out the thick milky liquid.

" What is it ? " Peter asked.

" Junior's escape tablets. He managed to get 'em through the search. What sort of time did you have in the cooler, Pete ? Did you have a visit from the chap who said he'd shot us down ? "

" Yes—he said you told him we were lost."

Wally laughed. " Sorry, Pete, I thought it would save a lot of awkward questions. He got pretty annoyed with me. I told him we were flying an Anson." He handed Peter one of the steaming mugs and, opening the bottom of the stove, raked out half a dozen potatoes which had been roasting there.

" Mac seems to have been pretty busy," Peter said.

" Commissariat, that's me ! " Mac handed the hot potatoes round among the sergeants. " You've got to have a syndicate in a place like this."

He's ruthless, Peter thought ; ruthless and loyal to his group. He could see that Mac would get all there was to get out of captivity, and return to civilian life as hard and ruthless as ever, but more experienced.

" We're being moved to Lamsdorf in a few days," Wally said. " We've all decided to stick together."

" Good show," Peter said. " I haven't heard what's happening to me."

" You'll go to an officers' camp." Mac said it without bitterness. " You look after yourself, Pete—no one else will."

" I'll look after myself," Peter said. " Have you thought about escaping ? "

" Not a hope," Mac said. " Lie low till the war's over."

" I'm going to study," Wally said. " Get some good out of it. We're lucky to be alive. Now's the time to catch up and get ready for a job when the war's over." Peter looked at the big, roughly carved head with its mop of unruly hair, and decided that Wally would come through, too.

" Then an old chap with glasses came in," Wally continued, " that was after the chap who said he'd shot us down. This one was an old chap in civilian clothes with a Red Cross badge in his buttonhole. He had a Red Cross form that started off quite normally, asking for your rank, name and number—then went on to ask other things like your squadron and your bomb load. I got as far as rank, name and number and then, when I realised what it was all about, I tore the thing up. The old chap was livid—thought he was going to have a fit or something. He didn't look too strong anyway. I made it up to him by telling him that I learned to fly on Tigers."

" Och, I had the same wee fellow." Teddy, the engineer, came from Glasgow. " He asked me if I'd like to broadcast to my people at home, but I told him they hadna got a wireless set."

" Where were you captured ? " Peter asked him.

" Och, I hadna got a chance. When I heard the skipper say bale out, I went to get ma parachute. I cuid have sworn I'd left it there on its rack at the rear of the aircraft. But when I got there it wasna there. And it was getting really hot there, in the back of the aircraft. So I thought for a bit, and decided I'd left it by the front escape hatch when I got aboard. I'd meant to bring it up with me but forgot all about it. I scrambled down to where I'd left it, but the flames were right across the aircraft by then and I had to crawl along the floor. There it was, though—balancing on the edge of the open hatch. I cuidna get down there quick enough, I thought it was going to fall out. I cuidna get out quickly enough either—the rest of you had gone hours before, except for Wally yonder and he was sitting there as calm as you like holding her steady. I must have baled out at about five hundred feet, because I knocked myself unconscious, and when I came round there were soldiers standing over me."

Peter turned to Wally to ask the question he had wanted to ask ever since he had entered the room. It still seemed impossible that the pilot could have escaped alive from that burning aircraft.

" How on earth did you get out, Wally ? "

" I didn't. I was just thinking of crash-landing when I suddenly saw a lake—so I ditched instead."

" Just like that ? "

"I was flying upwind anyway and the lake was pretty big."

"So you just ditched," Peter said. He knew that if it had not been for the lake Wally would never have survived. If it had not been for Wally, sitting there in his blazing aircraft, facing almost certain death so that his crew might escape, none of them would have survived. "So you just ditched," he said, "in the middle of Germany!"

"It wasn't Germany," Wally protested. "It was Holland."

At lunchtime Peter found himself a place next to John Clinton, who was now one of the few men in khaki. The North Africa people had changed their khaki drill for R.A.F. "other ranks" blue serge, and the scene reminded Peter of his early days in Training Command. The conversation was almost entirely of flying, and he felt sympathy for the silent figure by his side. "When did you get caught?" he asked.

"December the seventeenth."

"So was I. How extraordinary. How did they bring you here?"

"By air." The soldier grinned. "It's the only time I've ever flown, I'm afraid."

"Some of these chaps haven't done much more," Peter said. "The more they talk the less they've flown."

"I thought it was rather like that. I always thought it wasn't done to talk about flying in the mess."

"That was the 1914 war. Who's that other Army bod at the head of the table?" The man had intrigued Peter ever since he had entered the room. His face looked as though it had been hacked from red sandstone with a blunt chisel. He had one cauliflower ear, and was dressed in camouflaged paratroop's overalls.

"He's an M.O.," Clinton told him. "He's got a bed in our room. Most extraordinary character. He's brought a bag full of surgical instruments."

"Useful chap to have around. I wonder if he's got any food tablets."

Clinton lowered his voice. "We're thinking about a tunnel from our room. We wondered if you'd be game."

"You can count me in." Peter looked at the doctor eating in silence at the head of the table. He seemed a determined, methodical sort of chap; a man with a certain inflexibility. "He doesn't look much like a doctor," he said.

"He started life as a boxer," Clinton told him, "then he decided he had to be a doctor, so he took his degree. When the war started he was working for a mission in the East End. He's the most gentle creature I've met."

"He looks it."

"No—I mean it. He's so strong that he's gentle with it, like an enormous dog."

When the lunch was over Clinton introduced him to the doctor who suggested a walk round the huts. The man was certainly built like a boxer and walked with a rolling jerk. He had discarded the jumping jacket and was wearing a khaki sweater in which he looked like an American footballer or the hero of a strip cartoon.

He seemed doubtful about the tunnel. "I've been talking to the German M.O.," he explained. "He says that if I put in an application I can be moved to one of the P.O.W. hospitals, on the staff. I'd travel there on my own with one, or possibly two guards. I think I'd have more chance that way than by staying with you chaps. The only thing is that, if I don't make the jump, once I get to the hospital I shall be on parole and unable to escape. I'm rather worried about it. I don't know what to do."

"What about the tunnel from here?" Peter asked.

The doctor laughed. "That's really Clinton's idea. We haven't a hope, really. We haven't time. The German M.O. told me that we'll all be moved in a few days. I think you'd do better by jumping off the train than by digging anyway. A tunnel would take too long."

"We shall have plenty of time where we're going," Clinton said.

"I had a long train journey, coming here," Peter told them.

"It's not as easy to jump off a train as you might think. They watch you pretty closely. Besides, even if you got away you'd be in uniform. I'd say you stand a better chance to dig a tunnel from the permanent camp. Get out in the proper clothes and take your time over it."

"I'm not going to a permanent camp," Clinton said. "I must get away before then." He sounded almost desperate.

"Oh, I don't know . . ."

"I must. There are thousands of chaps in permanent camps. Escape will be pretty nearly impossible from there."

"I don't suppose they all try to escape," Peter said. "I've just been talking to some of my crew. They don't even seem to want to get away."

"They will." Clinton was striding at a terrific pace along the beaten path which ran round the compound inside the wire, walking as though he could walk away from his captivity. "They're just numbed now. Most of us are. Now is the time to try to escape. Before it is too late."

"I've been talking to the adjutant again," Peter said. "He still recommends waiting until we get to the permanent camp."

"He should be court-martialled." Clinton was almost running now. "We must strike while the iron is hot."

A few days later the sergeants left for Lamsdorf. Standing in the slush of the compound, watching them march away, Peter felt that his last link with the world he knew was being broken. He turned back into the camp, but could not face the crowded ante-room. It was all so mean, so sordid; squabbling over who was to have the slightly larger slice of bread, bolting breakfast to rush and bag a chair; queuing early in order to get the best seat at the concert. It was infectious, he was doing it himself. It was like it had been when he first joined up; a crowd of adults thrown together, without common loyalties or ties of any sort. Later, when they had started on the navigation course, there had been the common goal of the "Wings" exam, but here they had nothing. Not even the remote aim of trying to win the war. The future was grey and endless; endless feeble chatter, endless preoccupation with rations, endless lack of privacy. He thrust his hands deep into his trouser pockets and plodded slowly round the wire, head down, shoulders hunched ; a typical forlorn " kriegie " attitude.

That evening he heard that the paratroop doctor had been killed while jumping off the train on his way to the hospital at Obermassfeld.

CHAPTER VI

WELCOME TO OFLAG XXIB

EVERY WEEK a list of names of those who were to be "purged" to a permanent camp was pinned to the notice-board in the dining-room. This week the purge was to *Oflag XXIB* in Poland, and Peter's name was in the list. He was glad to see that John Clinton was going with him. There was something about the young Army officer's quiet self-sufficiency that had captured his respect. He had shaken off the first, almost panic-stricken frenzy to get away and spent most of his time reading. It seemed a complete reversal of his earlier frame of mind, but Peter sensed that he was holding himself firmly in check, realising that their stay in this transit camp was short, tiding over the time until he could concentrate wholly on the problem of escape.

As soon as Peter knew that at last they were really going, he began to make plans for his own escape. Convinced that he had not made the most of his opportunities, refusing to accept excuses from himself, he vowed that he too would make his getaway.

He sewed special hidden pockets into the lining of his great-coat, where he concealed the scalpels and the little food he had managed to collect. He spent hours in the library studying an encyclopædia from which the censor had omitted to remove the maps. He traced some of the maps on to toilet paper and hid them with the other things. But the doctor's death had made him even more pessimistic about jumping trains, and he knew in his heart that this preparation was merely a front to convince himself that he was doing all he could to get away.

At last the purge party was assembled outside the huts, complete with baggage. Peter was amazed at the quantity some of them had managed to collect in so short a time. They were made to march to the station, which was several miles away, and he was glad that he had decided to travel light.

John Clinton carried his luggage in his pockets, including a book that he had taken from the prison library. He marched with an amused expression in his eyes.

" What's so funny ? " Peter asked.

" These chaps with their bundles. They look like the lost tribes of Israel."

" Maybe they've got some sense. You don't know where we might find ourselves." Peter shifted his small bundle from one shoulder to the other. " Probably just as well to have something to start life with. It may be a perfectly new camp, with nothing there at all."

" There's no point in preparing to settle down," Clinton muttered. " If you set out with that idea you'll never get away. Look at that chap ! " He nodded towards a broad, stocky air-gunner named Saunders, who was staggering along under the burden of an unwieldy bundle wrapped in a blanket. He had a large " Bomber Command " moustache, and wore a balaclava helmet and flying boots.

" Old Bill looking for a better 'ole," Peter said. " I wonder what he's got in the bundle."

" Doesn't matter what it is. It shows that he's preparing to settle down."

At the railway station they were lined up by the *Feldwebel* and then addressed by the officer in charge. " Gentlemen," he said, " you will be some days in the train. If you behave reasonably, you will be reasonably treated. If you attempt to escape, you will be shot. This is not an idle threat. The guards have been given instructions to shoot any prisoner who attempts to escape. There is a live round in every barrel. That is all, gentlemen."

They were herded into carriages which were divided into compartments in the English fashion, but the seats were wooden.

Peter found himself squeezed into the corner of a compartment opposite a tall fair flight lieutenant and Saunders, who had arrived triumphant with his bundle, which he put on the floor between their legs. Next to Peter sat Clinton, already reading his book.

"Any more for Margate?" Saunders seemed determined to make it a pleasant journey. He handed cigarettes round, and soon the air was thick and stale with smoke. Four men at the far end of the compartment began a game of cards. Peter wondered which of them had been shot down with a pack of playing cards in his pocket—or had he picked them up at *Dulag-Luft*? Saunders had evidently been laying in a stock of something or other, judging by the size of his bundle. Peter looked at him closely. A red good-humoured face with a mouth that smiled easily under his grotesque moustache, a smile that was half-suppressed like that of a schoolboy. The mass of untidy hair, tow-coloured, and a quick dogmatic way of speaking that was not aggressive. An easy chap to get along with.

The flight lieutenant next to him was of a different breed. Fair and slim, even in his issue uniform he looked immaculate; his moustache was short and carefully tended. His name was Hugo, and he sat now as though the whole trip had been arranged as a sort of pleasure outing in which, although not entirely approving, he felt he ought to play his part.

Two hours later the train was still in the station. They had made several false starts, but had been shunted back to their original position again. At last, as though satisfied with the lesson it had taught them, the engine whistled in derision, and slowly the train pulled out.

Long hours of sitting on a wooden seat . . . nothing to read . . . falling asleep, and waking stiff . . . smoking, yawning, and moving restlessly . . . thinking of home . . .

Often the train stopped for no apparent reason, miles from

any station. Each time it stopped, the German soldiers jumped down on to the track, and stood with tommy-guns at the ready until it started again. Each time it stopped, Peter tensed himself to escape, but each time he saw that it was hopeless. There were raised sentry boxes, fitted with machine-guns, at both ends of every carriage.

John Clinton, when he had finished with his book, which was of no use to the others as it was Latin verse, proved himself a lively and interesting travelling companion. He told them that he had been born in Malaya, that his father owned a rubber plantation where he had lived until he was sent home to school in England. He had just gone up to Oxford when the war started, and he had joined the Army. He kept them amused for hours with stories of his troop of bren-gun carriers. It seemed to Peter that if he needed a partner in his escape he could go a long way and not find a better man than John Clinton.

Saunders, who together with his brother ran a greengrocer's shop in North London, did not appear disturbed at the prospect of several years' captivity. The business would go on and in time he would return to it. He took life as it came, finding it good and full of queer incidents which he invited the others to observe from his own original and slightly derisive viewpoint. Life to him, too, was something to be chuckled at, a chuckle in his case at once suppressed and followed by a quick look over his shoulder. He had started his career with a kerbside barrow off Oxford Street, and still retained that furtive, quick look round for the police.

Hugo on the other hand seemed almost devoid of humour. He was gentle, languid and charmingly self-centred. He made a perfect foil for Saunders. His main concerns at the moment were that there would be no facilities for washing in the camp —as, indeed, there were none on the train—and that he would not be given enough to eat. "What couldn't I do to a steak," he sighed. "With lashings of chip potatoes and red gravy. A T-bone steak."

"I'd settle for a plate of fish and chips," Saunders said.

"I'd settle for a tin of spam," Peter added.

" All you chaps think about is food," John said. " When I was in the desert——"

" Look out," Saunders said. " There's that sand blowing in again ! "

Beyond the steamed-up window miles and miles of pine forest, dark inside but with the tall trunks of the outer trees reddened by the sun ; inside the compartment boredom and depression, hunger and thirst, the smell of old socks, the choky heaviness of the smoke-filled atmosphere.

Then the failure of the heating plant, the cold.

The cold.

Icicles, formed by their breath on the window-pane—breaking them off to suck because they had no water.

By the third day they had eaten their rations and Peter had given up all hope of escape from the train. He took the food that he had saved from the hidden pockets in his coat, and shared it round among the men at his end of the compartment. Following his example, John Clinton produced a hidden store of food which he too shared. " Might as well eat it as let the Germans have it," he said. They looked at the others expectantly, but apparently any plans they had made to escape did not include a stock of food.

Late in the afternoon of the fourth day the train made one of its customary halts at a small wayside station, but this time it was different. The escort came down the train, shouting, " *'Raus, 'raus ! Ausgehen, alle ausgehen !* "

Looking out of the open door Peter saw that they had been surrounded by a cordon of soldiers, steel-helmeted and armed with tommy-guns.

" This is it," Saunders said. " Full military honours, too."

It was growing dark as they got down from the train. A fine sleet was falling, powdering their greatcoats and restricting their view. It was colder here than it had been in Frankfurt, and as far as Peter could see there was nothing but a flat unbroken sheet of snow. "Looks as though we've come to Siberia," Saunders said.

There were arc lamps hanging by the side of the track and the prisoners were paraded there for roll-call. They were counted three times before the guards could find the correct number and they were able to set out, at a shambling gait, for the camp.

The road led them straight across a plain towards a village whose few pale lights flickered wanly through the falling snow. It was little more than a track, seamed and furrowed by passing carts but improving as it neared the village, until they were marching on cobblestones which rang under the steel of their boots. The guards—there were nearly as many guards as there were prisoners—marched at their side, tommy-guns at the ready, while in front and behind the column were lorries with searchlights and machine-guns.

As they neared the village, some of the men at the head of the column began to sing. Slowly the song crept down the ranks until the whole company was singing. To Peter, it seemed that they were singing to show the villagers that, although captured, they were not defeated; he was thankful that they had chosen, not a patriotic song, but *Bless 'Em All* as their tune.

Leaving the village behind them they climbed a long hill, stumbling and slipping on the icy road. They were tired now, and had stopped singing. Presently they saw the lights of the camp ahead, the great circle of arc lamps, and the searchlights sweeping slowly across the empty compound. As they drew near a searchlight was turned on them, blinding them and throwing long shadows from the unevenness of the snow-packed road. It lit up their pale faces, dark beginnings of beards, the odd shape of scarves tied round their heads and the bundles they carried on their backs.

The gates were thrown open and the long straggling line of prisoners marched into the camp, peering through the darkness for some hint of what they were to expect. They could only see the wire, bright and hard in the light of the arc lamps, and the black and red-striped sentry box. Untidily they closed up on the leading ranks, who had halted. The gates were shut behind them with a creak and clatter of chains.

The prisoners eased the bundles from their shoulders. Some of them lit cigarettes ; a *Feldwebel* ran up and down the column telling them not to smoke, but they took no notice. The falling snow settled on their heads and shoulders as they stood waiting in the horizontal beam of the searchlight.

Then they were counted again, several times. Peter heard the Germans arguing about the count, and was filled with a feeling of sick futility. He stood in the cold muddy snow of the compound dumbly waiting for the guards to make a move. All he wanted was to get out of the snow. He thought with nostalgia of the dry room at *Dulag-Luft.* Even the railway carriage would have been better than this.

At last the guards agreed on the count, and the prisoners were marched into a large cement-faced building which stood just beyond the light of the arc lamps.

As he stood in the long queue, Peter wondered why they must be searched again. They had been searched before leaving *Dulag-Luft* ; what would the Germans imagine they would have picked up during the journey ? When his turn came, he stood and watched the guard trying to unravel the series of elaborate knots with which he had tied his bundle—the Germans never used knives, too salvage-conscious, he supposed. He wished he had added a few more knots for luck. The things the doctor had given him, together with the small brass compass and the maps he had copied from the encyclopædia were safe in their hidden pockets, and he managed to get them through undiscovered.

When the last man had been searched the prisoners were taken to a large hall, where they were handed over to the Senior British Officer. There were tables and forms set out in the hall, and the newcomers were given a cup of tea and two slices of black bread thinly spread with jam. When they had eaten they were addressed by the tall lean group captain, whose lined face looked haggard under his battered service cap.

" Gentlemen," he said, " before you go to your new quarters

I should like to say a few words about the general running of this camp. The organisation is simple, and I want to keep it that way. I, as Senior British Officer, am responsible to the German authorities for all that goes on inside the camp ; but I'll tell you more about that later.

" The building you are in is known as the White House. It was once a reformatory, but no prisoners sleep here now. It is used for the camp theatre and lecture rooms and for the library. Normally no prisoners are allowed in the building after dark.

" There are ten barrack blocks in the compound. Each barrack block is divided into twelve messes. In each mess there are eight officers. Each barrack block is under the command of a wing commander or a squadron leader. Each mess has a senior officer, who is responsible to the block commander for the conduct of his mess.

" All discipline is self-imposed. You will find, before you have been very long in the camp, that most of our energy is devoted to a ceaseless war against the enemy. To carry on this war, a spirit of loyalty and service is essential. You will find such a spirit in this camp.

" Our foremost activity is—escape. Do not forget that there are men here who have been escaping ever since they were captured. At the moment there is a tunnel half-way towards the wire. No—don't be alarmed. I can speak freely. The guards have gone, and we have stooges posted at every window. I tell you this because I want to warn you against ill-considered attempts at escape. If you rashly take the first chance that offers itself, it is more than likely that you will fail. That is not important ; what is important is that, in failing, you may uncover another, long-planned scheme that, but for your interference, might have succeeded.

" There is a special body of officers in this camp known as the Escape Committee. It is their job to co-ordinate and assist all escape attempts. If you have an idea, take it to them. Do not be afraid that by doing so you will lose control of the scheme. It is your scheme, and you will be the first man to leave the camp by means of it, if it succeeds. The Escape Committee will arrange for your forged passports and civilian clothes. We have special departments whose only job is making these things. If you have a scheme of escape, take it to the Committee. They are all experienced men, and they will give you all the help they can.

" The Germans have their own security branch. It is known as the *Abwehr*. They employ specially trained men we call 'ferrets.' You will recognise them in the camp by their blue overalls and the long steel spikes they carry. These men are dangerous. They all speak English and are expert in the discovery of escape activity. You will find them hiding under the floor and in the roof, listening at the keyhole and the windows. Look out for them.

" We have our counter-ferrets. We call them 'stooges.' Every ferret that comes into the camp is shadowed by a stooge. There are stooges standing at every window and door as I am talking. Before I began, they searched every possible hiding-place within hearing distance of this room. You, also, will be asked to volunteer for this duty. It is practically the only duty you will be asked to perform, and I hope you will do it cheerfully.

" If you attempt to escape—and I hope you will—you will find it an ungrateful task. Its greatest function is that it boosts the morale of your fellow prisoners. They feel that while there is an escape attempt in operation we are doing something against the enemy—not just vegetating. As I told you when we first met, there is a wonderful spirit in this camp. I hope that you will foster that spirit."

When the group captain had gone, the new purge was divided into groups to be distributed among the ten barrack blocks. Peter and John Clinton made up a party with Saunders, the air-gunner, and Hugo, the tall immaculate flight lieutenant.

As they made their way down the stairs of the White House Peter felt the warmth and integrity of the group captain still with him. Here was a man to follow, a man with something positive to offer. What a difference between this and the weak opportunism of *Dulag-Luft*. He was almost cheerful again, eager to take his part in the war that would continue in this camp.

Outside, it was still snowing. The roofs of the barrack blocks were covered in snow, but the ground inside the compound had been churned into thick black sludge. Duck-board rafts outside the doors of the long low barracks were half under water, and the newcomers cursed as they squelched their way through the darkness.

The door to their barrack block was secured by lock and bar —a modern lock, Peter noticed, and a wooden bar four inches thick, resting in heavy iron brackets. The guard unfastened the door and led them into a small vestibule. The by now familiar stench, which had so astonished them during their first days at *Dulag-Luft*, told them what lay beyond the door which faced them—typical German P.O.W. sanitation.

There were two more double doors on their right, and these the guard kicked open without ceremony.

After the freshness of the night, the fug inside was overpowering. The big low room was almost in darkness. Through the gloom of smoke and steam, Peter could see row upon row of two-tier wooden bunks diminishing into hazy perspective. As his eyes grew accustomed to the smoke he noticed that the bunks had been pulled out from the walls to form a series of small rooms. In each room stood a wooden table on which a guttering home-made lamp shed a feeble dull red glow. Smoke from these lamps joined with steam from rows and rows of damp washing which hung on lines almost down to head level, to form clouds which billowed and eddied under the roof. The concrete floor was puddled with the water which dripped incessantly from the rows of washing. There were windows in each of the side walls, but these were covered from the outside by black-out shutters. There seemed to be no ventilation whatever.

Round each small table sat a group of prisoners playing cards or trying to read by the light of the home-made lamps, which threw weird and distorted shadows on the walls, once white-washed, now grey and smeared by smoke and steam. Most of the men were wearing beards, their hair was long, and they shuffled round in wooden clogs or sat huddled on their bunks, blankets hunched round their shoulders, merging with the shadows that surrounded every feeble light. There was a buzz of conversation which dropped into curious silence as the new arrivals entered.

In one corner of the room a reedy gramophone ground out a dance tune, strident in the sudden hush.

A figure emerged from the shadows, and came towards them. He was wearing a worn R.A.F. tunic on which, below the pilot's wings, was the ribbon of the D.F.C with bar. On the sleeves, almost worn away, were the three rings of a wing commander. He was dark and bearded, and his feet were thrust into huge wooden clogs which he scraped along the concrete floor as he walked.

"Hallo, chaps—are you the new lot from *Dulag*?"

"Yes, sir."

"Good show. Sorry about the light—it'll come on again presently, I expect. Goon reprisal. My name's Stewart. Had a rough journey?"

"Pretty grim, sir, yes."

"Well, we've got some food fixed up for you. And by the way, don't call me 'sir'—we dispense with that sort of thing here. You'll want a wash before you eat. Just drop your things, and I'll show you round. You've got soap and towels, I expect."

He took them down the central gangway formed by narrow wooden lockers, which screened off the "rooms" which lay behind them. "You'll find us a bit bolshie, I expect, but the morale is pretty good—the Hun can't do a thing with us."

Peter, glancing in through the narrow doorways between the lockers, saw that the messes were divided one from the other by bunks standing at right angles to the wall. Each mess had a table and two long wooden forms, and seemed isolated, drawn round its own centre of fitful light. The effect of a squalid prolific slum was intensified by the festoons of washing which hung everywhere.

As they entered the washroom at the far end of the block, the electric light came on. There was a round of ironic cheers from the prisoners in the larger room.

" It won't be for long," Stewart told them. " The goons do it for fun. You'd better take advantage of it and get washed up while you can."

Peter looked at the two long cement troughs, above which ran an iron pipe with taps at intervals. There were wooden duck-boards on the floor, which was awash with greasy water. " The drains have stopped up again," Stewart explained. " We complain about it every day, but it doesn't do any good."

The newcomers set about removing some of the accumulated dirt of the four days' journey. The water was cold. As Peter washed, he thought of the wing commander's description " bolshie." What did he mean by bolshie ? The place was certainly primitive enough. He looked round him at the flooded floor and dirty walls.

There was a sudden burst of conversation and loud laughter from the large room, as the door opened and a man came out carrying a large tin which he began to fill under one of the taps. He was dressed in a short sleeveless jacket roughly cobbled from blankets. His hair was cropped down to a quarter of an inch in length, and as he waited for the tin to fill he sang softly to himself. Peter watched him furtively ; it seemed almost unbelievable that this could be a British officer. He felt as he had felt on his first day at school. When the man had gone, he looked across the trough at John, who was washing his beard. " What d'you make of this ? " he asked.

" Better than the last place," John said. " It's got a sort of discipline. You know where you are, in a place like this."

" Looks pretty grim to me." Hugo ran a wet comb through his hair, patting the wave into shape with his hand. " Almost a boy scout atmosphere."

" It'll be all right." Saunders was holding his dental plate under the running tap. Without his teeth his face looked old and drawn. " Better than the flak over Duisburg, any road."

" I didn't mind the flak." Hugo was now combing his moustache. " You can put up with almost anything if you've got civilised living conditions."

" Listen to him," Saunders said. " Civilised living conditions! He doesn't know he's alive." To Hugo, " I bet you've never been hungry in your life."

" Not until I came to Germany."

" Then you've been lucky," Saunders told him.

The wing commander called them together. Under the shadow of his beard his face was thin. " I know you've just had a pi-jaw from the S.B.O., so I'll make mine as short as possible. I'm going to put you chaps in the end mess, but for dinner this evening you will each go to a different mess, partly because we've drawn no rations for you yet and partly "—he grinned—" so that you can give all the gen about home. You're the first batch from England since we arrived here, so you'll have to answer a lot of questions. Do it as cheerfully as you can—the chaps have been away a long time.

" Flight Lieutenant Tyson is the hut representative on the Escape Committee, and if you want to escape we'll give you all the help we can. Your chances of getting back are practically nil. I'm telling you this because we don't want the game cluttered up with chaps who aren't prepared to put in everything they've got.

" Another thing: Don't be polite to the Hun. Don't let him be polite to you. If we behaved ourselves he could do with a tenth of the number of guards he has to use now. Relax for a moment, say a polite word to him—and you'll find yourself becoming a dead-beat. Don't forget for a single second that these are your enemies. Do everything in your power to make their job as difficult as you can.

" I'm putting you in the end mess. There's a chap there you might find a bit of a strain at first, he's a queer type. But there will only be six of you instead of the usual eight. You should be able to cope. Stick it as long as you can anyway, and if you find it too much let me know."

" What d'you mean," Saunders asked, " a queer type? "

" Oh, he's a bit round the bend, that's all. Strain, y'know. There's a Pole, too ; his name's Otto Sechevitsky. He more or less looks after Loveday. If I were you I'd be guided by Otto until you know the ropes. You'll find life a bit strange here at first no doubt, and Otto's got the thing buttoned up as well as anybody. If you follow him you won't go far wrong."

He took them to a mess at the extreme end of the block, near the entrance and unpleasantly close to the latrine.

Otto and Loveday were playing chess. The wing commander introduced them. " I'll leave you now," he said. " Otto will look after you."

As soon as he had gone, Loveday rose to his feet. He was a tall raw-boned man and his nose looked as though it had been squashed in below his protuberant forehead. The eyes, deep-set, slanted upwards and outwards, giving the face a cunning look belied by the wide slack mouth which showed red and moist through the tangled beard. He was wearing clogs, a greatcoat and a Balaclava helmet.

He cleared his throat. " *I'll* look after you individuals. You are all suffering from shock. You are all a bit unstrung. But I understand the position." He spoke slowly, punctuating each word with a stabbing movement of one of his large raw-looking hands. " I make allowances for newcomers. It's fate that sent you here. And fate that sent me to look after you. Ain't that right, Otter ? " He chuckled without mirth and looked at Otto, who smiled in an embarrassed way. " You may think an individual has free will—but he hasn't. Life's a chess-board and we're all pawns." He knocked one of the pieces from the board with a sweep of his mittened right hand and looked at Peter. " Ain't that right ? " he said.

Peter hesitated. " Er—yes," he said.

Loveday looked at him for a long time, while Peter felt himself coloured with confusion.

" You'll learn," Loveday said. " You'll learn soon enough. Won't he, Otter ? He'll learn in time." He looked round at the others. " You'll all learn." He looked at the chess-board and chuckled again. " Little pawns on a big board." He began to drum his fingers on the table-top.

" All the bunks are free," Otto said, " except these two." He indicated the two-tier wooden bedstead farthest from the doorway. He was a thin brittle-looking man whose grey eyes were calm and patient beneath a mass of straw-coloured hair. He looked oddly military and neat standing there beside Loveday's untidy bulk. " Just put your things down and I'll make some tea. The other chaps will call for you when they want to take you to dinner."

Dinner. Peter's stomach contracted and he felt a sudden spasm of nausea. Dinner. He had not eaten a hot meal since leaving *Dulag-Luft*. He hoped that they would not be too long before they called for him.

On each bunk was a sack filled with wood shavings, as a mattress, and a smaller sack, as a pillow. There were thin shoddy blankets, and two sheets and a pillowcase of coarse cotton. He chose the bunk above the one that John had chosen, leaving Hugo to share with Saunders, and began to arrange his few possessions on the rough shelf which the previous owner had fixed above his bunk. All his early enthusiasm had collapsed before the impact of this overcrowded slum. How could one escape, submerged beneath this turmoil ? The room was loud with the roar and chatter of a hundred voices, filled with the bustle of a hundred different aims. He worked in silence, conscious of the tall figure of Alan Loveday watching them unpack.

" I've got a book here." Loveday took down a large book from the shelf above his bunk. " It tells you how to handle people. An individual has to know how to handle people in a place like this."

Peter looked down at John and raised his eyebrows.

" What's the book called ? " John asked.

" *A Textbook of Psychology*. Psychology is the study of the mind. This is a good place to study psychology, because everybody is suffering from shock. Everybody is a bit abnormal round here."

"Yes," John said. "I suppose you're right."

"I don't need you to tell me when I'm right," Loveday shouted. "I'm telling *you*!" He glared angrily at John. "Just because you talk with an Oxford accent is no reason for you to tell me when I'm right!"

John was silent.

"This is a different world from the one you've lived in," Loveday continued. He was standing on one foot, the other resting on a stool at the end of the table. His mittened hands plucked restlessly at his beard. "This is a world where you have to study other individuals. Things are not the same here. Everybody——"

"Goon in the block!" It was one of the prisoners at the far end of the barrack. Soon the chanted cry was taken up on all sides. "Goon in the block! Goon in the block!"

"What's that?" Peter asked.

"It's the German guards doing the rounds," Loveday explained. "The other chaps always call out when they come in. It's a sort of warning. I always ignore them myself. When an individual . . ."

Peter went to the doorway of the mess, and looked down the central corridor. Followed by the jeers and catcalls of the prisoners, the tall, heavily-built guard walked down the centre of the barrack block, with his dog, a big Alsatian, on a chain.

"Two goons approaching," someone called, "one leading the other!"

The guard, ponderous in his heavy jackboots and his long green greatcoat girdled by a thick, unpolished leather belt, walked slowly down the corridor, the dog slavering and straining at the leash.

"What do they do that for?" Peter asked.

Loveday laughed. "It's psychological. They do it to frighten us. They turn the dogs loose in the compound every night. They're trained to savage everyone except the owner. One man to one dog. No one else can handle them."

CHAPTER VII

WIRE FEVER

PETER WAS collected for dinner by a flight lieutenant who introduced himself as Tyson. He went willingly, Loveday's insistent voice ringing in his ears.

" Loveday been holding forth already ? " Tyson was a tall man with a big jaw and a pleasant voice. He wore a black high-necked sweater under his service tunic, and strode quickly over the damp concrete floor in leather flying boots. " You mustn't mind him—he's a bit round the bend, that's all."

" Round the bend ? "

" Oh—wire fever. It comes in waves. Some chaps get it worse than others. With some it's acute depression, others definitely get a little queer. It's different with Loveday, though. I reckon he was a mental case before he was captured."

" You mean, he's always like that ? "

" More or less. He's never violent, you know. He's been in every mess in the block so far. No one can stand him for long."

" Poor devil." Peter could imagine him, friendless, pushed round from mess to mess.

" Oh, he's happy enough. Happier than a lot of us, I should think. It's you I'm sorry for. Here we are ! " He led the way into a mess in which three men were sitting at the table. They looked as though they had been waiting for him to arrive.

" This is Flight Lieutenant Howard," Tyson said. " Commander Drew, Flight Lieutenant Crawford, Lieutenant Simpson. The others are getting dinner ready." He motioned Peter to a seat at the head of the table. " Will you have a drink ? "

Peter must have shown his surprise, because they all laughed.

" No whisky or anything like that," the commander said hastily. " It's a little brew we make from raisins. We keep it for special occasions." He poured five small tots of colourless liquid from a tin into five large pottery mugs. " Forgive the glasses—they're all we have at the moment."

The brew was strong, it tasted like petrol. Peter was glad the tot had been a small one.

" Now, how long do you think the war will last ? " The commander, leaning across the table, spoke as though he were asking what would win the Derby—for a hot tip. He was big and gruff, and his blue eyes were set in laughter-lines above his wide, aggressively-curling beard.

Peter thought quickly. He hadn't the faintest idea how long the war would last. They obviously wanted to be reassured. " I give it a year," he said.

" Ah ! " the commander sighed, and leaned back as though a great weight had been lifted from his mind. " That's my impression, too."

" I'd give it longer than that," Crawford said. He was an older man than the others. He wore a long khaki overcoat, spoils of some forgotten army, and his knitted woollen cap was pulled low down around his ears. " We've got to get our full bombing force into operation," he explained. " We're only playing at it so far. Yes—I give it two years at least. Possibly two-and-a-half."

" Nonsense, Tom ! " The commander smiled at Peter. " You'll never win a war by bombing."

Simpson, who was younger than the others and wore the navy blue battledress of the Fleet Air Arm, held out a packet of cigarettes and offered Peter a light from a small lamp which was burning on the table, a round tobacco tin containing liquid fat. A metal bridge had been made across the open top of the tin, and through this bridge was threaded a woollen wick which burned with a small blue flame. " It's almost impossible to get matches here," Simpson explained, " so we keep a permanent light. What's the latest show in Town ? "

As Peter lit the cigarette he tried to remember. He hadn't seen a show in the West End since he joined the squadron. " *Blithe Spirit*'s a good show," he hazarded.

The commander snorted. " That was on before I was shot down."

Peter thought again. " There's a very good show at the Windmill," he said, " but I can't remember its name. I'm afraid I'm not very well up in that sort of thing."

" What were you flying ? " Tyson asked.

Peter felt safer here. " Stirlings," he said. " I started on Wimpeys and we converted on to Stirlings. I only did about five trips in Stirlings, and most of those were over Italy."

" Lousy kites, Stirlings." Crawford was obviously a reactionary. " Wouldn't be seen dead in one. Give me a Wimpey any day. What was the Italian flak like ? "

" Piece of cake," Peter told him. " They haven't a clue. We used to stooge around watching the fires."

" Where were you shot down ? "

" Over Germany. A night-fighter got us, chased us down to the deck and then set us on fire . . ." He was just getting started when the other members of the mess arrived with dinner. There were three of them and each seemed to be carrying something.

The commander attempted to continue the conversation but it was obvious that he was more interested in the meal than he was in flying over Italy. " The equipment's a bit primitive, I'm afraid," he said, indicating the seven pottery bowls, like pudding basins, which the others had set out on the bedsheet-covered table. " But we've got the best cook in the block—eh, Jonah ? "

" We've got the biggest appetite," Jonah said. He was a plump Canadian and apparently treated his cooking with all the seriousness due to that high art. There were tinned sausages, tinned tomatoes, fried potatoes and Smedley's peas ; all hot and arranged in attractive symmetry on a large roughly-constructed tray. On closer inspection Peter saw that the tray was made from dozens of small pieces of tin beaten flat and joined with folded seams.

Jonah hovered, reluctant to break up his artistic arrangement and put the food into the thick pottery bowls.

"Double up, Jonah!" The commander had taken his seat at the head of the table and was impatiently smoothing his beard.

Peter was seated at the commander's right hand. "Do you have a separate cook for every mess?" he asked.

"Yes, we all mess separately." The commander attacked his food with vigour. "In most messes they take it in turns to be cook. We're jolly lucky in old Jonah, he likes cooking and takes it all off our shoulders. We give him a hand with the potato peeling and the washing up."

"It's the only way I can get a decent meal," Jonah explained.

Peter's heart sank; he had never cooked anything more complicated than a boiled egg in his life. He hoped fervently that one of his mess would prove as great a gourmet as Jonah.

"Do you have a meal like this every night?" he asked.

The commander smiled. "No, I think Jonah's surpassed himself this evening. Each mess gets four Red Cross parcels a week. We usually manage one hot meal a day, but not as good as this. The other meals we make out with bread. Some chaps get used to it but I must admit I'm always hungry." He sighed.

As he ate Peter noticed the tactful manner of these older prisoners, the consideration with which they treated one another. They had obviously come to grips with their imprisonment and forced it to become as gracious as circumstances would allow. He remembered the frantic scrambling and pushing at *Dulag-Luft*, and wondered if these men had ever been like that. They were so quiet, with a calm reserve that made him feel soft and ineffective. He sensed that their disapproval would be a cutting and permanent thing.

After dinner they sat round the table drinking Nescafé out of the mugs which had contained the "brew" and asked him questions about home; questions that he found difficult to answer. If only I'd known I was going to be shot down, he thought. I'd have got all the dope ready. He managed to give them the current prices of beer and whisky, but when they asked him about food rationing and other topical news he realised his total inadequacy. He tried to change the subject.

" What about escape ? " he asked.

There was a pause in which he wished he had not spoken. Was it that they were against escape, or had he broken one of the unspoken rules of captivity by speaking of it ?

The silence was broken by Tyson who smiled wryly as he spoke. " Come and see us if you have any ideas. But take your time—have a good look round before you make any suggestions. If you get any ideas come and tell us first."

The sudden extinction of all the lights in the room saved Peter from further embarrassment.

" Blast ! " the commander spoke out of the darkness. " Where's that lamp of yours, Jack ? "

By the light of the small cigarette-lighter flame Peter saw Simpson cross to a cupboard and take down a lamp which he lit with a spill of paper. The lamp was made from old tins fastened one above the other and had one side cut away like an old-fashioned " dark lantern." It gave off a steady golden light, brighter than the smoky red glow in the other messes.

" That's a good lamp," Peter said.

" It's the fuel," Simpson told him. " It's margarine that's been rendered down to extract the water. Expensive, but it gives a clean light. Some of these chaps burn crude margarine, cooking fat or even boot polish—what can they expect ? "

" What d'you use as a wick ? "

" This one's made of pyjama cord, seems to be more absorbent than anything else. You can use bits of flannel, but I prefer pyjama cord."

Peter looked round at the other messes. The long room, plunged so suddenly into darkness, slowly assumed a new personality as one after another the flickering lamps threw their long shadows across the walls and roof. Conversation had fallen to a murmur, the prisoners closing in to make small groups huddled round the lamps. " What's wrong with the lights ? " he asked.

" It's the goons," the commander said. " The S.B.O. had a row with them about the sanitation, so they're carrying out reprisals."

Peter must have shown his bewilderment.

" S.B.O.—Senior British Officer. Goons—Germans," Simpson told him. " Kriegies—p.o.w.'s. You get used to it in time, it's another language."

" You'll forget you've ever been anything else but a kriegie in a week or two," Crawford said. " That's the danger."

When the lights came on again there were ironic cheers, the lamps were put out and the groups dispersed. Conversation swelled again, and the room was restored to its normal level of noisy shouts and long range conversation.

Back in his own mess Peter found that the others had returned from their dinner parties and were sitting round the table drinking cocoa. " You are just in time," Otto said. " We have a cup for you." He poured the cocoa from the tall metal jug.

" It'll make you sleep," Loveday said. " I've just been telling these individuals to get to sleep. They need all the sleep they can get. The most important thing about . . ."

" What sort of party did you have ? " John asked.

" I never knew I knew so little," Peter said. " I've made a date for you to go along and tell 'em all about the Middle East."

" That's O.K.," John said. " We had a lecture on it the day before I was captured. I've got myself into an amateur dramatic society."

" I've got myself into a rugger match—played on concrete," Peter said.

" We were wrong about that adjutant, Pete." John came and sat beside him on the bunk.

" Which adjutant ? "

" The permanent staff chap at *Dulag*."

" In what way ? "

" The chaps in the other mess were telling me. It's hush-hush, so don't spread it around, but he's working for us. He lets the Germans think he's a dead-beat and ready to work for them, and all the time he's getting information which he sends back to England."

" How does he send it back ? "

" Heaven knows, but he does. But what a rotten sort of job to have."

" You certainly need guts for a job like that," Peter said.

The lights flickered on and off twice.

" Five minutes," Loveday said. " In five minutes the lights go out, for the night."

Peter lay in the darkness trying to sleep. The sack of wood shavings was lumpy under his back. He was so near the roof that, if he raised an arm, he could touch its wooden beams. The air up here was acrid with tobacco smoke and thick with the sour smell of overcrowded living. He thought of the men in the mess he had just left; of how they had forced themselves to live in harmony, to make their unpleasant surroundings as bearable as possible. Perhaps we shall be able to do the same, he thought—smooth down the sharp edges, practise a little self-discipline. But that in a way was defeat. Far better to get out of the place, back to the danger and the freedom of the war. He would talk to John about it in the morning. There must be a way of getting out. The group captain had told them that a tunnel was being dug. How many men would they need for that? Perhaps there would be room for one or two more. Yes, he would find out all about it in the morning . . .

From time to time there was a crash and clatter as someone leaped in wooden clogs from an upper bunk, the scuff-scuffle of the clogs on concrete as the leaper hurried to the latrine, the creak of the opening door and the sudden stench.

All around him he could hear the snores and the heavy breathing of his ninety-odd fellow prisoners. At times a prisoner would shout or mutter in his sleep, sometimes scream in terror—a scream that would be cut short as his neighbour jerked him into waking. At intervals round the room sudden-glowing cigarettes told their story of sleeplessness and boredom.

He thought about the adjutant at *Dulag-Luft*—still carrying out his duty, but in the most unpleasant way. Bearing the scorn and contempt of his fellow-prisoners but all the time doing a hundred times more than they were doing to win the war. He thought of all the traitors of this war, who might, in reality, be spies. How unreasonable to judge, how impossible to give an opinion without being certain of all the facts. He offered a silent apology to that brave man, doing his lonely duty, despised by everyone, even by the Germans he was fooling.

PART TWO

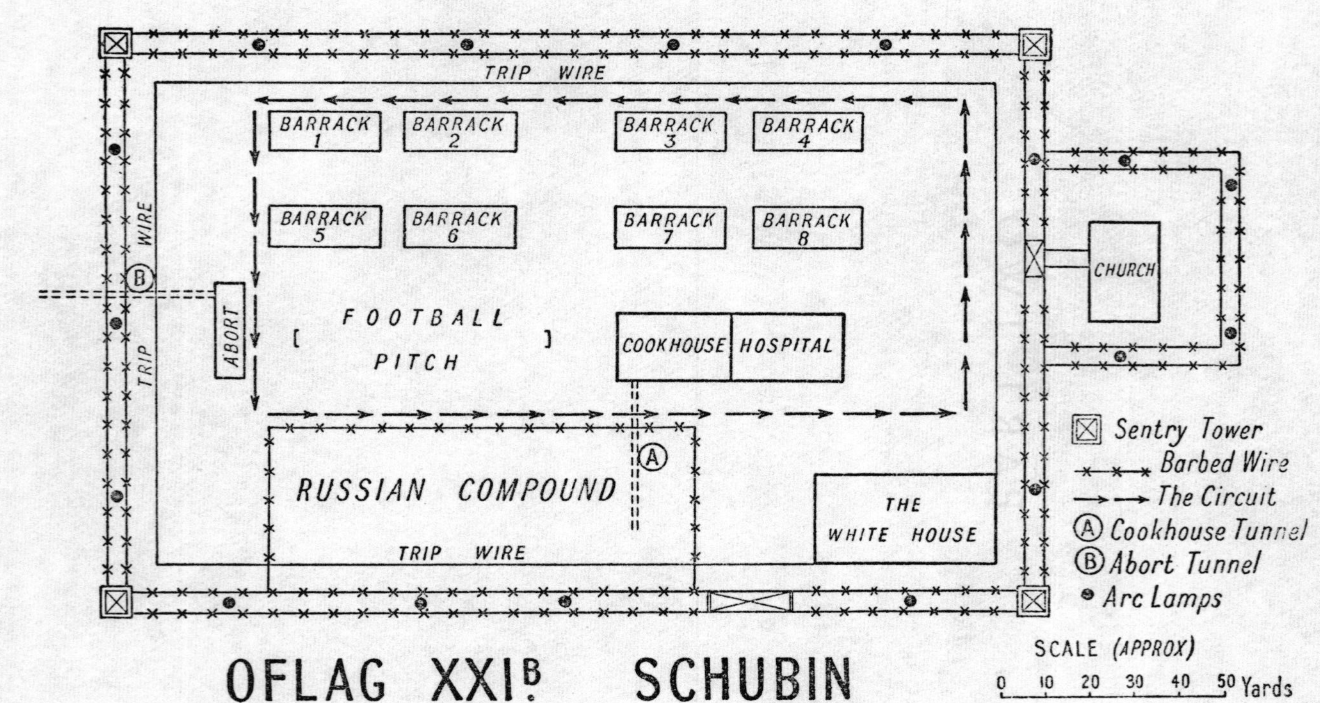

OFLAG XXI B. SCHUBIN

CHAPTER I

MARKING TIME

Before the war *Oflag XXIB* had been a boys' reformatory. When the Germans marched into Poland it was used as a concentration camp, and after the fall of France its barbed-wire defences were strengthened to hold French prisoners of war.

The camp was built on sloping ground and was enclosed by the usual double barbed-wire fence some twelve feet high, guarded at intervals by watch towers armed with machine-guns and fitted with searchlights. The two fences were six feet apart and the space between them, up to a height of about four feet, was filled with coiled barbed-wire.

Some time before Peter's capture, when the French military prisoners had been released to work in German industry, *Oflag XXIB* became a prison camp for British aircrew. Then there had been a number of escapes. The French had been kept in by the threat of reprisals on their families, but the British were not handicapped in this way. They were prisoners of long standing, and they knew the ropes. Before they had been there many weeks a good number of them had already been outside the wire. They did not stay out for long and by the time the *Kommondant* had sent for the help of the ferrets from their previous camp the punishment cells were already full.

The ferrets completely rewired the compound. They set a new trip-wire thirty feet inside the main fence, and told the prisoners that they would be shot at if they stepped across it. They built more sentry boxes raised on stilts above the wire, and buried seismographs in the earth under the wire. The seismographs were connected to a central control room where any vibration below the earth's surface, caused by tunnelling, was recorded with an ink pen on a revolving paper cylinder. The prisoners were locked in their barracks from dusk until dawn and during the hours of darkness savage dogs roamed the compound, sniffing at the doors of the barracks, discouraging the prisoners from venturing outside.

To the right of the compound gates at the bottom of the slope, the White House turned its blank and forbidding face towards the road that led to the railway station. Next to it and along the wire which lined the road was a narrow compound reserved for Russian prisoners who worked on the surrounding farms. This compound, inside the main camp, formed yet another barrier between the British prisoners and the world outside.

Behind the White House on slightly higher ground, was another building, once the home of the school staff, now used as the camp hospital and cookhouse. A small church stood in a compound of its own, an angular red-brick church in which a number of prisoners worshipped every Sunday. On the left of the hospital and separated from the road by the Russian compound were the stony football pitch and the latrine, known even to the English by its German name—*abort*. Inside the *abort* were two long deep trenches covered by rough wooden seats for forty-eight people. In the mornings the *abort* was always crowded and a long queue stretched half-way round the football pitch, almost to the hospital.

The rest of the compound was on steeply sloping ground, and terraced into this slope were the squat and ugly single-story brick barracks in which the prisoners lived a hundred to a room.

The gates of the compound were open now and a thin line of guards, their heads bent to the rain, rifles slung across their backs, filed in past the White House and struggled their way up the mud-covered slope towards the barrack blocks. It was early morning, and the rain fell inexhaustibly from a solid sky, hammering on the roofs of the sentry boxes, relentlessly pounding the sodden ground into a sea of sticky mud. Rain dripped from the barbed-wire and ran gurgling into the deep ditch which had been dug outside the wire to discourage tunnelling.

Inside Barrack No 4 the air was damp from the water that seeped up through the rotten concrete floor, from the moisture that oozed from the walls, from the rows of washing, from the breath of a hundred prisoners.

Peter woke slowly and thrust his head from under the thin German blanket. He was fully dressed, even to his issue R.A.F. greatcoat. He wore a woollen skull-cap on his head and mittens on his hands. The coal issue had been stopped again and they had gone to bed early, huddled fully dressed beneath their blankets. A film of water lay on the grey blanket over his head, and the woodwork of the bunk on which he lay was damp.

It was his turn to be stooge. Loveday and Otto had insisted on taking over the duty for the first few weeks in order to give the newcomers time to settle in. They had settled in all right. The last two months seemed more like two years.

He lay for a moment under the blankets, mustering the will-power to get out of bed. A bugle call from the German *Kommandatur* had been his alarm clock, and in a few minutes the guards would be here to unlock the doors and let him out. It was one of his duties to go to the cookhouse for hot water for the morning tea. There would be a concentrated rush of twelve stooges from eight barrack blocks; ninety-six men, all trying to get there first. Those at the end of the queue would find that the water had gone off the boil, and it would be nearly time for roll-call before they could get back to the mess, to face seven pairs of disapproving eyes.

He crawled from under his blankets, and was pulling on the wooden clogs which lay beside his pillow when the door crashed open and two guards, clumsy in their jackboots and camouflaged mackintosh capes, stood wetly in the doorway. "*'Raus, 'raus!*" they shouted.

The prisoners who were awake replied as one man. They breathed into their reply all their hatred of the German guards, all their contempt for the Third Reich. "—— off!" they

shouted, and buried themselves once more under their shoddy blankets. It was a fruitless gesture, they knew they had to get up; but it was a gesture. It was their morning litany.

As soon as the guards had gone Peter grabbed the tall metal jug from the table, threw in a handful of tea leaves and squelched in his clogs across the muddy compound towards the cookhouse. From all directions weird figures at various stages of undress were converging on this spot. The first dozen men in the queue would stand under the shelter of an overhanging corrugated iron porch. The rest would stand in the rain.

Peter found himself behind Bandy Beecham, who was wearing rugger shorts. Bandy's theory was that it was easier to dry your legs than it was to dry your trousers. He seemed unaffected by the cold.

"Coming over to the theatre to-day, Howard? We've still got two more sets to paint—the show has to be ready by Monday week." He looked at Peter accusingly over the turned-up collar of his cut-down issue greatcoat. Most of them had hacked their coats down to fingertip length, using the spare material to make slippers, costumes for the theatre or civilian clothes for the Escape Committee. Bandy's coat finished in a ragged fringe below which his red and naked legs curved aggressively into enormous wooden clogs.

"I'll come if I can, but I'm pretty busy at the moment. Perhaps I'll be able to look in for an hour this afternoon." Peter had been recruited by Bandy to help paint the scenery for the coming camp concert. His life was now so filled with necessary chores that he found it difficult to fit them all in. "How did the rehearsal go?" He wanted to show some interest, to atone for his failure to turn up the previous day.

"Complete chaos." Bandy assumed his role of the harassed impresario. "First we couldn't get started because they were using the theatre as a lecture hall, then the fairy queen had to go off to play rugger. If this goes on much longer I shall chuck the whole thing up. No one appreciates it anyway."

"You wait till you hear the applause on opening night," Peter said. "You'll think it's worth it then."

"If there ever is an opening night." Bandy retired into gloomy silence.

When Peter arrived back in the mess, he found that John had buttered two thin slices of black bread for each man and was spreading them thinly with jam. He remembered how, in the early days of their captivity, they had left the jam-pot on the table for each man to help himself. He remembered how unsatisfactory this had been; how an unjust estimation of the amount taken by one's neighbour had led to a rapid spiral upwards in the jam consumption of the mess.

He put the jug down and stirred in several spoonfuls of condensed milk. The milk, too, had once been left freely on the table. He remembered the row when Otto had discovered Hugo helping himself to a spoonful after the others had gone out to roll-call. Now everything was shared out by the stooges. It seemed fairer that way. He wondered if they would ever attain the equanimity of the older kriegies ; it didn't look much like it.

" Come on, show a leg ! Brew up ! " he chanted.

In each of the other eleven messes the morning's stooge was rousing his charges in his own way. There was a general stirring throughout the block ; groans, grunts, yawns and sleepy badinage. The men in the next mess continued the bridge post-mortem which had been suppressed by the angry shouts of their tired neighbours the night before.

In Peter's mess there was a feeling of strain. Loveday had been riding them ever since they had arrived. At first his advice, although given in a didactic, difficult manner, had been welcome ; but they had outgrown any need of Loveday's nursing. They wanted to be left alone.

John sat reading while he ate his bread and jam. It seemed to Peter that he used his book as a defence against Loveday's conversation.

" You individuals read too much," Loveday said. " Reading maketh a fool, man."

" What did you say ? " Hugo paused in astonishment, half-way between his bed and the table ; he was still continually astonished at the things the others said.

" I said, reading maketh a fool, man."

" It isn't fool," Hugo said. " It's full—F-U-L-L. Reading maketh a *full* man."

" Well, that's more than you can say for this breakfast." It was Saunders's attempt to stop the argument before it was under way. He might just as well have tried to stop the rain.

" It's fool," Loveday said. " Thomas Babington Macaulay."

" Bacon," John said it through a mouthful of bread and jam, without looking up from his book.

" Kindly do not address me with your mouth full, Clinton. We have all the time in the world here. There is no hurry at all. Now, what did you say ? "

" I said Bacon—Francis Bacon."

Loveday drew himself up to his full height, his face deep red. " Macaulay ! "

"*Bacon!*" Hugo shouted. John had retired from the argument, back into his book, as he always retired when the argument grew noisy.

A voice came from the next mess. "Are you chaps still arguing about food?"

"On *appell!*" It was Stewart, the block commander. "Come on, all outside." He stopped at the doorway of the mess. "Your turn to stooge to-day, chaps."

"Right," Peter said. "When do you want us?"

"Three o'clock in the *abort.*"

"O.K."

"All this stooging nonsense," Loveday said. "They'll never get out. Wasting everyone else's time as well as their own. Why don't they——"

"Officer at the gate!" It was Otto, watching from the window of their mess, the only window that looked out on to the path leading up from the main gate.

"All outside," Stewart shouted. "Officer coming up the hill. All outside!"

"I'm not going on *appell,*" Hugo said. "I'm *krank* this morning."

"O.K.," Stewart said. "Get back into bed."

"Come on, John." Peter snatched his greatcoat from the bunk and hurled it round his shoulders. John picked up his book, finished his mug of tea and collected his coat from the lower bunk.

"Good chap, Marcus Aurelius. Listen to this." He read from the book. "*They seek for themselves private retiring places, as country villages, the seashore, mountains; yea thou thyself art wont to long much after such places. But all this thou must know proceeds from simplicity in the highest degree. At what time soever thou wilt, it is in thy power to retire into thyself, and to be at rest, and free from all businesses.*"

"Free from all businesses, indeed," Peter said. "He didn't have to live in a prison camp."

Outside it was still raining, and a few of the prisoners stood miserably in small groups in front of each barrack block, watched by their no less miserable guards. The *Lageroffizier* was just coming into the compound, through the gate at the bottom of the slope. Stiffly returning the salute of the guard, he picked his way carefully up the muddy path.

Half-way up the slope, he looked towards the barrack blocks, and began to walk more slowly. It was a point of honour, a battle of wills. The officer refused to arrive before all the prisoners were ready on parade, the prisoners refused to wait on parade for the officer to arrive.

In the past there had been trouble on this score, and the morning *appell* had sometimes lasted long into the afternoon. This had been a punishment for all; for the prisoners, for the guards and for the officer himself. More for the Germans than for their prisoners, because the prisoners had little else to do with their time. It was, in a way, a victory for them. Eventually they had become bored with standing around, and came to a tacit understanding with their guards. It was understood that they would parade in their own time, but would be ready when the officer reached the top of the hill. But he never trusted them. Seeing the ranks still incomplete by the time he was half-way up the hill, he always became frightened and walked more slowly. He would lose face if he reached the top of the hill before the prisoners were ready. But he had to keep on walking; he would lose face also if he stopped. The stooges, watching him from the windows, left it until the last minute before shouting " Officer coming up the hill." There was then a sudden and astonishing exodus through doors and windows by half-dressed, seemingly panic-stricken kriegies. The officer resumed his normal pace and honour was satisfied.

He was met at the top of the slope by the British adjutant, a short man who always manœuvred to obtain the advantage of the higher ground, so that he could look down on the sallow bespectacled German as he returned his morning salute.

The prisoners stood in fives and slowly the guards walked up and down the ranks, counting them. It was said that the guards could only count in fives. Another guard went through the barrack block to count the *krank im Zimmer*. The officer stood watching, the rain dripping from the shiny black peak of his service cap and soaking into the olive-green of his cape. The prisoners waited like a herd of passive cattle, wet now, but knowing that the rain would stop sometime.

The guard who had counted the sick in bed reported to the *Obergefreiter*, who in turn reported to the *Feldwebel*, who reported to the *Lageroffizier*. The *Lageroffizier* saluted the British adjutant, and the prisoners were dismissed. They would not be bothered again by the Germans until the afternoon *appell*.

Back in the barrack block, John took the breakfast things to rinse them under the cold water tap in the washhouse, while Peter stayed behind to sweep the floor and scrub the wooden table. Otto and Loveday lay full length on their bunks. Hugo sat on the edge of his, studying his hair in a small hand mirror.

Peter attacked the rough damp concrete floor with a broom he had borrowed from the next-door mess. It was bad enough to sweep up after people when they were not there, but when it was raining and they lay all over the place so that he had to sweep round them, it was worse. He lifted Hugo's feet from the floor and swung them on to the bed.

"Here, steady on!" Hugo said.

"How d'you expect me to sweep under the bunks?" Peter asked.

"Shouldn't bother, I never do." Hugo returned to his study.

On the other side of the table Loveday, in the lower bunk, was explaining to Otto, in the upper, exactly why it was that Poland lay so far behind England in the forward march of civilisation. Otto listened politely. He had spent some months in a *Gestapo* gaol where, it was rumoured, torture had been used to extract information. He never spoke of it, but for Peter he still retained that aura of mystery which cloaked all those to whom violence had been done. He would have liked to talk to Otto intimately, to hear his story, but Otto never encouraged intimacy. He lived quietly within the secret reclusion of his past experience, giving himself only to Alan Loveday, whom he treated with a tenderness that the others could not understand.

Saunders usually spent the morning walking round the circuit or watching a football match. He was not a reading man. Wet mornings were a trial to him, and now he came and stood awkwardly by the table. " Pete, d'you mind if I light a *Stufa* ? "

" For heaven's sake ! " Peter was angry at first, but saw the look in Saunders's eyes. " Oh, all right—but mind you clear the mess up after you. You'd better open the window, too."

Saunders took the *Stufa* from under his bunk. It looked like a rusty battered coffee percolator. The top section held water, the middle was fitted with a patent draught-forcing arrangement of his own invention, and the bottom, made from a Klim tin, was the firebox. The *Stufa* burned small shavings of wood that Saunders had cut from a plank with one of the table knives.

Soon the mess was full of smoke which quickly spread to the adjoining rooms.

" PUT THAT THING OUT ! " The shouted protests came from the nearby messes.

" Nearly boiling." It was Saunders's boast that he could boil half a cupful of water before anyone else knew that the *Stufa* was alight. " O.K., chaps, it's out now." Shaking with suppressed laughter, he put the *Stufa* back under the bunk, closed the window and sat down at the table, preparing to shave.

" SHUT THE WINDOW ! " someone shouted from the next mess.

" It's all right, it's all right," Saunders said. " I've shut it."

" You're not shaving here, are you, Saunders ? " It was Hugo speaking from his bunk.

" Why not ? "

" The washhouse is the place for shaving."

" I can't shave there, it's fully occupied."

" What d'you mean ? "

" I mean it's fully occupied. If you'd had the energy to go and wash this morning you could have seen it yourself. You're no more sick than I am."

" I'm sick of you turning this mess into a gentlemen's lavatory." Hugo put the mirror back on the shelf above his head. " Also, it may surprise you to hear that I had a cold shower and a shave before any of you were awake this morning. I just didn't feel like going on *appell*, that's all."

" Lucky we don't all feel like that," Saunders said.

When John came back with the breakfast things, Peter had finished the floor and was scrubbing the table with a nail brush.

" There's a hell of a mess in the washhouse." John seemed amused. " Go and have a look."

" I'm too busy," Peter said.

" Go on—have a look. I'll finish the table."

" Ah, well, if you insist. I'll get some more water while I'm there." He took the metal jug from the shelf and made his way down the long room, through a small lobby just large enough to house the brick cooking stove, and into the washhouse which they shared with the next-door barrack.

It was a simple brick-built room with whitewashed walls and a concrete floor. There were long cement troughs with rows of dripping taps, and wooden benches on which some prisoners were washing their clothes. Beneath a rough shower made from a length of rubber hose and a punctured tin, a naked figure danced under ice-cold water, while his laundering neighbours, cursing, clutched their washing and retreated from the broadcast splashes.

The place was even more crowded than usual this morning, and more noisy. Above the tumult of shouting, singing and slapping of wet clothes on the wooden benches, Peter heard a cautious tap-tap-tap. In one corner of the room a man was breaking through the concrete floor with a chisel made from a window-fastener.

Tyson and the bearded commander were washing their shirts on one of the benches near the door.

" What's all this in aid of ? " Peter asked.

" The crazy gang from the next block." The commander's beard bristled with indignation. " How can a man do his dhobying in a row like this ? "

" They haven't a chance," Tyson said. " Just making a nuisance of themselves."

" It won't be for long, that's one thing. They'll have the goons round here like flies round honey." The commander slapped his washing with a hand the size of a spade. " A damn' fool effort like that won't last for long."

When Peter arrived back in the mess Saunders was carefully sorting out his " rubbish," the mysterious blanket-covered bundle he had brought from *Dulag-Luft.* At first the rest of them had been enthusiastic about the cooking utensils—saucepans made from old cans, and baking dishes from rolled-out jam tins—that it had contained. They had not been so enthusiastic about the mass of raw material which he had brought along. There were short lengths of wire, pieces of string, tins of rusty nails, nuts and bolts, a penknife with a broken blade, bunches of flattened-out tins, photographs torn from magazines—all the hundred and one things once jealously hoarded by the schoolboy, now valuable again in the eyes of the prisoner of war.

Hugo, impelled by moral indignation, had gone for a walk. John was reading through the argument between Otto and Loveday, which had now progressed to religion and psychology—the ultimate goal of all Loveday's arguments.

" What's going on out there ? " Saunders asked, looking up from his litter-covered blanket.

" Some chaps from the next block starting a tunnel," Peter told him.

" Then we shan't have any peace until it's discovered," Loveday said.

" Can't say we have much now," Saunders muttered, " chaps nagging at you all the time."

" It's stopped raining, Pete," John said. " Let's go for a walk."

"I haven't time, I've got to get the lunch ready."

"Morning, chaps!" A stranger stood at the doorway of the mess. "D'you mind if I stooge from your window? We've got a *dienst* on in the washhouse."

"There you are," Loveday said. "What did I tell you?"

"O.K., John," Peter said. "Let's go for a walk."

Out in the compound, the prisoners were taking exercise. Round and round, just inside the wire, pacing the eternal treadmill of the path they had worn with their restless feet; parallel to that other, fainter pathway a few yards outside the wire, worn by the feet of their guards.

"Thank goodness it's stopped raining," Peter said. He looked at the camp, sodden underfoot but washed clean by the rain. "Life's impossible when everyone's inside."

"It's pretty impossible anyway," John said. "It's time we got cracking and got out of it."

"You can say that again," Peter said, "and go on saying it. Every idea we've had has been squashed by the Committee. We were taken prisoner about three years too late, that's our trouble. Every possible place has been used at least once already. Look at that job they've just started in the washhouse. They only started it there because there was nowhere else. Even Tyson says they haven't a hope."

"He amuses me," John said. "He's always so furtive. He's the typical cloak-and-dagger merchant—I'm sure he talks to himself in code."

"He knows all there is to know about tunnelling," Peter said. "He's got it all buttoned up."

"He may have, but he's still here."

"He's been out several times. Once you're outside the wire, it must be a matter of luck how far you get—absolute luck. It's getting out that takes the ingenuity."

"I suppose a tunnel is the only way?"

For Peter, the next best thing to escaping was talking about escape. He began to ride his hobbyhorse. "Examine the

problem," he said. " What is it ? To get outside the wire. Right. There are three ways—over the wire, under the wire, or through the wire. You've only got three choices."

" The first one's out as far as I'm concerned," John said.

" I agree. You'd never get away with it—and even if you *did* get over you couldn't take any kit with you. You wouldn't get very far."

" There are two ways of going through : By the gate or cutting through the wire itself." John was riding with him now, knee to knee.

" Cutting through the wire is pretty impossible," Peter said. " That leaves the gate. And there are two ways of doing that."

" A bluff or a stowaway."

" Exactly. To stow away there's the bread cart or the rubbish cart. Bluffing is no good unless you look like one of the goons, and neither of us do." He looked at John with his fringe of downy beard and grinned.

" The carts have just about had it," John said. " They've been tried so often that the goons examine every inch of them. There's the night-cart, too—you'd forgotten that."

Peter shuddered.

" A chap did it once," John said. " Bribed the Pole who was driving it only to half-fill the tank and sat up to his neck in the stuff. Stark naked, with his clothes tied up in a groundsheet on top of his head."

" Wonder he didn't die before he got outside," Peter said. " Did he get away with it ? "

" He was caught at the gate. Now they make the Poles fill the carts right up to the top."

" It'll have to be a tunnel," Peter said. " It's the only way." It was the conclusion they had reached so often before.

" It certainly seems like it," John said. " But where ? The only place we haven't thought of is the church." He suddenly became excited. " Why not ? It's quite near the wire and I don't believe the goons ever go in there."

"How should we get in? There's a wire fence round it, y'know." This was no longer wishful talking; this was a possibility.

"Go in with the morning service, stay there all day digging, and come out with the chaps from evening service. A Frenchman called Atger did it in the last war, I remember my father telling me about it. We could take enough food in with us to last all day, and work in comfort. We could make the trap right underneath the altar."

"How should we dispose of the clay?"

"Oh, I expect we could tuck it away under the floor, or in the roof. Or failing that we could distribute it among the people at evening service and get them each to bring a bit out."

"I wonder what the padre would say." He felt that there must be a snag in it somewhere.

"He needn't know."

"It's well worth trying," Peter said. "Let's go and have a word with Tyson."

"Better keep this one to ourselves," John said.

"Tyson's all right," Peter told him. "I promised I'd tell him if we had an idea. It'd be silly to go into it alone, it's too good a scheme to mess up by not preparing properly. Besides, he's on the Escape Committee."

"I'd rather try it on our own."

"We can't do that. Someone might be working there already without our knowing it. There probably is." He suddenly became despondent. "There's bound to be a snag of some sort. It's too good a place not to have been tried before."

"Come on," John said. "We'll go and see him, we can't do any harm."

They found Tyson sucking an empty pipe and putting the finishing touches to a civilian jacket he was making out of a blanket.

" 'Morning," Peter said. " May we come in ? " It was the mess in which he had dined on the night of his arrival.

" Come in, come in ! " Tyson cleared a stool and moved from his own seat to the bed. " Come in and sit down." He looked at them inquiringly.

" We've got a scheme for a tunnel," Peter said.

Tyson grinned. " What, another ? "

Briefly they outlined the plan. It sounded good to them. While they were talking Tyson filled his pipe and lit it from the stub of John's cigarette.

" Yes, it's a good idea," he said. " I've had it suggested before. Unfortunately the chapel is on parole and must not be used for escape purposes. That also applies to anything to do with the theatre. I'm afraid you'll have to think again."

Peter looked at Tyson quietly smoking and sewing at his jacket and felt the hopelessness of it all. Here was a man who had been here for years, and had tried to escape ever since he had been here. And they were only on the fringe ; had not even started. At first he had thought it would be easy. " Get to a permanent camp and then make your plan." He looked round him at the now well-known squalor of the large room and felt the misery rise inside him like a sudden wave of nausea. He fought it down again, tried to drive it back, refuse to acknowledge it.

" Is there any chance of getting into a scheme that's already started ? " he asked.

" There are only two tunnels going at the moment," Tyson said. " The one from the *abort* and that crazy idea from next door. The *abort* one's full up and I wouldn't advise the other." He hesitated for a moment, then, having considered, spoke with more enthusiasm. " As a matter of fact, I'm thinking of opening up an old tunnel that's been lying derelict for some time. We had to abandon it because of flooding. It's worth having another shot at, anyway."

" D'you want any help ? " Peter asked.

Tyson puffed at his pipe. " We haven't decided to open

it up yet. I'm going down this afternoon to have a look at it."

" Where's it from ? " John asked.

" It's from the cookhouse behind the hospital—where you get the hot water in the morning. If we do open it up again we shall need some enthusiastic types and I'll keep you two in mind. You won't get into the digging team right away but I might be able to start you off in one of the dispersal squads."

" Thanks very much." Peter rose to his feet. " It's a pity about the church."

" We must stand by our word," Tyson said, " even if the goons don't."

Out on the circuit again John was enthusiastic. " Well, we've got somewhere," he said. " It was worth having the idea just for that."

But Peter did not want to be enthusiastic. They had been enthusiastic too often during the last few weeks. He wanted to wait now until it was certain. To talk about it now would spoil it. But he felt the excitement inside him, making him walk faster, walk as though he were really going somewhere instead of marching like a processional caterpillar round the circuit of the wire.

They walked quickly without talking, overtaking others, slipping on the damp clay as the path dipped down towards the football pitch. They passed the *abort*, skirted the Russian compound, passed the White House, the hospital and the cookhouse, significant now because of its abandoned tunnel. They climbed the far slope, came round behind the barracks and down past the *abort* again.

" Did you know that Otto was in the *abort* scheme ? " John said.

" No, is he ? "

" Nor did I until the other day. I found a heap of old clothes covered in damp clay under his bed. I was looking for a potato I'd dropped. When I taxed him he told me all about it. D'you know, the thing's about fifteen feet deep. I think they stand a pretty good chance of getting away with it."

"How far have they got?"

"They've done about ninety feet already. They'll be out in about a month—that is if the goons don't decide to dig another *abort* and fill in the old one."

"It's certainly time they did," Peter said. He could still smell it from where they were, on the far side of the football pitch. "Where does the tunnel actually start?"

"From the side of the trench. You have to get right down into it to get into the tunnel. Not a job for the squeamish. They struck water about half-way, and they have to crawl through inches of it. Those clothes of Otto's stank to high heaven—he usually keeps them down the tunnel, but they had to get out in a hurry the other day and they hadn't time to change."

"How did they manage to get from the *abort* up to the barrack block in their tunnelling clothes without being spotted by the goons?"

"I didn't ask him. I suppose they put greatcoats on or something. They couldn't have chosen a more unpleasant place to start a tunnel from, really . . . Although a kriegie never gets a chance to get far from an *abort*. I tried to escape from the window of one coming up through Italy, and I've been hounded by them ever since."

"Did you do that, too?" Peter was amused. It was extraordinary how like Roy John was, with his dark vitality hidden beneath a cloak of indolence.

"What?"

"Try to climb out of the lavatory window."

"If anyone wants to escape he's almost forced to go to the *abort* to do it," John said. "If he wants to eat or change his clothes while he's escaping, he has to do it in the *abort*." He laughed. "I used to eat my tuck in the lavatory at prep school. It was the only place one could be alone."

"It's the only place you can be alone here," Peter said. "You *can* be alone there—but at what a cost!"

"Not in the big one you can't," John said, "not in the forty-eight seater!"

In the lower *abort* behind the football pitch, Peter found the tunnellers already assembled.

"Come on!" Stewart said. "Where've you been?"

"Sorry, I've been cooking."

"So've I for that matter. There's your contact, standing on the corner over there. See him?" He pointed to a muffled figure who stood at the far end of the football pitch, apparently watching a group of prisoners throwing a rugby ball about. It was Saunders. "If he blows his nose, give us a shout." Stewart began quickly to strip off his clothes.

Peter watched the figure at the far end of the football pitch and listened to the clipped conversation of the men behind him. They were talking of the air pump and of wood for shoring the tunnel. Presently he heard the clack-wheeze, clack-wheeze of the pump, and knew that they had started work.

He began to grow stiff and cold. He knew that many yards below his feet men were sweating and straining in the slime of the tunnel. He knew that he was helping them, but that was not enough; he wanted to dig. He wanted to be in a scheme himself. If only Tyson decided to open up the tunnel from the cookhouse he would have a chance. At first he would only be stooging as he was now, but he would have a footing. He would know that if the tunnel succeeded he would have a place in it, however low down. And he might eventually get into the digging team. Since his arrival at the camp he had looked on the tunnellers as a special breed of men, much as at school he had looked on those with tassels to their caps.

At intervals seven-pound jam tins full of clay were hauled to the surface. The clay was emptied into the adjacent *aborts*, and pushed under with long poles. The smell was almost overpowering. He pressed his nose close to the draughty window, and concentrated on Saunders, whose muffled figure was becoming difficult to see in the gathering dusk.

Suddenly he saw a flash of white. Saunders was blowing his nose. " Goon approaching," Peter shouted. " Stewart ! "

" O.K., watch Saunders." Hurriedly Stewart began to dismantle the air pump. " If he scratches his head it means that the coast is clear again. Give us a shout if he does."

He heard the air pump being hidden and the scuffling as the men who had been working on the surface dispersed to various seats in their role of involuntary visitors.

He saw Saunders scratch his head, and gave them the " All clear ! "

He heard the pump begin to work again, and presently the splash of falling clay.

At four-thirty Stewart called a halt. It was time for the tunnellers to come up and wash before their tea.

" Let's have some jam," Saunders pleaded. " I'm frozen through to the marrow."

" The rule is," Peter said, " jam yesterday, jam to-morrow, but never jam to-day." He cracked the old, old joke, hiding his hurt beneath the badinage.

" I know, I know," Saunders said. The joke was wearing a little thin, even for him. " But we've had the mail to-day—let's have a bash."

" If we have jam for tea, we have no jam for breakfast," Peter said. " Please yourselves—we'll have a vote. All those in favour ? . . . Fair enough—let to-morrow look after itself."

" Bandy Beecham called in this afternoon to see why you hadn't gone down to help him with the scenery," Hugo said. " I told him you were busy. He wants to know if you'll go over to-morrow."

" Thanks." Peter put a minute quantity of jam on to each slice of bread and butter.

Otto came in and sat down ; he looked tired. " Ah, we have jam. That is good."

" Sheer prodigality," Peter told him, and gave him some extra jam.

" I've had a letter from my Aunt Grace," Hugo said. He was cutting his slice of bread into thin fingers, maintaining the convention of afternoon tea. " She's got a Siamese cat. Used to write to me every week while I was on the squadron."

" What—the cat ? " Saunders was spreading his jam lovingly into every corner of the slice of bread.

" No, the aunt—about the cat. She's worried about his habits. Used to send me bulletins regularly every week. She's sent telegrams before now. I thought I'd got away from it all when I was shot down, but now she's started writing to me here. I suppose I'll have to use my precious letter-forms to write to the old bitch."

" I shouldn't bother." Saunders took a bite that accounted for a third of his slice of bread.

" Oh, but I must. I have expectations, great expectations." Hugo took a small bite from one of the fingers of bread and jam and replaced the remainder on the table in front of him.

" This also is funny," Otto said. " I have a letter to-day. I do not have many letters ; this one is the first I have received in six months. Many months ago I receive a sweater from the Red Cross, and inside the sweater is sewn a piece of paper with the address of the lady who had knitted the sweater. I write to this lady in South Africa, and thank her for the sweater. I have now a letter from her. She says that she is sorry and it is all a mistake, she knitted the sweater for someone on Active Service."

" She ought to try it sometime," Saunders said. " What d'you think—my old woman's joined the W.A.A.F. Says it'll be more companionable. I'll give 'er companionable when I get back . . ."

" Were there any letters for me ? " John asked.

" They all looked like bills," Saunders said. " I threw 'em on the fire."

" There was nothing for you." Loveday's meditation was over for the day. " I looked specially," he added darkly. " I've been observing you, Clinton, and I've come to the conclusion that you're the type that can't exist without extraneous stimuli. Letters are very important to you, aren't they ? "

" Well—I like getting them."

" There you are. Now, the only way a man can be complete——"

" Young Simpson got caught this afternoon," Saunders said.

" Caught doing what ? " John seemed grateful for the interruption.

" Trying to get out in the rubbish cart. He hid under some old tins they were carting away from the cookhouse. They got as far as the gate, and one of the ferrets started poking about in the rubbish with his steel spike. He got young Simmy right on the hip with it, and that was that. Marched 'im straight off to the cooler."

" You'll never learn," Loveday said. " Why run away from life ? If only you individuals would realise that this incarceration was sent to try you. Then you would grasp it with both hands, instead of running away from it."

" Why running away from life ? " Peter said, fighting down his misery. " Surely it's just as much running away to stay here and accept it."

" If it was your fate to be taken prisoner," Loveday said, " it was your fate. There's no running away from that."

" How d'you know it isn't your fate to escape ? " He knew that it was useless to argue with Loveday, but now he could not help it.

" You'd be given a sign," Loveday said.

" You treat fate like a fruit machine," Peter said. " Stop it working when it's most convenient. How did you know that it wasn't your fate to go down with the aircraft ? Why did you bale out with a parachute ? "

" The pilot told me to."

" Supposing he hadn't ? Supposing he'd been killed ? Would you have baled out then ? "

" It was fate that he wasn't killed," Loveday said. " Everything is ordained by fate."

" What absolute cock ! " Peter could contain himself no longer. He rose to his feet and blundered out on to the circuit. To escape from the mess and take his misery with him, out on to the now deserted and muddy path. He too, had received a letter that afternoon, a letter from his mother, written on an official letter-form, telling him that Roy had been shot down over France. " I pray that he has been taken prisoner," his mother had said, " and that one day he will join you in the camp . . ."

CHAPTER II

PLANS FOR ESCAPE

ON HIS way to the camp theatre the next morning, Peter saw Otto walking alone, hands in pockets, round the circuit.

"Hallo, Otto. How's the hole going?"

Otto looked at him sharply.

"John told me," Peter said.

"It goes well enough."

"When d'you think you'll be out?"

"In a month—perhaps two."

"Where are you making for—the Baltic?"

"I shall go to Warsaw," Otto said. "I do not think it is possible to get to England. In Warsaw I shall fight underground."

"What are the others doing?"

"I do not know about the others."

"Is there any chance of getting in, d'you think?"

Otto smiled. "I really do not think so. There are so many now. The nearer we get to finishing, the more there are who have places. There are now thirty of us."

"Where do you come?" Peter asked.

"I am third. There is a man, I do not say his name, who has offered me a thousand pounds for my place."

"A thousand quid! That's expensive digging."

"I do not dig for money," Otto said.

"No, of course not."

They walked for some time in silence, while Peter cursed himself for asking if there was any chance of getting in at this stage, when all the work was done. " How did you get started ? " he asked.

" Started ? "

" In the escape game—how did you first get into a scheme ? "

" First I escape from Poland," Otto said. " I go to Constanza and there I get a ship to Marseilles. In France I join the French Air Force, because I am already a pilot. I train in France, and while I am still training the Germans come. So I go to Oran and Casablanca. From there I go to Gibraltar and to England. In England, I train again. I train for a long time, and then I fly and I am shot down."

" So when you get back to Warsaw you complete the circuit."

" Yes, I complete the circuit. And I do not go away again. I do more good at home, I think."

" What I meant was, how did you get into the escaping game here in the camp ? " Peter said. " It seems a pretty closed shop to me."

" That is because you are late arriving," Otto said. " Now you must start a scheme of your own. All the prisoners of experience are banded together. There is not room for anyone who is not experienced like themselves."

" You can say that again," Peter said. " It's all very well to say start a scheme of your own, but all the possible starting places have been exhausted." He did not trust the possibility of Tyson's tunnel. He believed in having as many irons in the fire as he could.

" You will have to think . . . Perhaps when you are moved to a new camp . . ."

" D'you think we shall be ? "

" I have been in four camps already. They do not believe in keeping us in one place for very long." Otto took his hand from his pocket and with a quick flick of his wrist threw a small parcel through the wire into the Russian compound. One of the Russians, a skeleton dressed in rags, made a quick dive at it and thrust it inside his coat.

" What was that ? "

" Bread," Otto said.

" But we already give up part of our rations to feed the Russians."

" That is given to the Russians who work. The men who are too ill to work get nothing. One of them died some time ago, and they kept his body in the hut three weeks before they told the guards."

" Good God ! "

" They drew his rations. You English do not realise. You say the German is not too bad. Perhaps he is not—to you. You have the Red Cross, and you have many German prisoners. Do you think that the nations who have not these threats are treated in the same way as you ? You do not know the Germans. You are blind in your own shell of " good sport." You English are so sporting that you shame the Germans into treating you also sporting. But you could not do it without the strength behind you. The Russians do not have Red Cross parcels—no, they are treated like pigs——" Otto stopped himself. " I am sorry. You will think that I am fanatic. But it is true, what I tell you."

" I've heard that the Russians don't treat the German prisoners too well," Peter said. " Perhaps if they treated their prisoners decently the Germans would do the same."

" It is not a matter of treating decently ! " Otto shouted. " What would you do without your parcels from England ? Could you live on the German ration ? "

" No."

" Then do not talk of treating decently ! "

What is the use of talking at all, Peter thought. What is the use of trying to generalise. He thought back over his captivity, of the friendly, decent Germans who had been his guards and captors. Little men, men with a sense of humour, caught up in the vast machine of their own making which had got beyond their power to control. Then he thought of Otto and his torture at the hands of the *Gestapo*. Of the Russian prisoners, starved, worked to death, hoarding their dead for the extra rations. The concentration camps. The prisoners there were Germans themselves.

They did not have Red Cross parcels. What would he and the others be like without them? How would they behave?

They came round by the Russian compound again. The smell of the huts was strong, even out here in the open air; a sharp, acrid odour, with a cloying, almost sweet aftertaste—like the smell of the monkey-house at the zoo. There were some torn thin blankets hanging on a line, and in sheltered corners of the compound queer thin figures with large heads and dirty drawn faces sat nodding in the late winter sunshine.

Down on the football pitch there was a rugger match between Block 3 and Block 5. The teams were cheered on by their supporters, who formed a thick margin all round the pitch. At the sound of cheering borne by the wind the nodding figures in the Russian compound looked up as though in wonderment.

"I should like to talk to you about Alan," Otto said.

"What about him?"

"You find him difficult, I think."

"He's a bit of a nuisance at times."

"It is not his fault," Otto said. "He has a good heart."

"I don't doubt it. But you need more than a good heart in a place like this, as you know well enough. If he'd only give it a rest at times."

"He is unhappy, you know."

"So are a lot of other chaps."

"It does not help to tease him," Otto said. "It will only make him worse."

"I don't tease him—I keep away from him as much as I can."

"The others tease him," Otto said. "You have some influence with the others. Perhaps you will persuade them."

"It does him good, I think. If you don't rag the man he'll get worse and worse."

"I do not think so. He is very lonely."

"What do you want us to do—talk psychology?" Peter felt a distinct aversion to this lobbying on Loveday's behalf; perhaps it was the flattery of Otto's assumption that he had influence over the others.

" He should not be here," Otto said. " He should be in the hospital."

" Come off it—he's not as bad as that."

" He is very unhappy," Otto said. " It is understanding that he needs. I do not like to think what he will do when I am gone."

" Haven't you told him that you're in the *abort* scheme ? "

" I have not told him, because we may not succeed. There is no point in hurting him without cause."

" You will tell him, though ? "

" If we succeed I shall tell him the night before we leave. If we fail, then he need not know."

" You pander to him too much," Peter said.

" I know him," Otto said. " I do not think it is a good thing to tease. Understanding will help him more than teasing."

" But he won't co-operate," Peter was suddenly impatient with Otto because of Loveday. " I asked him to help me with the scenery once, but he said he had no time for such childish activities. He doesn't seem to want to co-operate . . . That reminds me, I promised Bandy I'd go down there this morning. I must get along."

The camp theatre was in the White House, and when Peter arrived Bandy Beecham was in the middle of a rehearsal. The chorus, complete with long flaxen wigs and built-up brassières, were shaking the floor as they " Can-Canned " furiously up and down the flimsy stage.

" Stop ! " Bandy said. " Stop ! I can't bear it." He put his hand to his forehead. " How many times have I told you ? Lightly, lightly—remember you're supposed to be young ladies. And you, Rowe—tighten up that brassière a bit. It looks indecent."

Peter's scenery was behind the stage and he took advantage of the lull to walk across. " How's it going, Bandy ? "

" Fine, fine, old boy. Will you have those flats finished by to-morrow ? "

" Providing you don't alter it again."

"That's all right—it's fine now," Bandy told him. "Just the job . . . Now, girls, let's run through once more—then we'll do the seduction scene."

Peter fetched his brushes from where he had hidden them under the stage, and began to mix his colours. He was painting the backcloth and wings for the baronial hall scene—panelled walls with plenty of scope for trick perspective. He enjoyed painting scenery. There was something in the large scale of the drawing, the wide sweep of the brush, that gave him a measure of release. He enjoyed making water colours of the camp and pencil sketches of life inside the barrack block. He enjoyed the rugger matches when captivity was forgotten in the dominating urge to get the ball across the line. But none of these gave him quite the satisfaction that he found in painting scenery. Perhaps it was the very falseness of it all, the glamour that coloured the production of even the camp theatre shows, that made him forget his present surroundings and lose himself in the scene that he was painting.

It was nearly lunchtime when John came to fetch him and while Peter was cleaning his brushes Tyson came across to them.

"You two still keen on the cookhouse job?"

"Yes," John said.

"Meeting in my room this afternoon," Tyson told them. "Come straight along as soon as you've finished lunch."

As they walked past the hospital towards the barrack block Peter told John of his conversation with Otto, about Loveday.

"Ragging's just what he needs," John said, "take him out of himself."

"That's exactly what I said, but Otto doesn't agree."

"Loveday's got too many sharp corners," John said. "They need wearing down a bit, that's all. Otto's too easy with him."

Peter did not reply.

"I wonder how far they'd got with the cookhouse tunnel before they had to abandon it," John said. "I wonder if we'll get out before Otto."

"They couldn't have got very far or they'd have carried on," Peter said. "They'd never abandon a tunnel that was nearly finished."

"We'll be out before the washhouse chaps anyway," John said. "They haven't even cut through the concrete yet."

They found Loveday wrestling with *A Textbook of Psychology* and Hugo asleep on his bunk. Both Saunders and Otto were out of the mess but by the window stood the inevitable stooge from the washhouse tunnel. Ever since the work had been started there had been a stooge at their window, the only one which gave a good view of the path which the Germans would have to use to reach the barrack block. Yesterday Peter had been irritated by the silent obsessed figure which stood, blocking the light and overhearing all their conversation, peering sideways out of the window, making their mess a public property. Now, warmed by the thought of their own tunnel, he asked the stooge how the work was going.

"Dunno," the man said. "I've never seen it. I expect it's getting on all right." He turned furtively back to the window.

"I'll go for the hot water," John said. "You stay and collect the soup." He took the metal jug from the shelf and set out for the cookhouse.

Saunders came in. "Soup up yet?"

"Not yet," Peter said.

"It's up in Block 2." He sat disconsolately on one of the bunks and began to pick idly with his fingernail at a splinter which projected from the side of his wooden bunk, until the soup arrived in a galvanised iron dustbin carried by two of the British soldiers who worked as orderlies in the cookhouse. There were about a dozen of these men who boiled the morning tea water in huge cauldrons and made the midday soup with the meagre German rations. They dumped the dustbin in the corridor where it was taken over by the barrack messing officer. "Soup up!" he shouted. "SOUP!"

Peter joined the queue of stooges in the central corridor. Each man carried a pile of eight basins. As each stooge reached the head of the queue he shouted out the number of his mess and his fellow prisoners came to collect the bowls into which the soup, evil-smelling and dark green in colour, was slopped by the messing officer.

Hugo had found a piece of meat in his soup and when Peter brought in the last two bowls the others were trying to identify it.

"I think it's horse-meat," Hugo said.

"Dead Russian," said Saunders.

"I shouldn't joke," Loveday said. "We found a cat in it once."

"Probably a rabbit," Hugo suggested.

"I know a cat from a rabbit," Loveday said. "Since when did a rabbit have claws?"

"Let's not talk about it." Hugo decided he was not hungry and pushed his bowl to the centre of the table.

"Aren't you going to finish that?" Saunders asked.

Hugo pushed the bowl towards him.

"Gash soup! Gash Soup! GASH SOUP!!" It was the messing officer shouting from the corridor. There was a rush of stooges to collect their share of the surplus soup. John came back with half a bowlful. They drew lots for it, and Loveday won.

"What's for dinner to-night?" Saunders asked, finishing the last of Hugo's soup.

"Salmon pie," Peter said. "Come on, step on it." He wanted to get the washing-up done so that they could go to Tyson's meeting.

"What, again? We had salmon pie yesterday."

"We had two lots of salmon this week."

"O.K.," Saunders said. "Try to pep it up a bit more this time. What's all the hurry about—anyone would think you were going to the flicks or something."

The meeting had started when they arrived, and they squeezed in behind a dozen or so prisoners who had crowded into Tyson's mess at the end of the room. "Well, that's the first two teams," he was saying, "all men with experience. We shall work two shifts and when these chaps have had enough we can ring a change with one of the dispersal teams. That means we'll need two dispersal squads and two complete sets of stooges."

Peter and John found themselves in one of the stooging teams.

"Now—just a brief outline of the scheme." Tyson sounded enthusiastic. "It's to be in the central cookhouse, under one of the boilers which is no longer used. It's an old tunnel that we had to abandon last autumn because of water seepage. I went down myself yesterday, and it seems to have dried out quite a bit. There have been one or two small falls but I reckon we can shore it up and get it working again. Now I don't want anyone to come in with any false illusions. As I say, it's a derelict tunnel and we abandoned it because it wasn't considered safe. We may work for months and then find we have to give it up again. But that's up to you.

"The next problem is how to get the excavated clay away from the tunnel—that usually *is* the difficulty. Stewart's lot are lucky in that respect because their dispersal is right on their doorstep as it were. So are the chaps who are using our washroom—not that I think they'll get very far. Now in our case we shall utilise the fact that stooges go to the cookhouse every morning and lunch-time to fetch the tea water. The clay from the tunnel will be carried away in the water jugs."

"What about the morning tea?" someone asked.

"I was coming to that. At present each stooge collects about half a jugful of tea. In future every alternate mess will collect a full jug of tea, which will be shared with the mess next door. The stooge from that mess will collect a jugful of clay."

"It'll never work." It was the same small dark man who had spoken before.

"Why not?"

"Suppose they don't wash the jugs out?"

"They can keep the jugs separate, and use the same one for the clay each time."

"I don't think the chaps would agree to that," the dark man said.

" Nonsense, of course they will. By doing that we can take out as much clay as we like. The guards are used to seeing a constant stream of men with jugs at mealtimes. The earth will be brought straight back here and then we can disperse it at our leisure. It's a perfectly watertight scheme."

There was a roar of laughter, at which Tyson looked surprised. Then he saw the joke. " Perhaps foolproof would have been better than watertight—although foolproof is a bit too strong with some of you chaps around." He looked pleased, as though he had scored a point.

" How shall we get the wood for shoring into the cookhouse without being spotted ? " someone asked.

" Firewood for the boiler. Any more questions ? "

" Yes—when do we start ? "

" Early next week. We're just making a new frame for the trap, and getting the stooging system organised. We want to work it so that we don't get too many chaps coming in with their jugs at the same time—and not too few. Everything must go on exactly as it always does."

" How far have they already dug ? " John asked.

" About a hundred feet—there's still a long way to go. But if everything goes smoothly we should break sometime in the spring."

" Where will it come up ? " Peter asked.

" We're going under the Russian compound. It's under their wire already. I have considered coming up and making a dispersal under their huts—but I don't altogether trust 'em. We'll do it if we have to but at the moment the intention is to cut straight through and come up on the other side of the main road. Any more questions ? "

There were no more questions.

" Right," Tyson said. " The first team will meet here at nine o'clock on Monday morning."

CHAPTER III

THE TUNNEL

FOR THE next few weeks Peter and John did little more for the cookhouse tunnel than they had done for Stewart in the *abort dienst.* They stooged on draughty corners, stood for hours looking out of windows or sat propped against the wall of the White House counting the Germans as they came in and out through the compound gates. But now they had a place in the tunnel, even if they were only thirty-two and thirty-three on the list, and the stooging had more purpose.

As Tyson had foreseen, the digging teams were forced to spend a considerable time in strengthening the shoring and repairing damage to the tunnel walls before they could start to push their way towards the wire. As time went on Peter and John listened to his reports with diminishing hope; it seemed that they would never begin to move.

But their spirits rose again as a number of their fellow stooges and some of the dispersal team, unable to stand this period of frustration and delay, dropped out. Slowly, place by place, they began to move up the list towards a place in the digging team.

When digging finally started in earnest, they spent most of their time as members of a dispersal gang, bringing the clay to the barrack block in the water jugs and packing it into small bags made from shirts and underclothes. They took some of these bags, suspended round their necks under their coats by a piece of string, to the *aborts*, and disposed of their contents in the usual way. The rest of the bags they hid under the bunks, and in the short interval between dusk and lock-up they buried the clay they held in the ground outside the huts. It was slow, tedious, uninteresting work, but it was one stage better than stooging.

Then, one afternoon as they were finishing their lunch, Tyson came into the mess. " You two all right for a spell below this afternoon ? "

" On the ball," John said.

" Right. Come to the cookhouse as soon as you can. Wear your tunnelling kit under your ordinary clothes, and bring a handkerchief or something for your heads." He went out, leaving behind him an awkward silence, which was broken by Saunders.

" You didn't tell us you were on a *dienst*," he said. " How long has this been going on ? "

" Oh, not long," Peter said, minimising it. " We haven't much chance of getting out, I'm afraid—we're not in the first ten."

" It's all a stupid waste of time," Loveday said. " Why don't you individuals settle down ? Settle down and study like I do. I'm improving my mind." He tapped a finger on his forehead. " It's a natural psychological reaction to want to escape. When an individual is locked up he wants to get out. You ought to overcome it. Look at Otter here—he doesn't waste his time trying to escape, he's an old kriegie. Eh, Otter ? " He poked Otto in the ribs with a large raw finger. " We old kriegies don't try to escape, do we, Otter ? We study and improve our minds."

Peter looked at Otto, who smiled and shrugged his shoulders.

" How did you two manage to get in ? " Saunders glanced at John engrossed in his book again. " Why pick on you two of all people ? "

John looked up ; innocent. " Well, as a matter of fact, they spotted that we were outstandingly good tough types, and asked us if we'd run the tunnel for them."

" Good types ! " Loveday shouted. " There's conceit for you. Good types indeed ! Nothing but read, read, read. Because we're not good enough to talk to, I suppose. Captain Clinton has to withdraw himself from the others. Good types indeed——"

" He was only joking, Alan," Otto said it gently. " He didn't really mean it."

" Then he should say what he means," Loveday said. " All this double-dealing and cross-talk. How can an individual live in peace while all this deceit is in the air ? Why didn't you two tell us you were in a tunnel? "

" Didn't think you'd be particularly interested." Peter was hurriedly getting their football clothes out of the locker.

" So you didn't think I'd be interested, eh ? What d'you think I am, eh ? So you think I'm not loyal to the mess—you think——"

" Come on." Peter threw John's bundle across to where he was sitting. " Time we were going down, John."

" O.K., chum." John put his book on the shelf above his bed and began to change into his tunnelling clothes.

The scene in the central cookhouse reminded Peter of the setting for a modern ballet. The four boilers, like enormous witches' cauldrons, stood side by side on an apron of concrete against the farthest wall. Beneath the end boiler, now dead, was the narrow entrance to the tunnel, open ; and by its side lay the trapdoor made from concrete in a shallow wooden tray. In each of the side walls small high windows threw their spotlights on to the figures of the orderlies, who tended the boilers, and the early shift of tunnellers, who had just come to the surface. The tunnellers were dressed in woollen undervests and long pants, patched like harlequins, bright yellow from the puddled clay. On their heads they wore woollen caps or handkerchiefs knotted at the corners and, dancer-like, they wore no shoes.

Tyson, already in his tunnelling clothes, was waiting for them. " Hurry up, chaps," he said.

Peter and John quickly took off their outer clothing and joined the new shift, who were waiting to go below. It was cold and they shivered as Tyson slid under the boiler and, after much grunting and straining, disappeared from view. Peter, following, found a hole in the floor about two feet square. There was a rough ladder fixed to the side of the shaft at the bottom of which the flickering rays of a lamp showed Tyson's legs as he crawled out of sight. Presently his face appeared where his legs had been. "Go easy down the ladder," he said.

At the bottom of the shaft was a square chamber about six

feet by four in which a man crouched, working a crude concertina-like air pump made from a canvas kit-bag. By his side the goon lamp cast its lurid glow across his sweating face as he swung to the rhythm of the creaking pump. The walls and ceiling of the chamber and the mouth of the tunnel which opened from it were of solid wood, bedboards jammed together side by side; but the floor was liquid clay.

Tyson was crouching half in and half out of the tunnel. In his hands he had two smoking lamps, one of which he passed to Peter. "Follow me!" He spoke in a whisper, as though he could be heard through twelve feet of solid earth.

The tunnel, once they had left the chamber, was no longer lined with wood. The walls and ceiling dripped with water which gathered in long puddles on the floor and, as he wriggled after Tyson into the blackness, Peter felt this water soak through his woollen vest and grip him with its icy fingers.

After crawling for about fifteen feet the light in front stopped moving, and when Peter caught up with it he found Tyson crouching over a hole in the tunnel floor, about three feet from where it came to an abrupt end. " It goes down another six feet," he whispered. " The real tunnel starts from the bottom of this shaft. The upper tunnel is only a dummy. We camouflage the trapdoor over this shaft whenever we leave it, and then if the goons discover the upper tunnel they'll think it ends here. They'll just fill in the top shaft and this bit of tunnel—and then when the flap's all over we can strike the lower tunnel from another shaft. That way we only lose the short upper tunnel, and save the lower one." He chuckled and climbed down the second ladder into the lower gallery.

Peter, stifling his feeling of panic, followed. This was what he had wanted. He'd got the chance, and now he must go through with it.

It seemed deep, deep down in the earth. Somehow the second shaft seemed a hundred times deeper than the first. It seemed completely beyond help from the surface. At intervals, where there had been a fall, patches of wooden shoring bulged ominously inwards. He had to fight hard to force himself to carry on.

He seemed to have been crawling for about half an hour before he again caught up with Tyson, who had reached the end of the tunnel. " You work here," Tyson told him. " Here's a knife. Put the clay you dig out into this toboggan." He showed Peter a rough wooden trough about eighteen inches long by twelve inches wide. " When you pull the rope twice I'll haul it back to the lower shaft. I pass it up to the top tunnel, and Clinton will send it back to the upper shaft in another toboggan. You see now why we need such a large team."

When Tyson had left him there was silence; more complete

silence than Peter had ever known. It seemed as though the eighteen feet of soil above his head was pressing down, pressing inwards. Then, in the silence, he heard the faint hiss of air pushed by the man at the pump through its life-line of jam tins joined end to end. This metal pipe, coming along the upper tunnel, down the shaft and along the wall of the lower tunnel, was his connection with the outside world—that, and the rope which pulled the toboggan. He took the knife and began to hack away at the clay in front of him.

An hour later Tyson called a halt. John took Peter's place at

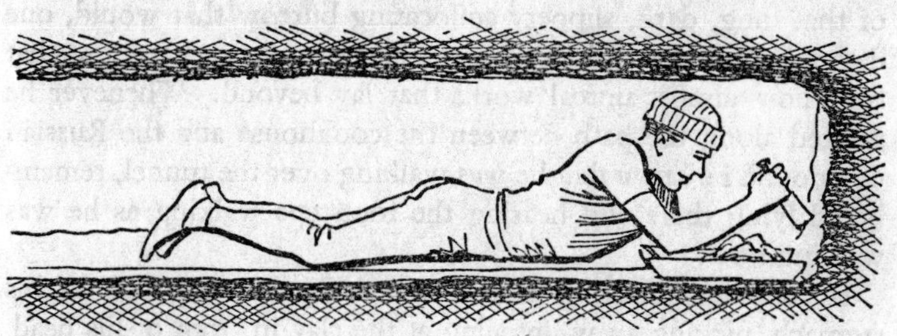

the head of the tunnel, while Peter pulled the clay back to the lower shaft. The rope, thinly plaited from the sisal string off the Red Cross parcels, cut deeply into his hands, and the strain of pulling the heavy toboggan through the thick sludge of the tunnel floor made his shoulders ache. He had blisters on the palms of his hands from the handle of the knife and, as he unloaded the clay into jam tins and passed them up to Tyson at the top of the shaft, he began to realise that there was more to tunnelling than he had thought.

At the end of the two-hour shift they came to the surface. Peter knew now why the earlier tunnellers had staggered as they crossed the kitchen floor. He had been sweating for the last two hours, and his woolen underclothes were wringing wet with sweat and moisture from the tunnel.

The stooges had a hot bath waiting for them; a real, galvanised iron bath. Peter had not known that such a thing existed in the camp. As he sat in the luxury of the warm and muddy water, he began to think that perhaps tunnelling was worthwhile after all.

As the tunnel moved steadily on towards the wire the possibility of escape loomed larger and larger in Peter's mind. He still played football for his block, still painted scenery for the theatre, talked on the circuit and made sketches of his fellow prisoners; but always at the back of his mind was the tunnel. From waking until sleeping he carried with him the warm comforting thought of that long, dark, slippery suffocating burrow that would, one day, take him and John under the barbed wire and away to that free, now almost unreal world that lay beyond. Whenever he walked along the path between the cookhouse and the Russian compound he knew that he was walking over the tunnel, remembered lying there and hearing the footsteps walking as he was walking now.

He enjoyed working at the tunnel face. Lying flat on his stomach, picking away unseeing at the clay in front of his head, he felt that he was really getting somewhere, really doing something towards getting out of the camp. Moreover he was alone, lying there in the darkness and dank air of the tunnel: alone in a small world of silence, a world bounded by the feeble rays of the lamp that guttered by his head. He was more alone than he could be anywhere else in the camp. Up there in the crowded barrack block, on the teeming circuit, he was aware all the time of his fellow prisoners; their habits of speech and the almost maddening physical proximity—the body odour and the unconscious elbow in the ribs. But down in the tunnel it was dark and lonely, and he sang to himself as he picked away at the hard clay, and felt sorry when it was his turn to leave the loneliness of the tunnel to go back to his place in the shaft.

CHAPTER IV

THE SEARCH

SUDDENLY IT was spring. It seemed to Peter, as he walked from the barrack block to the White House for his shower, that the last few months had passed without his knowing it. He had been working hard on the tunnel, making his civilian clothes, planning a route; living in the future so intensely that he had not noticed the winter passing into spring. Now there was a hint of warmth in the air, even at this early hour, and outside the barrack blocks prisoners were shaking their bedding and flinging it over the clothes-lines which bordered the paths between the buildings. The sky was blue, and even the dark earth which not long since had been mud seemed to be expanding, stretching itself in the friendly sun. The air was strangely scented, and the warm sun on his face and hands quickened his blood, making him feel that life was good.

As he walked he decided that in future he would join Hugo in his cold shower before breakfast. It would be a discipline, something to get him fit for the trip that lay ahead. He would walk too, increasing distances round the circuit; two miles the first few days, then four, then six, up to twenty miles a day. He would not fail because he couldn't stay the distance. He would start to-morrow; for the moment he would make the most of the monthly hot shower, and change into the clean clothes that he carried under his arm.

" I paid sixpence to see
A tattooed Scotch lady,

She was a sight to see
Tatooed from head to knee——"

The words came through steam, the accompaniment was falling water, the tune *My Home In Tennessee.* Beneath a battery of twelve showers controlled by a German guard the prisoners unfolded like seedlings under a gardener's hose.

" *Under her jaw*
Was the Royal Flying Corps
And on her back
Was the Union Jack,
What could you ask for more?
Up and down her spine
Were the King's Own Guards in line
And right around her hips
Was a fleet of battleships——"

Peter, lean and hard from hours of sweating in the tunnel, soaped himself all over and sang with the others. He was no longer just wasting his time, he had an objective now. Beside him John was singing in a high clear tenor.

Someone, a deep bass at the back of the room, began to sing *Wir Fahren Gegen England.* It was a good song to sing in the bath, and this was a typical bathroom. Their voices boomed and reverberated, aping the German Labour Corps who, in white cotton trousers, naked and bronzed above the waist and carrying burnished spades instead of rifles, marched past the camp in the mornings; marching on England by way of a road they were building through the forest.

"... *England, England* ..."

Then, high above the noise of the singers, Peter heard the shrill expostulation of the guard. " *Bitte, bitte!* " he was saying. The prisoners took no notice. Peter saw the guard's entreaties turn to fear, fear of the approach of a superior.

The fear turned to anger. He began to shout, as the Germans

always shouted when they were nervous. The prisoners still ignored him. In desperation he turned off the water. It stopped suddenly, a few last miserable trickles mocking the soap-covered prisoners, who stared impotently at the guard. Slowly the singing subsided as, one by one, they admitted defeat. It was uncomfortable standing there in the cold, covered in nothing but wet soap. One or two of the more obstinate continued for a few bars, until the last was finally silenced by his comrades.

"*So!*" The *Obergefreiter* smiled, a smile of triumph. He turned the water on again.

"*I paid sixpence to see*
A tattooed Scotch lady . . ."

On their way back to the barrack block they noticed a crowd of prisoners gathering round the main gate. "What's going on down there?" John said.

"Let's go and have a look."

As they walked down they met other prisoners converging from all directions, making towards the gate.

"What is it?" John asked one of them.

"New purge from *Dulag*."

"Come on," Peter said, "there might be someone we know."

He hurried down to the gate, trying to curb his impatience, telling himself that his brother was not, could not, be there. Ever since his mother had written to tell him that Roy had been posted "missing" he had tried to stop himself from hoping that he would, one day, walk into the prison camp. To hope unreasonably, he felt, was a weakness. Nevertheless he knew the old choking sensation as he forced himself to walk more slowly as he neared the gate, could not prevent himself from almost running the last few yards.

Down at the gate the new purge was still standing in ranks outside the wire; pale, unshaven, bewildered men, most of them wearing the stiff new uniforms drawn from the stores at *Dulag-Luft*. Among them were some Americans, and these wore strange bulky flying boots and khaki jockey caps. They all looked tired, and there was an expression of horror on their faces as they regarded the uncouth bearded figures behind the wire. The kriegies were throwing over packets of cigarettes and calling out the numbers of their squadrons.

" Anyone from Seventy-five Squadron ? "

" Yes—here ! "

" How's old Handlebar ? "

" Never heard of him."

Peter looked along the ranks of strange faces, looking for the mop of black hair, the upright, slim, disdainful figure ; quickly at first, and then again more slowly. All around him other prisoners were crowding against the trip wire, only kept from the main fence by the machine-guns of the guards in the sentry boxes.

" Anyone from Seven Squadron ? "

" Dick ! I thought you'd fetch up here sooner or later ! How's Jimmy ? "

" Anyone from Coastal there ? "

" Anyone from Thirty-five ? "

Peter shouted the number of his squadron with the others and discovered a New Zealander who had been with the same squadron, but they did not know one another. He asked, casually, after his brother, but the man had never heard of him.

" Come and have tea with us this afternoon," Peter suggested. " Block Four, the end mess. You can't miss it, it's next to the bog."

Then the gates were opened and the newcomers, hoisting their bundles on to their backs, straggled into the compound between the automatic rifles of their escort, who kept the older kriegies at a distance. As they passed the trip wire one of the Americans therw a small parcel which was caught by a kriegie. A guard, who haq seen the parcel thrown, made a dart after it, but the kriegie duickly lost himself in the crowd. The American dodged unobtrusively behind his friends as they were marched up to the White House to be searched.

"Good show," Peter said. "That's something the goons won't get, anyway."

"Come on," John said, "we'll be late for lunch."

"I didn't see any Army chaps there," Peter said as they walked slowly away from the wire. He was ashamed that in his disappointment he had forgotten to introduce the New Zealander to John.

"There never are," John said.

"I've never understood how you came to be in an Air Force camp at all." Peter wanted to enter into John's life for a moment, to bury the insistent vision of his brother grimly holding his aircraft in that last screaming dive to the dark earth or sea below. "Why didn't they send you to an Army camp?"

"I was caught so far behind the German lines they thought I was a paratrooper," John said. "Apparently they always send paratroops to Air Force camps."

"That's because their paratroops are part of the *Luftwaffe*," Peter told him. "What were you doing behind the German lines—sabotage?"

John grinned. "As a matter of fact—I wouldn't tell anyone else, mind—I was going in the wrong direction."

Peter laughed, glad of the excuse to laugh. He knew John well enough to be certain that he had not been captured easily. He knew John's shame at having been captured, a shame not shared by aircrew as their surrender had not involved a laying down of arms. He changed the subject. "You looked exactly as though you'd suddenly found yourself in a zoo, that first day at *Dulag*. Absolutely lost. It was being surrounded by the R.A.F., I expect."

"It was a bit disconcerting," John said, "but nothing to the first day I came here. When I saw my first authentic kriegies I swore that whatever happened I'd never let myself get like that."

"And now look at us—I bet those new chaps are thinking exactly the same about us."

"Some of us still keep pretty smart," John said. "Look at Hugo—he shaves every morning and even polishes his buttons with brickdust. I admire him for it, in a way. It's a sort of self-respect."

"I don't think much of a self-respect that demands clean buttons to keep it alive." The vision was fading now. "That sort of thing's all right on the barrack square, but it doesn't do much good out here. He's not adaptable that's all it is. He's the type that takes a dinner jacket on safari with him."

"That's the type that built the Empire," John said.

"Don't you believe it, old son—not Hugo's type. The Empire was built by jokers without backsides to their trousers. You're thinking of the people who run it now."

"Better tell that to Loveday to-night in the mess," John said.

As they climbed the hill towards the barrack blocks they saw that their barrack was surrounded by small groups of prisoners who were being kept at a distance by armed guards. They began to hurry up the slippery path, wondering what had happened, Peter's private sorrow lessened now by the thought that something, anything, unusual was taking place.

They found Stewart arguing heatedly with a German in front of the door. "But it's lunchtime," Peter heard him say.

"I cannot help that, Mr. Stewart. If you will break the regulations by digging a tunnel from your barrack, you must expect to take the consequences."

"But this is mass punishment."

"Come, come, Mr. Stewart. You cannot call this mass punishment. It is merely a precaution."

There was a sudden crash as one of the small lockers, made by the prisoners from bed-boards, came hurtling out of an open window.

"You can hardly call that a precaution," Stewart said.

"You know perfectly well, Mr. Stewart, that it is against the regulations to make furniture out of the bed-boards."

From inside the block came the heavy bang, bang, of crowbars on the concrete floor, the rending crash as one of the lockers was pushed over on its side.

" Oh, go to hell ! " Stewart said.

" There is no need to be violent, Mr. Stewart."

Peter and John stood among the other prisoners and watched their cherished possessions being hurled from the doors and windows to lie, sometimes broken, on the ground outside; mutilated books and photographs, carefully made shelves and cooking utensils, drawings and clothing, scattered or in heaps on the muddy ground.

" That's the end of the washhouse tunnel," John said " Tyson said it wouldn't last for long."

Towards the end of the afternoon the search was called off. The washhouse tunnel had been found, so also had a number of *verboten* articles which were wrapped in blankets and taken away by the guards. The tunnel, flooded with water for the night, would be filled in in the morning.

The end mess was in chaos. Mattresses had been ripped open, photographs torn from the walls, their small stocks of clean clothing lay scattered and trampled on the floor. " We'd better get cracking," Peter said. " We've got someone coming for tea."

" My pin-ups have gone ! " Saunders shouted. " That goon's pinched my pin-ups ! "

Slowly they restored the room to some sort of order. Saunders, still devastated by the loss of the pin-up girls, grumbled as he worked, full of schemes to get even with the goons.

The others took it in good spirit; only Loveday failed to respond. He sat on his bunk nursing *A Textbook of Psychology* which he had found with its back torn off among the debris on the floor. He did nothing towards cleaning up the mess, but sat brooding, the book held listlessly between his hands.

" Come on, Loveday," Saunders said.

" Leave him," Otto said. " He will be all right in a minute."

He began to sort out Loveday's things and put them away in his locker.

By the time the New Zealander arrived the room was more or less in order again. He hesitated in the doorway, as though afraid to enter.

"Come in," Peter said. "Excuse the chaos, we've just had a blitz." Then he remembered his own mystification on his first night in the prison camp. "The Germans found a tunnel in the washhouse," he explained.

"What are the chances of escape from here?" the New Zealander asked.

It had been one of Peter's own first questions, and he shelved it. Now that he was on a scheme himself he guarded it as jealously as the early gold prospectors had guarded their lucky strike. He felt that talking about it would minimise its value. Instead, he introduced the newcomer round the mess, but when he came to Loveday there was no response. The man seemed dead to the world. Peter passed it over as lightly as he could, and began to question the visitor about men he had known in the squadron. But he could find no point of contact. They had all been shot down, or posted to another squadron. Even the doctor and the padre had been changed.

When Hugo brought in the tea they sat down at the table.

Loveday remained obstinately on his bunk.

"Come on, Loveday—teatime!" Peter said. He put his hand on Loveday's shoulder, but there was no response. As he sat down he noticed the visitor glance as if fascinated at Loveday and then quickly look away.

We do look a queer lot I expect, he thought. He looked at the others; Saunders with his vulgar red good-humoured face, his impossible moustache, under his habitual knitted cap; Otto, pale and thin with woollen wrist-warmers showing below the cuffs of his tunic; John, a student from the Latin Quarter; Hugo, a stage Russian émigré, presiding at the head of the table; and Loveday sitting on his bunk like patience on a monument, brooding over the damage to his book.

He looked at the visitor and saw the hungry way in which he wolfed his bread and jam. His stomach will shrink, he thought, it'll take time, but in the end he won't be quite so hungry.

"Any good shows in Town?" Hugo made the opening gambit.

Peter saw the newcomer frantically searching his mind, and

felt for him. "I don't suppose you had much time to go to shows," he suggested.

"No—used to spend most of the evenings with the boys."

"What's the beer like in England?" Saunders asked.

"It's all right. Pretty scarce."

"Ah," Saunders said. "It would be. How long've you been shot down?"

"Five days."

"Five days!" Saunders pushed his woollen cap to the back of his head. "Blimey, they aren't half pushing 'em through now. How long d'you have in the cooler?"

“ The cooler ? ”

“ Blimey,” Saunders said, “ he doesn’t know he’s alive.” He examined their guest with renewed interest.

“ How many trips had you done ? ” Hugo asked.

“ This was my first trip.”

Poor kid, Peter thought, what an end to your first trip. A year’s training, one flight and now this. It was like the life of a butterfly. “ You’ll soon settle down,” he said. “ This isn’t a bad life. It’ll seem a little odd at first.” What can I tell him about it, he thought, how can I advise him ? “ Have some more tea,” he suggested.

“ This is the end.” Loveday’s voice, deep and full of doom, coming from behind him, made the New Zealander choke into his mug.

“ Hallo, Lovey.” Saunders turned and looked at him. “ Feeling better now the work’s all done ? ”

“ I’ve been meditating.”

“ Good thing,” Saunders said. “ Nothing like a little meditation when there’s work to be done.”

“ They’re frightened that I shall succeed now,” Loveday said.

“ Don’t you worry, chum,” Saunders told him. “ Nothing you can’t do if you put your mind to it.”

“ I *shall* succeed ! ” Loveday beat with his fist on the side of his bunk. “ You individuals fail to realise how organised they are. They even try to destroy my work.”

“ You’ll disorganise ’em.” Saunders winked at the New Zealander. “ Just keep on the way you’re going.”

Loveday came to the table and glared at them. “ So we have strangers in the mess.”

Otto poured him a cup of tea and passed his three slices of bread and butter, while Peter began to tell the New Zealander about the events of the afternoon. All the time he was talking he could see the boy stealing furtive glances at Loveday who, eating stolidly through his bread and butter, fixed him with a malevolent stare.

" Well, I'd better be getting on." The guest rose to his feet and moved towards the doorway. " Thanks very much for the tea."

" Not a bit," Peter said. " Come and see us again some time."

" I will." The New Zealander stole one more frightened glance at Loveday and escaped into the corridor.

CHAPTER V

THE OTHER TUNNEL BREAKS

As SPRING slowly relaxed into summer the two remaining tunnels were driven painfully inch by inch at right angles to one another towards the wire. The *abort dienst* was well in the lead, and for the past few weeks Tyson's team had worked desperately to catch them up. If they could make sufficient headway both tunnels could break on the same night, and a record number of prisoners would get away. If Stewart broke first, the second tunnel would be handicapped by the stringent security measures that would inevitably follow the first escape. It was a back-breaking race against time and, hampered by water seepage, the cookhouse team were unable to maintain the pace. By the middle of May the *abort* attempt was ready to break. The escapers had prepared their forged papers and their civilian clothes, and now they waited for a suitable night to make their getaway.

Tyson had decided to suspend work on the cookhouse tunnel until after the others had broken out. As he explained to his disappointed team, "We could hardly expect them to wait for us and it would be a pity if we made a boob now and gave the other show away. We can't possibly get ready to break on the same night so we'll just have to lie low until they've gone. As soon as the flap's lifted we can get cracking again."

Peter and John, stifling their impatience, used this period of idleness to perfect the plans for their own journey. They had decided to walk down through Poland and attempt to make contact with the partisan forces in Yugoslavia. They would travel as Italians and John, who already had a smattering of the language, was working hard at his Italian grammar. At the same time he was learning the part of Lysander for the new production of *A Midsummer Night's Dream*, which was to be staged in the early summer. Peter knew that he regarded this as an insurance against their tunnel being discovered.

On the day that the *abort* tunnel broke England played Australia at rugby football. Under cover of the enormous crowds Stewart's team, their escape clothing hidden by greatcoats, wandered down to the *abort* and, one by one, lowered themselves into the trench and so into the narrow tunnel. In addition to the digging team there were the dispersal squads, some stooges, and one or two of the prisoners who had helped to forge the identity papers or make the civilian clothes. Some of these had never been down the tunnel before and there were long delays while they re-arranged their packs and clothing before they could squeeze into the narrow hole. At last there were more than thirty of them, lying head to heels along the suffocating length of the muddy burrow.

Peter had given up football now that his own escape seemed possible. To risk a broken leg at this stage would be foolish. He helped Tyson to get the last man down a few minutes before lock-up time, and went back to the barrack block. Most of the thirty escapers had come from Block 2, but the vacant spaces had been evenly distributed over the entire camp. Several people had gone to spend the night in another block, and in the empty bunks cleverly made dummies lay under the grey blankets, wigs made from human hair and empty boots protruding naturally.

It was a perfect night for escape. Heavy clouds were massing in an angry sky. Gusts of wind went humming through the wire, blowing into the camp, and causing the guards to turn their backs to its source—turn their backs on the potato patch which lay in the path of the bitter wind, and which intricate calculations with line and home-made theodolite had told the tunnellers would cover the exit of their tunnel.

Under the potato patch the working party dug away the last few feet of subsoil and waited for complete darkness.

In Peter's block all the preparations had been made. Following the discovery of the escape, there would be a search such as they had never had before; a search that would sweep in its ruthless path everything that was in the least suspect. During that afternoon most of them had buried everything of value in the ground outside the barrack. Peter and John had buried their home-made civilian clothes and their store of carefully hoarded food; but Peter could not bear to part with his small brass compass and the maps he had brought with him from *Dulag-Luft.* He had sewn these into the waistband of his trousers.

Now he sat with the others who, trying to appear as usual, were all the time half-listening for the sudden rifle shot or the angry stutter of machine-guns which would tell them that the escapers had been seen by the guards outside the wire.

"Dinner's an hour early to-night," Saunders warned them.

"Good show," Peter said.

"They've made them all an hour earlier in case . . . you know," Saunders said.

"What are we having?" John asked.

"Salmon pie."

"Not again!"

"Well . . . I can do it quickly, you see—in case anything happens. By the way"—defensively—"there's no chocolate this week."

"How's that?" Hugo liked his chocolate.

"I gave it to Otto."

"Oh, you did, did you?"

"Well—I didn't really *give* it to him. After all, we've got the rest of his parcel this week."

"Yes, that's right."

"I gave him the raisins too," Saunders said. He seemed to expect censure for this.

"That's O.K.," Peter said. "You're the cook. As long as you dish us up a meal each day——"

" There's no sweet," Saunders said quickly. " I gave him the sugar too."

Loveday kept to his bunk all evening, speaking to no one, refusing to be drawn into conversation. He had been like this ever since Otto had told him that he was leaving. He had told him alone, out on the circuit, and the others did not know how Loveday had taken it. They only knew that this strange silence, instead of being a blessing, was a curse. His brooding cast a blight upon them all, and they were unable to settle down.

The whole barrack block was quiet, everyone listening with half his mind for the sound of a shot and the whistles of the guards. Everyone, with half his mind, was crawling out through the muddy exit through the rows of growing potatoes, away from the camp. Everyone shared the feeling of naked vulnerability, the " crab-without-shell " feeling of the man with a gun behind him; the feeling they had all known at least once before, when their aircraft had heeled and spiralled down in flame.

" What about a game of cards ? " Saunders's suggestion was tentative.

" Not to-night," Hugo said.

" Where's Otto making for ? " Saunders asked.

" Warsaw," Peter told him.

" Rum sort of place to make for."

" He was born there."

" Oh, yes, of course—he's a Pole."

There was a silence. Someone in a mess at the far end of the room started the gramophone. They sat listening to it; the first time they had ever listened to it consciously, as anything other than a background to their conversation.

" Damn' stupid lyric," Peter said.

" All dance lyrics are stupid," Hugo said.

Half-heartedly Saunders picked up a paintbrush he was making for Peter; rolling sisal string into a hank, cutting the loops with a razor blade, fraying them out and binding the rest to form a handle.

" I wonder if they're all out yet ? " John looked up from his book.

Peter glanced at his watch. " Not yet. There are thirty of them. If you allow an interval of three minutes between each, it's going to take an hour and a half. Better allow another hour for safety. If we hear nothing by nine o'clock we can reckon they're all away."

" Another hour and a half," Saunders said.

" It's going to be a hell of a day to-morrow." Hugo was darning a sock, using a tin of baked beans as a mushroom. " What are you doing about your job ? "

" Leave it alone for at least another week," Peter told him. " Wouldn't be safe to go near it before then. The goons will tighten up like hell for a bit after this."

" That's the worst of tunnels," Hugo said. " Everybody suffers. It isn't only you chaps."

" Every tunnel that breaks means one less starting place," John said.

" It must have been wonderful for the chaps who were the first ones here," Peter said. " Fancy being in a camp from which no one had ever started a tunnel . . ."

" It would be very pleasant, I agree," Hugo said. " But sooner or later chaps would start digging and the goons would start imposing restrictions. It's a sort of vicious circle, one chasing the other. Far better not to start it."

" Far better not to be here at all," John said.

" It makes you think." Saunders sat hunched over the table, wearing the woollen cap that seemed so much part of his face, the paintbrush forgotten in his struggles to express himself. " It makes you realise that no man has any right to lock a fellow up for any length of time. Look at us. Compared to Dartmoor this place is a holiday camp. We've got our friends, and the goons leave us pretty well alone. Yet we think it's awful here. Fancy going to Dartmoor for twenty or thirty years. A hundred and ninety-nine years they can give you in America. Rather get the chop."

"We don't know how long we've got," Hugo said.

"I'd rather not know," Peter said.

"I like to know where I am." Hugo bit off an end of wool and moved the tin round inside the sock, looking for more holes. "If we only knew how long we'd got, we'd know how long we had to wait."

"We're not doing so bad," Saunders said. "Think of those chaps in Dartmoor. For what? Because they stole to feed their wives and kids most likely. And why did they steal? Because no one had ever taught them how to earn their living."

"They broke the law, they must face the consequences," Hugo said. "Our case is different, we're not criminals."

"We all got caught," John said.

"We're just as guilty as they are, if it comes to that," Saunders said. "Look at me—I've killed innocent women and children, bombed hospitals and churches——"

"The Bermondsey Basher, they call him," John said. "Slit-throat Saunders."

They sat in silence after this, in the strangely silent room. The gramophone was still playing, but quietly now, in a mess at the far end of the room; and Peter imagined the sentries stamping up and down outside the wire, swinging their arms to keep warm, fleetingly illuminated by the passing searchlight beams.

John took a tattered piece of paper from his pocket. "I'll read you a poem if you like. That'll cheer you up." He straightened the paper and announced:

NIGHT BOMBERS

"*Monstrous shadows moving in the darkness*
In sudden bursts of power in near-dawn darkness;
Huge ungainly lumbering shapes
Wallowing blindly towards dispersal points,
Waved onwards and finally brought to rest
By two dim lights
Wielded commandingly by an airman,
Cold in the exterior darkness.

"*From the belly of the nearest shadow*
Descends a ladder, down which climb
Seven leather-huge dwarf men.
Michelin-men of uncouth shape ;
Helmeted and visored like men from Mars.
And, as they stiffly clamber down,
The wind blows freshly ; brings the friendly smell
Of earth and meadows in the moonlight.

"*For nine hours these have been away from earth,*
Sucking oxygen through narrow tubes,
Cold and cramped and deaf with noise,
Each in his lonely station ;
While searchlights, flak and fighters all combine
To tear them down ;
To tear them fiercely burning from the sky,
In which they try in vain to hide themselves.

"*So slowly down they clamber,*
Remove their masks and sniff the air ;
They light a cigarette and stretch their arms
And look around them at the sky.
They are glad to be alive these men ;
These seven leather-huge dwarf men
As thick-booted, gloved and helmeted they stand
Beneath the belly of that monstrous bird."

"That's not a poem," Saunders said. "It doesn't rhyme."

"You didn't write it, did you ?" Peter spoke to John.

"No."

"Who did ?"

"I don't know. I found it when we were putting the dummies in the bunks."

"If you want some poetry," Saunders said, "I know a bit of *Gunga Din*."

"I wonder who wrote it," Peter said.

"Kipling, of course !" Saunders said it with scorn.

" No—I mean this. Let's have a look, John." He took the paper from John's hand. " Why, this is Otto's writing."

" Blimey," Saunders said. " I didn't know Otto was a poet. He couldn't speak English, hardly."

" His English was good," John said. " It was only his accent that was a bit ropey."

" That happens to be my property," Loveday said, from his bunk, " and I'll thank you to give it to me."

" Sorry." Peter passed the piece of paper to Loveday who took it, folded it and put it under his pillow.

" I think it's jolly good." Peter would have said more, have tried to tell Loveday that they understood, that they realised that this evening meant more to him than it did to them. But it had grown beyond that. Loveday had put himself beyond their reach.

While Hugo and Saunders were preparing dinner Peter sat and listened for the sound of activity from outside but heard nothing.

He went to the latrine whose window looked out on to the wire, and found Tyson there, gazing intently out into the darkness.

" Anything happening ? " Peter asked.

" They must be all away by now," Tyson said. " I'd give my ears to be with them."

" We'll be out soon," Peter said.

" It's too much to hope for, two tunnels so close together," Tyson said. " We'll be lucky if we survive the search."

That night Peter could not sleep. He lay on his bunk wondering about the escapers, where they were and what they were doing. He imagined those who had decided to go on foot walking along the deserted roads of the Polish countryside; free. Free to go wherever they liked. And now, if the cookhouse tunnel weathered the search and was not discovered, they could start on theirs again. He and John were well up on the list. The bad air and the damp of the tunnel had already taken its toll of the diggers. One by one they had dropped out, and place by place he and John had crept towards the top. Now they were well within the coveted " first ten " and would be certain of getting away when the tunnel broke.

He would soon have to arrange for the rest of his civilian clothes and his papers; he wouldn't worry about these until after the search. Too bad to get all ready and then lose the lot. Far better not to make too many preparations—too much to lose if you were discovered.

In the early morning, still unable to sleep, he went out to the washhouse for a mug of water. The place was lit by a feeble low-powered bulb, and beneath the light Tyson, muffled in coats and blankets, sat reading a book. He did not look up as Peter entered the room, nor did he speak. As Peter filled his mug quietly, anxious not to disturb him, Tyson slowly turned a page, and when he left the washhouse the man was still sitting there, his head bent to the book in the dim light, alone in the night-quiet washhouse.

CHAPTER VI

OPEN WARFARE

THE FOLLOWING morning the usual body of miserable green-clad German soldiers with fixed bayonets marched into the compound, separated to the various barrack blocks, unlocked the doors and shouted their usual "*'Raus, 'raus!*" to call the prisoners to another day. In Peter's block the prisoners shouted back their usual reply.

But here ended the similarity to any other morning. Instead of breakfast of three thin slices of black bread, Saunders and Hugo had prepared a substantial meal—not as a celebration, but because very soon the whole camp would be turned out on to the football pitch to stand, perhaps all day, while the tunnel was excavated and the barracks searched.

This morning, to make the columns look their normal length, the prisoners paraded in ranks of three instead of five. They were all fully dressed and carried sandwiches, some of them cardboard boxes full of food. No one knew what to expect, and it was wise to be prepared.

To Hauptmann Mueller as he walked up the hill, everything looked as it normally did. There were the long lines of prisoners, each line nearly as long as the barrack before which it stood. Peter's block was the first to be counted, Wing-Commander Stewart's place being taken by Tyson, who in unaccustomed full uniform looked tired and apprehensive.

As Mueller approached, Tyson saluted. The German returned his salute.

"Where is Mr. Stewart?"

" He is not here this morning."

" *Ach so ?* " Mueller looked slowly down the ranks of grinning men. It was not until the guards began the count that he became aware that everything was not in order. His round face turned white, then red, then white again. Peter could see the effort that he was exerting to retain control.

He turned to Tyson. " In fives, please," he said in a quiet voice. " Always in fives, Mr. Tyson."

" O.K., chaps—close up ! "

Untidily the long straggling line of prisoners closed up to a compact bunch three-quarters of its normal length. Mueller, determined not to betray his feelings, stood silent while the count was taken. There were fifteen prisoners missing.

He moved to the next block, where the same performance was repeated. He counted all the blocks, and then stood talking to the *Lagerfeldwebel* in the middle of the square. By now the triumphant prisoners could see from his face that he was beside himself with worry. Presently the *Feldwebel* called one of the guards, who saluted and set off at the double to the *Kommandatur*.

The prisoners waited expectantly. Then the rumour got around that Mueller had sent for the *Kommandant*. He was an almost mythical being, rarely seen in the compound. Mueller walked up and down, his hands behind his back, while the *Feldwebel* loosened stones from the path with the toes of his jackboot and kicked them against the wall of the barrack block.

Presently the compound gates were opened, and a squad of guards, armed with tommy-guns and wearing steel helmets, marched towards the football pitch. They were halted and turned to face the prisoners, their tommy-guns at the ready.

" Mass execution at *Oflag XXIB*," John muttered.

" They're only closing the stable door," Peter assured him. In spite of the danger to their tunnel, he was enjoying himself, as most of the prisoners were enjoying this break in the normal routine.

There was a murmur of appreciation as the *Kommandant*, a slight figure in cavalry breeches and a long flowing cloak, appeared at the gates. He walked stiffly, like an ancient crow, his cloak held tightly across his narrow chest. Hauptmann Mueller walked down to meet him, the roll fluttering in his hand. They met, watched by nine hundred prisoners. The *Lager-offizier* saluted and stood stiffly to attention while the *Kommandant*, having returned the salute, stood arms akimbo, his cloak blowing in the wind.

"He's tearing old Mueller off a terrific strip," John said.

"Wouldn't be in his shoes," Saunders said. "Not for six months off my sentence." He chuckled nervously.

The two Germans talked for some minutes while the troops drawn up on the football pitch stood stiffly, pointing their tommy-guns at the prisoners. Then Mueller saluted again, turned on his heel, and walked back towards the barrack blocks. When he reached the top of the hill his face was set in a frozen grin; the British prisoners must see that he was "sporting."

"You will return to your quarters, gentlemen," he said.

The prisoners filed back into their barrack blocks, and were locked in.

The rumour spread quickly; the *Kommandant* had sent to Berlin for the *Gestapo*. In Peter's block there were long queues for the windows that looked out on to the football pitch. The fortunate ones who had obtained the point of vantage were relaying the news to those inside the room.

"Here come some more goons."

"They must have turned out the whole unit," another said. "There are hundreds of goons marching down the road."

"They've deployed into the fields now—they're surrounding the camp. They're making a loose cordon about fifty yards deep."

"They've no idea where the tunnel comes out, that's why."

"They've no idea where it starts either."

There was a silence, while those at the back grew restless.

"What's happening now?"

"Nothing much—they're just hanging around looking stupid."

"Here come the dogs."

"Where—I can't see them!"

" There, look—coming along the road behind the sentry-box."

" Hell, yes—it won't be long now chaps."

" Here comes a car. Two cars—three—a whole convoy. They're Mercs, they're stopping outside the gates. Brown uniform—must be the *Gestapo.* They're all saluting one another now. Heiling Hitler as hard as they can go."

" What are the dogs doing ? "

" They're quartering the fields outside the wire. They've found the tunnel ! "—excitedly—" they're hopping about like mad—they're shouting their heads off at one another. How typical! Someone's run off for the *Kommandant.* He's fallen over his rifle. What clots—they're pointing their rifles down the hole—as though anyone's still down there ! "—shouting out of the window—" You clots, you silly clots ! They went hours ago ! "

" Shut up, Bill," someone said. " They'll put a bullet in here if you don't shut up."

" Sorry, but they *are* silly clots. Look at them standing there as though they expect the whole camp to come out of the hole."

" Here comes the *Kommandant.* And the wily Gest-a-po. And the cameramen. They look as though they're going to a funeral."

" Have you fellows had enough yet ? Let someone else have a look."

The window party squeezed their way out, those immediately behind taking their places.

" What's happening now ? "

" They've got to the hole. They're all waving their arms about. I can't see what they're doing, I think the *Kommandant* is telling old Mueller to go down the hole. He's refusing to go."

" Mueller's telling one of the goons to go down—he's refusing to go too."

" Good show, that's mutiny. Hope they shoot the whole lot."

" What are they doing now ? "—impatiently.

" One of them's got a bicycle—he's cycling back to the compound."

" The *Kommandant's* lighting a cigarette. They're taking a photograph of the hole. Fat lot of good that's going to be."

" That's for the records, old boy. The Scene Of The Amazing Break At *Oflag XXIB*. Thirty Desperadoes Loose in Poland. The *Luft-Gangsters'* Break For Freedom."

" Hallo, there's a squad of goons coming into the compound. They're marching across to the *abort*. They must know the tunnel starts from there."

" Left right, left right, left right . . ." the prisoners chanted in time with the marching soldiers. Slowly they changed the time of their shouting, and burst into laughter as the Germans altered step. It's just like school, Peter thought. He stood at the back of the crowd listening to the running commentary. He felt the victory of the prisoners over their guards and, as always in moments of victory, he felt pity for the vanquished.

" Left right, left right . . ." There was a sudden rattle like the sound of a stick brushed across corrugated iron as a salvo of tommy-gun fire flew low across the roof of the barrack block.

" Better pack it in, chaps," someone said. " The next lot'll be through the windows."

" What's happening now ? "

" They've locked the door of the *abort*, and posted a couple of goons outside."

" Perhaps now they've found the tunnel they'll let us out of here."

" Not a hope, we'll be here for days."

" I bet they don't find the trap from this end. We sealed it down pretty thoroughly."

" Here come the working party. They've got some Ruskis with spades. They're going to make 'em dig it up."

" Where from ? The *abort* end ? "

" No—the exit. They're telling a Ruski to go down—they're putting a Ruski down the hole. Poor devil, he'll come out right into the trench of the *abort*."

" He's lucky—they'll have to give him a bath now."

"He'll never get through it. I expect half the chaps left their food down there because they couldn't carry it all."

"Old Kee went out loaded like a camel."

There was silence as the green-clad Russian prisoner was seen to crawl headfirst into the tunnel. Presently there was more excitement.

"Look—here come some charabancs. They're pulling up outside the camp. They're full of goons—hundreds of 'em—complete with kit and everything."

Saunders came and joined Peter and Loveday at the back of the crowd. "They haven't got a chance," he said.

"There are too many of them," Peter said. "If only one or two had gone they wouldn't have taken all this trouble. Thirty going all at once has scared them stiff. They're turning half the army out."

"It's going to make it difficult for your lot when you break," Saunders said.

"They'll forget all about it before then," Peter told him.

"I hope Otto gets away," Saunders said. "I reckon he's got more chance than the others."

"More chance of getting shot if he's caught." Peter saw the look on Loveday's face and wished that he had not spoken.

The prisoners were locked in the barrack blocks all that day and night, and the following morning the whole camp was herded on to the football pitch, where they were surrounded by a ring of armed guards while the buildings were searched. They spent the morning sitting and standing—there was not room for them all to sit at the same time—or queuing to use the temporary latrine that had been erected in one corner of the pitch. Saunders had brought his patent portable *Stufa* and Peter and the few prisoners who surrounded them were able to drink a mug of luke-warm tea.

Later in the morning the Germans set up a trestle-table under one of the goalposts. One by one the prisoners were made to approach the table, where they were identified with the complete personal record kept by the Germans—photograph, fingerprints, birthmarks and a chart of tooth fillings. After each man had been identified he was stripped and searched; and then he was released to walk freely round the circuit, but was not allowed to enter the barrack blocks.

The prisoners quickly realised that the longer they could spin out this identity parade, the greater start would the escapers have. They milled around inside the cordon of guards, each one, as he was caught and taken to the table, hanging back like a frightened steer about to be branded. Once he was in front of the table deliberate misunderstanding and stupidity, if handled intelligently, could gain a valuable ten minutes. After half an hour of this the guards used their bayonets to enforce their commands, and the identification was speeded up.

As the football pitch thinned out and Peter realised that it would soon be his turn to be identified, he began to worry about the few *verboten* possessions that were hidden in his clothes. There would be a serious shortage of maps and compasses for the next few weeks and he did not want to go out unprepared. In spite of Tyson's pessimism he was still confident that their tunnel would remain undiscovered. Surely the goons would be content with one tunnel unearthed this week.

Looking round him to see what the others were doing, he could see several earnest bearded figures diligently but furtively scraping away with their hands at the loose earth of the football pitch, or patting the surface soil tenderly back into place. He knew a moment's indecision and then quickly slid his maps and compass from their hiding-place in the waistband of his trousers and buried them in the ground. Shortly afterwards he was taken by the guards and marched to the trestle-table where Mueller, a chastened man, sat glowering through his round, dark-rimmed spectacles.

"Number?"

"Eh?"

"Number?"

"Number?"

Mueller kept his temper. "Your P.O.W. identity number!"

"Oh . . . I've forgotten it."

"Where is your disc ?"

"Disc ?"

Mueller signalled to one of the guards, who lowered his rifle and gently pushed the bayonet into the small of Peter's back.

"Oh, my *disc* !" Peter fumbled with the front of his shirt, taking as long as he could to discover the metal disc which hung from a piece of string round his neck. When, at last, he found it, the string was too short to enable him to read the number. He leaned across the table and held the disc in front of the officer's face.

Mueller drew back hastily. "*So ! Neunundachtzig !*" He flicked through a small box file and extracted a card, in one corner of which Peter could see a photograph of himself with set expression, holding a number across his chest.

"Flight Lieutenant Peter Howard." Mueller studied the photograph, then looked hard at Peter. "So you have been in bad company. Do not congratulate yourself, my friend. They will not be out for long." He signalled the guard to take him along to be searched.

At last, when all the prisoners had been identified and released on to the circuit, a close line of guards walked methodically across the football pitch, turning over the loose soil with their jackboots. Peter, standing by the touchline, watched anxiously as penknives, compasses, maps, Indian ink, packets of dye and other escape material were unearthed and placed in two large blankets which the ferrets carried off to the *Kommandatur*.

As soon as the prisoners were allowed on the pitch he went to where he buried his things ; but the compass and maps had gone.

During the next ten days the prisoners were awakened five or six times every night to be counted, land-mines were placed in the earth outside the wire, and series of snap *appells* were held. These were carried out independently of the usual fixed roll-calls and were heralded by the blowing of a bugle. As soon as the bugle sounded the prisoners had to leave whatever they were doing and assemble outside the barrack blocks. While they were being counted ferrets searched the blocks, the *aborts*, the cookhouse and the washhouses in the hope of finding a tunnel which the sudden roll-call had forced the prisoners to leave uncovered.

Under these conditions it was impossible to dig, and Tyson decided not to resume work on the cookhouse tunnel until this security mood of the guards had passed. Peter and John, chafing at the delay, passed the time in walking round the circuit to keep fit and in making their plans for the long journey across Poland and Hungary to Yugoslavia.

Gradually the excitement subsided and one by one, sometimes in pairs, the would-be escapers were brought back grinning sheepishly, into the fold. The cooler was already filled with the victims of the *Kommandant's* displeasure on the morning after the break, and the returned escapers were locked in the White House where they lay awaiting trial. Often on their daily walk round the circuit Peter and John would catch a glimpse of the white strained faces peering from the upper windows. A levy was made on all rations, and food was sent to these prisoners within a prison.

Eventually only Otto and an English lieutenant-commander were still at large. As the days grew into weeks their fellow prisoners began to hope that these two had got clean away. When at last the news came that they had been "shot while resisting arrest," the camp refused to believe what they hoped was merely a rumour. Then it was announced publicly on parade by the S.B.O. and the prisoners were forced to accept it.

They retaliated by increasing their goon-baiting activities until there was open warfare between the prisoners and their guards. The Germans, frightened by this hatred, used their rifles to maintain order, and it was only the tact of the S.B.O. that saved the lives of several of the wilder spirits.

CHAPTER VII

ORDERS FROM BERLIN

THE TUNNEL was nearly finished, and as Peter lay hacking away at the hard, tenacious clay he felt that nothing could now stop them from getting out.

They had recently come to a layer of large, flat smooth stones which, Tyson said, had probably once formed the bed of a river. The ground was even wetter here, but once beyond it they had begun to drive the tunnel upwards towards the surface where it was drier. But the air was bad at the head of the tunnel owing to the upward slope, and Peter was forced to crawl back to the bottom of the slope at intervals for air. He had just returned to the face for another spell of work when the lamp at his head guttered out and filled the tunnel with its acrid smoke.

I'll crawl back and have a chat with John, he thought. Give the air time to clear a bit.

He crawled back to the lower shaft where John should have been working, but there was no one there. Thinking this odd, he climbed the ladder in the darkness and edged along the upper tunnel. There was no light, only the darkness and the silence, and he had a sudden fear and quickened his crawl towards the chamber at the base of the upper shaft, fighting hard to keep from utter panic. He thought that he was alone, that the others had gone and sealed him down. He could hear himself panting in the darkness as he pulled his body through the puddled clay.

Suddenly he bumped into John. " What's wrong ? " he asked. " Why are all the lights out ? "

" The goons are searching the cookhouse," John whispered.

" I was coming to fetch you. The chaps have shut the trap down —we'll have to stay here until the search is over."

" Hope they don't call an *appell.*" Tyson's voice came softly out of the darkness. " We've had it if they do."

" D'you think they suspect anything ? "

" I doubt it," Tyson whispered. " Just a routine check, I should think. It's getting cold down here."

Peter realised that he, too, was cold ; that the damp clay was drawing all the warmth from his body. He shivered. " I'll go for a crawl up the tunnel, I think."

" I'll go with you," John said.

They stopped at the top of the lower shaft for breath. " How long shall we have to stay down here, I wonder ? " Peter said.

" It'll be lunchtime soon—they're bound to pack it in by then."

They sat opposite one another in the upper tunnel, their legs dangling down the shaft.

" Getting pretty stuffy down here, isn't it ? " Peter said.

" I could do with a smoke."

" That'd make it worse. Heaven knows what it'll be like when there are about forty of us lying down here waiting to get out."

" We'll have the exit open then, that will let some air in," John said. " I'm glad we shall be up at the front end, in more ways than one."

" So am I," Peter said. " I don't think this air will last much longer."

" It'll see us out," John said. " There's enough down here to last for hours."

" Let's go back and see what's happening." Peter wanted to get back near the shaft, away from the compressing darkness of the tunnel. They felt their way back to where Tyson crouched at the bottom of the upper shaft.

" There was a hell of a row going on just now," he told them. " It sounded as though the whole German army were in the cookhouse."

" Probably a blitz search," John said.

"The air's pretty bad down here." Tyson sounded worried. "We'd better give 'em a bit longer, then if we hear nothing we'll assume that the goons have cleared everyone out. If we lift the trap carefully we can have a look round and get some air."

For the next half-hour they lay panting in the darkness of the tunnel. The air was getting worse, so bad that it was advisable not to move about. By huddling together in the chamber at the bottom of the shaft they were able to generate some warmth. Tyson had disconnected the tube from the air pump and worked the pump to change the air at intervals.

Peter sat with his back propped against the wall of the chamber and hoped that the Germans would not find them. He realised now that he had banked everything on this tunnel; that the nearer they got to breaking out the more important the tunnel had become.

"Half an hour must be up," John said. "It must be well after lunchtime."

"I expect the goons have called another *appell*," Tyson said.

"What'll happen when they find we're missing?"

"They won't, if the chaps can manage it. They should be able to cover our absence all right—after all, we're only three."

That's what it is, Peter thought, they must be on *appell*. The others will cover us all right. They *must* cover us, we can't be discovered now. A few more days and we shall be away. They can't possibly discover us now.

Some time later they heard the thud of footsteps on the floor above, the scrape of the stove being moved. The trap was lifted. The head and shoulders of one of the stooges appeared in the opening.

"Sorry, you chaps. It was the Swedish Commission. Some Red Cross blokes came in to inspect the cookhouse. We thought we'd never get rid of them. You'd better hurry up—the goons have laid on a special lunch."

"We've saved your lunch." Hugo indicated the two bowls of

barley soup, two small pieces of raw-looking sausage and two rolls of white bread which stood on the table.

"The tea's still hot," Saunders said. "I put the jug on the stove."

"I suppose you've heard the news," Hugo said.

"About the Swedish Commission?" Peter asked.

"About the move."

"Move?" Peter stopped eating. The sausage felt like lead in his throat. He knew before he said it what Hugo was about to say.

"We're going in about four purges. *Stalag-Luft III*, I think they call it. Supposed to be a pretty good camp."

"When are we going?" Peter managed to ask. Perhaps there would be time to finish the tunnel before the move. Perhaps there was still a chance.

"First thing Monday morning. We're going in four purges," Hugo repeated. "Personally I shall be jolly glad to get out of the place."

Peter could have murdered him. He sat in front of the special lunch, feeling that everything was finished. To have been discovered would have been bad enough; but to be moved to another camp just before breaking was the last straw. He turned to John.

"We'll just have to leave it, that's all," John said. "There's another week's work at least. We can't possibly do it before the move." He spoke lightly, as though the tunnel were of no importance; but Peter knew what it meant to him, knew the control he must be exercising to be able to speaklike this.

"It's jolly tough luck," Saunders said. "Especially after you'd got as far as that."

"Is the whole camp going?" Peter could hardly believe it, even now.

"Every man jack," Hugo said.

"Who's coming into this camp after us?" Peter asked.

"They say it's not going to be used as a military camp any

more," Hugo said. "Too insanitary. They'll probably turn it over to the *Gestapo.*"

"What a find, for anyone who does come in!" Saunders chuckled. "A ready-made tunnel, just waiting for 'em."

"Don't talk about it," John said. He opened a book and began to read.

"Why did it happen so suddenly?" Peter wanted to get it straight.

"Orders from Berlin," Hugo said. "After the last escape, I expect."

"But that was weeks ago."

"The news just got through, I expect. Everyone has to be evacuated within forty-eight hours."

"I bet it was the Swedish Commission," Saunders said. "I bet they said the place wasn't fit to live in."

"No, it wouldn't be that," Hugo said. "They wouldn't work so fast on that recommendation. The Berlin rumour seems more like it."

"It's definite we're going?" Peter still thought there might be a hope.

"The day after to-morrow," Hugo said.

Having been prepared for disappointment for so long, Peter was able to hide it.

"What's *Stalag-Luft III* like?" he asked. "Is it a new camp?"

"I think so—it's in a pine forest, I believe."

Peter could imagine it. Virgin ground. They'd get in early and stake their claim for a tunnel. Get cracking as soon as they arrived. The last tunnel had been good experience, now they would make one on their own. Keep it small and take no unnecessary risks. "Which purge are we going in?"

"The first. We leave at eight o'clock in the morning—we'd better start getting packed right away."

Stewart came in with a handful of letters. "Last post you'll get for a few weeks—better make the most of it."

"Is it a fact we're all going?" Peter asked.

" Yes," Stewart said. " Rotten luck on you chaps. You'd nearly finished, hadn't you ? "

" We were going out next Friday," Peter said. " What's the new camp like ? "

" Wooden huts," Stewart said. " Eight in a room."

As he packed for the move Peter had an idea. The Russian compound. Why couldn't a group of them drive a shaft up from the middle of the tunnel and come out in the Russian compound ? They could hide there until the others had gone and then complete the tunnel at their leisure. He pulled on his clogs and hurried down to Tyson's room.

Tyson was sitting alone at the table, sewing bars of chocolate into a watertight packet made from a rubber groundsheet.

" I've got an idea," Peter said.

" It's all right," Tyson said. " There are stooges out."

" Why not come up in the Russian compound ? " Peter said. " Hide there until the others have gone ? "

" We'd thought of that." Tyson's smile was almost gentle. " I've just spoken to their head man about it, but he won't play. Says they'd all be shot if we were caught. I expect they would be too. He even went so far as to say he'd tell the goons if we tried it."

" Need the Russians know ? "

" They know where the tunnel is, they've heard us digging. They'll be on the look-out for it now. Can't blame them in a way, you know."

" I don't blame them," Peter said. " It's just rotten luck."

" I'm going to hide down there," Tyson said, without looking up from his sewing.

Peter waited.

" I'll stay down there till you've all gone, then I'll come up from our end. There's just a chance the compound will be left unguarded."

" You can't get out from inside," Peter said. " We found that out this morning."

" I've arranged for the Pole who drives the night-cart to come in and let me out."

Peter felt a deepening of his admiration for the man. He certainly hadn't wasted time in useless regret since he had learned of the move. And here he was calmly sewing food into waterproof bags, giving his life into the hands of a man he hardly knew.

" Supposing he doesn't come ? " Peter said.

Tyson went on sewing.

" He might be too scared," Peter said. " Or there might be Germans here."

" It's worth the risk," Tyson said.

" Is there room for two ? " Peter, as he said it, felt that he was abandoning John ; but there obviously wouldn't be room for three.

" I thought you'd ask that," Tyson said, " and the answer is no. There's not enough air for two. I've talked it over with the Committee and they've decided it's a scheme for one."

Sitting in the train which was taking them to *Stalag-Luft III* Peter remembered that other journey, four months ago, when he had first met his fellow-prisoners. He and John had not wasted their time. They had learned a lot and in the new camp they would start another tunnel.

He looked across at Tyson sitting quietly in his corner. The Germans had found him in the end. Tyson would do thirty days' solitary confinement when they reached the new camp. But he would try again. He was that sort of man.

He looked at John, once more immersed in his book of Latin verse. John too would try again. To try was the important thing. They must learn to treat each failure as a preparation, a preparation for the next attempt. There was no giving up now. They would go on trying until they had dug their way out—if not from *Stalag-Luft III* then from another, unknown camp.

Publisher's Note

But it was from *Stalag-Luft III.*

Peter and John had no sooner arrived in the new camp than they were plotting ways of escape. Again they found that all their ideas had been tried before. Then John remembered the Wooden Horse which had helped the Ancient Greeks to get into another enemy stronghold, the city of Troy. He and Peter adapted the ruse and by means of a Wooden Horse got out of *Stalag-Luft III.*

Their escape from the camp itself is only a part of the story. Once outside the wire they were still faced with the problem of getting out of Germany. They had many adventures and time after time disaster threatened to overwhelm them.

You can read the whole story in *The Wooden Horse*, Eric William's thrilling account of his famous escape.

The Man Who Saved London

The Story of Michel Hollard
D.S.O., Croix de Guerre

by

GEORGE MARTELLI

TO MICHEL HOLLARD

to his comrades of the *réseau* "*Agir*"
and to the memory of those others
who gave their lives for freedom

Capitaine de Réserve Michel Hollard

DISTINGUISHED SERVICE ORDER

CITATION

This officer in January 1942 organised and conducted, with the greatest skill and devotion for two years, a highly successful information service in favour of the Allied Cause in Northern France.

He, at great personal risk, reconnoitred a number of heavily guarded V1 sites and reported thereon with such clarity that models thereof were constructed in this country which enabled effective bombing to be carried out.

His courage, devotion to duty and unsparing efforts were a constant inspiration to his team.

Finally arrested in February 1944 by treachery, he was deported to Germany, from where, after severe privations and despite torture under which he revealed nothing, he succeeded recently in escaping.

Acknowledgements

The main source of material for this book is Michel Hollard himself, to whom I am principally indebted for his breaking down, after ten years' resistance, and allowing me to tell his story. I have also been assisted by many others and wish particularly to express my gratitude to Mme. Hollard, M. Maurice Guchuy, M. Joseph Brocard, Captain V. C. Farrell and Mr. E. J. Kruger for much essential information; to Captain B. H. Liddell Hart for lending me the papers of the late Chester Wilmot; and to Count F. G. von Saurma, formerly technical director of the flying bomb sites, not only for expert advice, but for allowing me a glimpse of the "other side of the hill."

G.A.M.

Foreword

by LT.-GENERAL SIR BRIAN HORROCKS

K.C.B., K.B.E., D.S.O., M.C.

During the preparation of my recent "Men of Action" television programmes I have been privileged to read many stories of incredible courage. This, however, is the most remarkable story of them all, for Michel Hollard was the man who literally saved London.

When France capitulated in 1940, he determined to continue the struggle against the Germans by acting as an Allied agent, and he built up a network of spies, called the *réseau* "*Agir*" which soon became familiar in British intelligence circles for the accuracy of its reports. The success of the organisation was due entirely to his own outstanding capacity for leadership. He chose the agents himself, collected their information and nearly always handed it over personally to our intelligence officers in Switzerland. It sounds quite incredible but he succeeded in crossing this heavily defended frontier on ninety-eight separate occasions.

The *réseau* "*Agir*" was completely self-contained; no wireless was used and it did not rely on parachute drops for supplies. It was entirely dependent on the initiative of one quick-witted, cool-headed and extremely brave Frenchman.

It was typical of Michel that hearing about some new curious buildings which the Germans were constructing he obtained employment as a labourer there. And in spite of the strict screen of secrecy maintained by the Germans his agents subsequently uncovered one hundred similar sites. One day, even, while a German engineer was in the lavatory, an "*Agir*" agent succeeded in stealing the drawing of a site from his coat and making a quick tracing. From this the first blueprint of a V1 launching platform was made, and despatched via Switzerland to England.

With this information available, in December, 1943, the RAF struck with such devastating effect that the Germans were forced to abandon their original plan of despatching 5,000 flying bombs a month to London and to adopt a much more modest programme.

It has since been estimated that had it not been for Michel's information the V1 attacks on this country would have been six times more severe and would have lasted six months longer. Not only would London have suffered terribly but our invasion of Europe would unquestionably have been made much more difficult. This was the climax of his success as a master spy. But the charmed life he had been leading could not continue for ever and shortly afterwards he was betrayed to the Germans. Michel was subjected to every sort of barbarity: the bath torture, flogging, a ghastly train journey which lasted for three days and three nights when the prisoners were packed so tight—100 to a wagon—that they all had to stand wedged against each other, and ultimately incarceration in the Neuengamme extermination camp.

This sort of treatment was calculated either to kill the prisoners or at any rate reduce them to the state of animals. In ninety-five per cent of cases it succeeded. Michel belonged to that rare five per cent of remarkable men who had the courage to resist to the end.

Finally, when the victorious Allied armies were approaching, the prisoners were forced into the holds of merchant ships (which the Germans intended to scuttle) and taken out to sea where they were bombed by the Allies; the majority perished. Michel's escape from death was almost a miracle.

No one reading this book could have any doubt that Michel Hollard was entitled to the highest decoration for bravery which we can give to a foreigner under these circumstances, namely, the D.S.O. But it seems to me that many statues have been erected in London—the city he saved—to less deserving people.

THE MAN WHO SAVED LONDON

Contents

Part One

Part Two

Maps

PART ONE

1. First Venture

Michel was forty-one when the war started. Five foot seven, of spare but athletic build, with dark hair brushed back, lively eyes and a quick-changing expression, dressed usually in a neat dark blue suit only distinguished by the ribbon of the Croix de Guerre, he appeared no different at first glance from any other French business man of medium prosperity. However, there was something about him—a sort of inner intensity—which, to a student of character, would have announced that here was no ordinary man.

At sixteen he had run away from home to join up in the First World War, working for a year as an orderly in a military hospital until he was of age to be accepted as a combatant. Even then, being physically undeveloped, he had been obliged to fake his chest measurement in order to pass the medical!

At nineteen he was already a veteran, decorated for valour, and a year later was leading his platoon in pursuit of the retreating Germans when the armistice put an end to his military career. By then he had already gained more experience of men than many people acquire in a lifetime.

By comparison the years between the wars were an anti-climax: he did not find the return to civilian life easy. His schooling had been erratic. Now he had to complete his own education and at the same time earn a living, since his father, a distinguished scientist but with five daughters to provide for, was not in a position to assist.

To complicate matters still further, he had fallen in love and become engaged, against the opposition of both families, to a girl who, like himself, was a Protestant and a descendant of a Huguenot family, but better educated than Michel. To separate her from her fiancé, she was sent abroad for three years, and he employed the interval making himself worthy of her. Finally the parents gave their consent to the marriage. Three children followed, and to provide for the growing family absorbed all Michel's energy, leaving little time for the other interests—political, musical and literary—to which he was really drawn.

To qualify for his chosen profession of engineering, while keeping himself alive, he had attended night classes at the *Conservatoire National des Arts et Métiers* (corresponding to the London Polytechnic), gaining a diploma in mechanics, machinery and metallurgy.

Armed with this and by dint of industry and strict economy, he made his way in the fiercely competitive world of the inter-war years, holding a variety of posts including—for a short time—that of proprietor of a small taxicab business.

At the date when the war broke out he had abandoned this and was employed as technical representative by an important French firm specialising in the manufacture of brake linings.

As an officer on the reserve with the rank of Captain of Infantry, Michel hoped to rejoin the army. But his class was not called up, and in spite of his efforts to be accepted for active service he found himself mobilised in a civilian job under the auspices of the Ministry of War.

He threw up this on discovering that the *Centre d'Études* under which he worked, with all the resources of the French armaments industry at its disposal, was working for the enemy with the full approval of the Vichy Government.

The question was what to do next.

The most urgent task, of course, was to find a new job. The war might be lost, France prostrate, the Germans masters of Paris, but one still had to eat, with a wife and three children to support.

Once, however, one had decided to do nothing to help the enemy, obtaining a job became extremely difficult. In agreement with the authorities and with the acquiescence, more or less willing, of the majority of the nation, the French economy was being rapidly harnessed to serve the Occupying Power. In the engineering industries especially, for which Michel was qualified, almost every big firm was working directly or indirectly for the German war machine.

It was probably from the shock of this discovery that Michel's own rebellion dated. For one had to take a line: either adjust oneself to the situation or reject it—utterly.

It did not take him long, after his return to Paris, to decide which course to adopt. In fact, it scarcely required a conscious decision: it was rather a reflex action, an instinctive attitude, deriving less from any intellectual process than from some fundamental element in his make-up.

Having rejected the idea of defeat, the only logical consequence was to go on fighting; and this is what Michel now resolved to do, even if it meant fighting single-handed, and although at the moment he could not see how such a thing was possible.

Meanwhile the search for a job continued. Michel answered advertisements, attended interviews, received offers—but invariably turned them down on discovering that acceptance would mean violating his principle.

Early in August, when he was getting very short of money, he saw an advertisement in a Dijon paper which appeared to fulfil his conditions. An engineering firm, producing gas engines for motor cars, required a Paris representative. These engines, which ran on charcoal, were in great demand owing to the shortage of petrol.

Although applicants were requested to reply by letter, Michel decided to do so in person. Tearing up the letter he had started, he took the first train to Dijon and presented himself without warning at the firm, which was called the *Maison Gazogène Autobloc*.

The next day he returned to Paris with the job "in the bag." He had obtained the agency for half Paris, and a promise that no one else would be appointed for a fortnight.

Thanks to his pre-war employment he had excellent contacts

in the motor industry and by the end of the two weeks was back in Dijon with a first batch of orders.

He now demanded the agency for the whole of Paris and another fortnight during which no other agent should be accepted. This was willingly conceded.

Finally, after much running about and a couple more journeys to Dijon, he was appointed by the firm as their sole concessionaire for the Seine Department, with the title of Agent-General and powers to sign contracts and appoint his own representatives.

This position, besides making him financially independent, was for the next four years to provide the perfect "cover" for Michel's clandestine activities. Although he obtained it by pure chance and at a moment when he was desperate to find work to keep himself and his family, it would have been difficult to find another, as it turned out, which could have served his purpose as a *résistant* so effectively.

Worrying as his time of unemployment had been, Michel had not allowed it to oust his main preoccupation: how to carry on the war against Germany; and as soon as he was installed in the new job, and the financial problem solved, he applied himself to ways and means.

This was not easy. Although the B.B.C. were already talking of the French Resistance movement, in fact at this date it hardly existed. Michel made inquiries, followed clues, but they all led him nowhere. Finally he decided that the only solution was a direct contact with the Allies; and during the winter of 1940–41 he gave his mind constantly to this project.

Meanwhile the gas engine business flourished. Orders flowed in and the difficulty was to meet them. There would have been many more but for his refusal to supply the Germans.

This could have got him into trouble—in fact, it eventually did so—since the Germans themselves were short of petrol and made increasing use of gas. But for the time being he managed, by skilful tactics, to keep the enemy at bay, while satisfying his genuine French customers. At first he used his flat to work in, but soon was rich enough to rent offices in the Avenue Parmentier.

The more the business prospered the freer he felt to devote himself to his plan. He considered the various alternatives. A Channel crossing was out of the question: every inch of the coast was guarded. The frontier of Spain was remote from Paris and he knew nothing of its conditions.

That left Switzerland. The frontier was relatively near, he knew the region, above all it possessed the priceless advantage of affording an excuse for his journey. For it was rich in forests, forests produced charcoal, and as a salesman of gas engines Michel had a special and legitimate interest in charcoal.

Indeed, it was so much in demand and so difficult to find, that he had been obliged to undertake the additional business of procuring and supplying it to his customers. Otherwise the gas engine enterprise would have collapsed for lack of fuel.

So there, without his seeking it, was a ready-made "cover story." What more natural than that the Agent-General of *Gazogène Autobloc*, which also supplied charcoal to its customers, should himself go prospecting for that increasingly rare commodity? Or that he should choose for his searches that region of France which produced the kind of timber from which charcoal is made? And if his quest happened to take him rather close to the Swiss frontier, who could blame him for that?

There was only one snag. In order to reach the frontier it was necessary to cross the *Ligne d'Arrêt Nord-Est* and enter the *Zone Rouge*. This was a corridor varying in width from fifty to sixty miles and running the whole length of France's eastern frontiers.

For anyone living outside the zone special permission was required to enter it, which Michel knew there was no chance of his obtaining. Merely to ask would have invited suspicion.

But nothing venture, nothing gain. He decided he must take this hurdle when he met it.

Early in the spring of 1941 he started to make his preparations. Each week he saved some money to finance the expedition, and by casual remarks accustomed his staff to the idea that he would be going on a journey to look for charcoal.

At last all was ready: his secretary briefed to answer questions in his absence, enough money in his wallet to last a fortnight, and a return ticket bought. On the evening of the 15th May he boarded the night train for Dijon. With him he took a bicycle, a brief-case and a haversack.

Arriving at Dijon early next morning, he went straight to the *Gazogène* factory. There he spent the morning attending conferences and discussing his charcoal project.

Having thus established his alibi, he left the factory, and taking the Langres road set out on his great adventure.

He had chosen the Langres road, which runs north-eastwards from Dijon, after careful consideration of the main obstacle in his path. This was the Canal de la Marne et Saône, which formed the western boundary of the *Zone Rouge*.

The canal ran north and south to the east of Dijon and for much of its way through built-up areas.

To avoid these, Michel had decided to make for a place called Cusey, twenty-five miles north of Dijon, which appeared to lie in fairly open country, and where there was a lock as well as bridges.

His road ran straight through level country and he cycled along easily, enjoying the fresh air, the summer afternoon and the pleasant country sights. It was hay-making time and the air was filled with the sweet scent of sun-dried grass. He planned to reach the canal at dusk, and it was about seven p.m. when it came in sight.

As he rode along beside it he saw that crossing was not going to be easy. Every bridge was guarded by sentries, while access to the lock was barred by a fence of spiked railings reinforced with barbed wire. In addition a large notice warned anyone approaching that the fence was connected to a mine, which it would detonate on being touched.

It began to look as though he would have to swim. As the

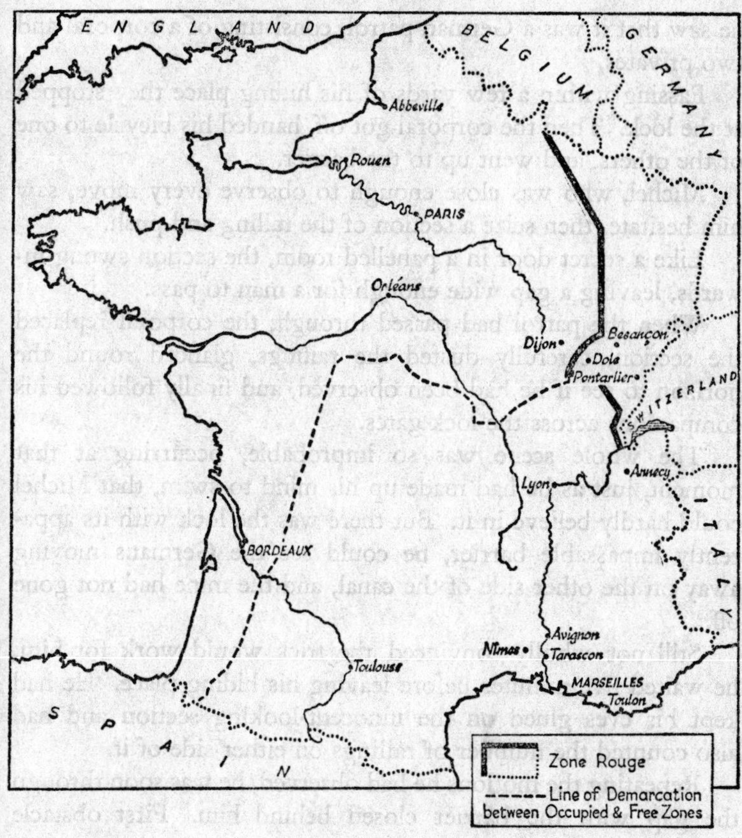

France, showing the Occupied Area and the *Zone Rouge*

canal was quite narrow and probably fairly shallow, that was not impossible, even with a bicycle; but it was inconvenient, to say the least, and, what was more serious, liable to attract attention. There seemed, however, to be no alternative. He did not mind the barbed wire, but the mine was another thing.

While he was considering the problem, concealed behind a hedge, three cyclists appeared in the distance. As they approached he saw that it was a German patrol, consisting of a corporal and two privates.

Passing within a few yards of his hiding place they stopped at the lock. Then the corporal got off, handed his bicycle to one of the others, and went up to the barrier.

Michel, who was close enough to observe every move, saw him hesitate, then seize a section of the railing and push.

Like a secret door in a panelled room, the section swung inwards, leaving a gap wide enough for a man to pass.

When the patrol had passed through, the corporal replaced the section, carefully dusted the railings, glanced round the horizon to see if he had been observed, and finally followed his companions across the lock gates.

The whole scene was so improbable, occurring at that moment, just as he had made up his mind to swim, that Michel could hardly believe in it. But there was the lock with its apparently impassable barrier, he could see the Germans moving away on the other side of the canal, and the mine had not gone off.

Still not wholly convinced the trick would work for him, he waited five minutes before leaving his hiding place. He had kept his eyes glued on the innocent-looking section and had also counted the number of railings on either side of it.

Repeating the motions he had observed, he was soon through the gap with the barrier closed behind him. First obstacle passed.

Just inside the barrier was a small square house, presumably occupied by the lock-keeper. There had as yet been no sign of him, but as Michel was passing, the door was opened by an elderly man. In his shirt-sleeves and slippers, rather lean, with reddish hair and a fair moustache, he looked at any rate like a Frenchman.

Michel was unprepared. He had his story ready for the Germans, but had not considered what he would do if caught behaving suspiciously by one of his own compatriots. Should he run for it or put his cards on the table?

He stopped and placed his finger over his lips.

"Listen," he said, "I'm trying to reach the frontier. And I'm not particularly anxious to run into Germans."

The lock-keeper looked him up and down, then jerked his head towards the house. Michel followed him indoors. In the small living-room there were the remains of a supper and a bottle of wine.

The lock-keeper filled a glass and handed it to Michel. Then he replenished his own, raised it and said: "*Salut.*" No further explanation was asked or needed.

The lock-keeper, whose name was Vrignon, would have pressed supper on his visitor, but it was now getting late and Michel was anxious to be under cover before curfew. So after thanking his host and promising to return, he bade him *au revoir* and set off again.

This encounter raised his spirits amazingly. The discovery both of a safe place to enter the zone, and also of a reliable accomplice, was the first encouragement he had received, and it seemed to him to augur well for his plan.

M. Vrignon had advised him to keep to side roads. Since, however, it was now nearly dark and he still had fifty miles to go to reach the place where he had planned to spend the night, he decided to risk the main road and take the shortest route.

He had covered about forty miles when just outside a village he saw two German soldiers walking in the same direction. Pedalling madly he dashed past, ignoring their challenge, and kept going till he was out of range.

An hour later he arrived at Dole without further incident and booked in at the only hotel.

It was about six o'clock the next evening when Michel rode into the small hamlet of Le Cernois, a few miles this side of the Swiss frontier. He had been bicycling since early morning, it had been raining all day and he was tired and soaked through.

The choice of Le Cernois as the springboard of his attempt was the result of a chance conversation in Paris. One of his customers had happened to mention that he knew the local *douanier*[1] and had found him a friendly person.

The customs house, which also served as a residence for the *douanier*, was the largest of the three or four buildings in sight, the others being farms. As Michel waited outside, after knocking at the door, he could see through a passage into a courtyard at the back, where several bicycles were propped against the wall.

When the *douanier* came to the door, Michel said: "I'm a friend of Monsieur X. I'd like to talk to you."

The *douanier* looked him over.

"All right. You'd better come inside."

He led the way into his office.

"I suppose you know I've got Germans here."

"No, I didn't, but I saw some bicycles at the back."

"That's them. It doesn't matter but you'd better be quick."

Michel then made a clean breast of it. He was trying to cross the frontier and he'd be coming back. He'd chosen Le Cernois because his friend had told him the *douanier* might be helpful. Could the latter show him a good way? If he met any Germans he would say he was looking at forests.

The *douanier* nodded understandingly. Then he went over to the wall, where a large-scale map of the district was displayed and traced with his finger the route for Michel to follow.

While they were talking a German officer entered the room. Without turning, and slightly raising his voice, the *douanier* remarked: "But you know nearly all the best wood has been cut down."

The officer crossed the floor, opened the door to an inner room, and disappeared.

"When is the best time to try?" Michel asked.

The *douanier* looked at his watch.

"Now. Everybody is at supper. You'll make it before dark if you hurry."

"What about my bike?"

[1] Customs guard.

"I'll look after that. You can call for it on your return. Go fifty yards down the road and turn right. You'll find the path straight ahead."

A quick handshake, "good luck," and Michel was on his way.

But not for long. He had gone half a mile and not yet reached the woods, when there, straight ahead of him, was another German patrol: two soldiers, rifles slung over shoulders, sauntering down the path towards him.

He stopped and searched desperately for cover. There was none in sight: besides they had already seen him. There was nothing for it but a bold face.

When he was five yards away from the Germans they stopped. In his town suit, carrying his brief-case, wet and bedraggled, Michel was conscious of the effect his appearance must produce on a lonely country path at that hour.

One of the soldiers started questioning him in German.

Where was he going? What was he doing? What papers was he carrying?

Michel, who could speak it a little, answered in German. He repeated the story he had so often rehearsed: he was on his way to look at forests. At this time of night? Well, it had been raining all day, and as it was now clearing up, he thought he would save some time.

The Germans were not convinced. He must accompany them, please, to the *Feldgendarmerie*.[1]

Back at the customs house there was no sign either of the *douanier* or the officer. But there was a military truck waiting outside. Michel and his escort climbed into it and the truck was driven off.

Michel now began to feel some alarm. The soldiers had scarcely glanced at his identity card but it seemed certain that the *Feldgendarmerie*, when they saw he lived in Paris, would ask him how he had entered the *Zone Rouge*.

After a short drive the truck stopped in a small town called Mouthe, where the *Feldgendarmerie* had its local headquarters.

[1] Military police.

Michel was taken to a small room and locked in for the night. There was neither bed nor couch, so he lay on the wooden floor, and, tired and dispirited, was soon fast asleep.

The next morning, he was removed to the Hotel du Grand Poste, at Pontarlier, for questioning. The interrogating officer, a youngish man in German army uniform, looked stern. He was obviously not disposed to credit Michel's story.

The only document the latter carried, apart from his identity card, was a statistical report he had obtained from some Ministry in Paris. It showed the monthly production in French factories of military vehicles for the Germans. This he now produced with a flourish, explaining that he had been given the information in connection with his gas engine business.

Since the document carried the official stamp of the Ministry, it made some impression on the German, but it was clear that he was still not happy about the affair.

For some reason he had not put the one question Michel feared: how he had crossed the *Ligne d'Arrêt* without a permit. But at any moment it might be asked, which would be fatal. It was essential to get away before that happened.

The interrogation had been proceeding for half an hour, without any sign of its concluding, when Michel had a happy inspiration. Why, he suggested, not hand him over to the French authorities? He would then be able to explain himself in his own language and the French magistrate would be able to judge whether he was telling the truth.

The officer hesitated. Clearly he was tempted, it was the easy way out. At the same time he was pretty sure there was something fishy. He studied the prisoner's face and Michel returned the stare blandly. Finally he stood up.

"All right. We'll send you across to the French."

2. *Behind the Mountain*

The action of the *Feldgendarmerie* in handing over Michel to the French was consistent with Hitler's policy at the time. The Germans were trying to rule with the velvet glove, using the French authorities to enforce their rule. To show themselves worthy of this confidence the Vichy Government applied the new laws with zeal. At the same time they could exercise a certain discretion.

In consequence the examining magistrate at Pontarlier, when Michel was brought before him the next day, having spent the night in the police station, was less anxious to find fault with the prisoner than to make sure he did not release a dangerous malefactor whose crimes would later recoil on his own head.

Michel, of course, was all innocence: had no idea that his search for charcoal would take him so close to the frontier. Admittedly he should have looked at a map, but it had never occurred to him that he was doing anything wrong, etc., etc.

Nobody could look more honest than Michel and his story was plausible enough. There was only one flaw in it: his illegal entry into the *Zone Rouge*. It seemed inevitable that sooner or later he must be questioned on this, and the truth then discovered.

In fact, the point was never raised. It was so elementary that doubtless the magistrate supposed that the *Feldgendarmerie* had already raised it and received a satisfactory explanation. Otherwise there was no charge which could be laid against Michel and after half an hour's interrogation he was allowed to go free.

One condition, however, was imposed. He must take the first train back to Paris; and to make sure he complied with it two policemen were detailed to escort him to the station and put him on the Paris express.

At this point, and after so narrow an escape, Michel might well have decided to abandon the attempt, and return to Paris to recuperate before trying again. As it was, the only result of the incident was to make him more determined than ever.

Trustingly the two policemen did not wait to see him off. Having seen him comfortably settled in an empty compartment, they bade him *bon voyage* and took their departure.

Michel gave them a few minutes, then opened the door away from the platform, jumped down on the track, crossed the line, and, after circling the station, arrived back at the entrance, where he had previously noticed that a bus was waiting.

The bus was still there. It was the bus for Morteau, a smaller town fifteen miles from Pontarlier and somewhat closer to the frontier.

Michel hung about, keeping out of sight, until the Paris express had pulled out. Then he boarded the bus and sat down behind a newspaper. Soon it started off.

So ended his first encounter with the enemy. He had pitted his wits against the Germans and their French accomplices and come off best. It was an encouraging start and gave him a new confidence in his plan.

Morteau, where he arrived about noon, was a quiet little place in the foothills of the Jura, washed by the River Doubs. Michel liked the look of it: there were no Germans and no police.

He bought a map of the district and studied it while eating a snack at a café. Morteau was only four miles from the Swiss frontier by the main road, but this was obviously to be avoided.

As he was searching the map for an alternative route his fancy was caught by two curious names, not very far apart: Au-Dessus-de-la-Fin (Above-the-End) and Derrière-le-Mont (Behind-the-Mountain).

He liked the sound of these places: it smacked of small and

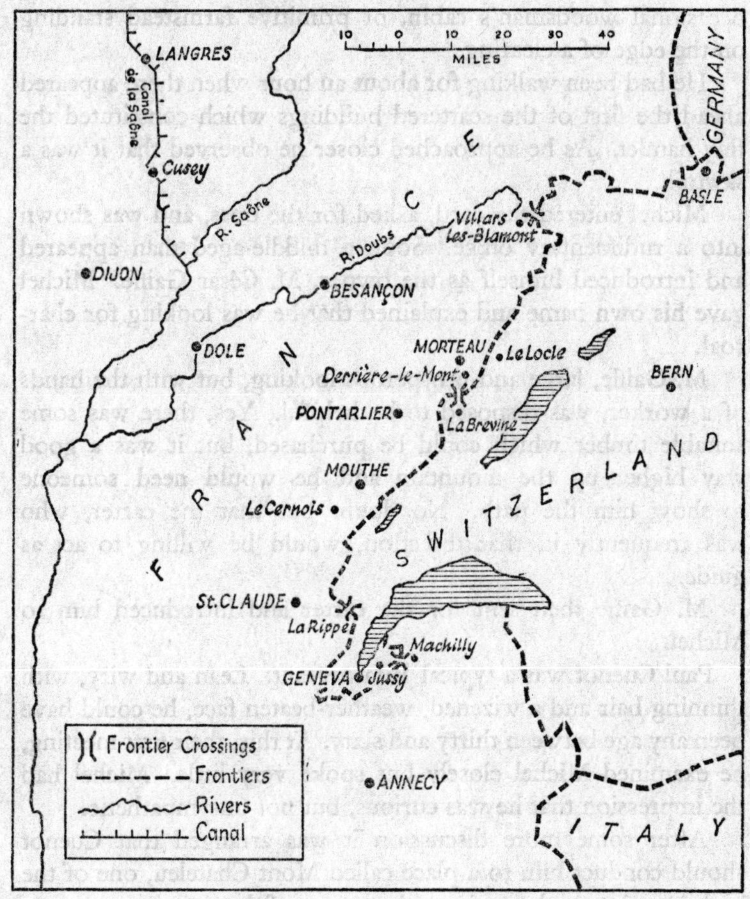

Michel's frontier crossings

lonely outposts, remote from the beaten track. Furthermore, the road that led to them seemed to end at Derrière-le-Mont. He therefore decided to make this his first objective. Leaving Morteau on foot he found a side road, which soon began to climb as it entered the forest. Here the only sign of life was the occasional woodsman's cabin, or primitive farmstead standing on the edge of a clearing.

He had been walking for about an hour when there appeared ahead the first of the scattered buildings which constituted the tiny hamlet. As he approached closer he observed that it was a sawmill.

Michel entered the yard, asked for the boss, and was shown into a rudimentary office. Soon a middle-aged man appeared and introduced himself as the owner, M. César Gaiffe. Michel gave his own name and explained that he was looking for charcoal.

M. Gaiffe, large and prosperous-looking, but with the hands of a worker, was disposed to be helpful. Yes, there was some suitable timber which could be purchased, but it was a good way higher up the mountain and he would need someone to show him the path. No doubt but that the carter, who was frequently in that direction, would be willing to act as guide.

M. Gaiffe then sent for the carter and introduced him to Michel.

Paul Cuenot was a typical Jura peasant. Lean and wiry, with thinning hair and a wizened, weather-beaten face, he could have been any age between thirty and sixty. At this, their first meeting, he examined Michel closely but spoke very little. Michel had the impression that he was curious, but not unsympathetic.

After some more discussion it was arranged that Cuenot should conduct him to a place called Mont Chateleu, one of the highest points in the region, where trees of the right type were to be found. As it was now growing late they would start early the next morning. For the night he could get a room *chez* Jacquot, a primitive sort of guest house open for occasional summer visitors. Apart from the dwellings of M. Gaiffe and Paul Cuenot, this was the only residence in the place.

So far so good, thought Michel, as he lay in the Jacquots' only spare bed that night. He still had no idea how he would proceed the next day; but he could see from his map that Mont Chateleu straddled the frontier, and felt sure that once he was there some plan would suggest itself.

Punctually at seven Cuenot was outside. The carter was leading a small horse and cart—the latter a home-made affair on rubber tyres. It was used for carrying timber and was the only kind of transport practicable on the narrow forest paths.

Michel was ready, having already breakfasted, and set off at once with his guide. The morning was fine and cool and there was a scent of pines which Michel, accustomed to the urban smells of Paris, sniffed with appreciation. The narrow path wound through the trees. All around was silence and solitude, only disturbed by the occasional flapping of wings, or the gurgle of a mountain stream.

As they proceeded, climbing steadily through the forest, he considered alternative plans of action. Should he take the carter into his confidence, or wait till they were near the frontier and then give him the slip? He was pretty certain that Cuenot would not betray him deliberately, but there must always be a danger in sharing his secret.

While he was still debating the pros and cons with himself, they arrived at a point where the path divided. Cuenot stopped and turned to him.

"That's the quickest way," he said, pointing to the left, "but I think we'll take the other. Less chance of running into the *boches.* After all, there's no point in having to explain oneself to them."

This was enough to make up Michel's mind.

"You are quite right," he replied, "especially as I'm planning to cross the frontier."

Cuenot nodded understandingly.

"I suspected as much—as soon as I saw you. You might as well have told me. And all that story about charcoal?"

"Just a blind."

"I guessed it was. Well, now I know, I can take you to the right place."

"Good. That's just what I was hoping."

After they had climbed for another hour the trees began to thin and they came on another track which led gently downwards. They followed this a little way, then Cuenot stopped. They had come to the edge of the forest.

Concealed from below by bushes, Michel found himself looking down on a little valley. Covered with lush grass and partly shaded, it looked pleasantly cool and refreshing. Immediately ahead of him the ground fell steeply. At the bottom was a stream and beyond that another grass slope, rising to where the forest began again. From there onwards the ground, densely covered with brush and pine trees, ascended steeply to the skyline half a mile away.

Cuenot pointed to the summit. "At the top you'll find a wall," he said. "That's the frontier."

As Michel gazed he felt he was seeing the promised land. After all the vicissitudes of the last four days, he could scarcely believe that he was actually in sight of his goal. For six months past he had been living for this, and the odds had always seemed against him. Now success was almost in his grasp.

Below and a little to the right of where they were standing a large chalet-like building stood in the fold of the valley. This, Cuenot explained, was an abandoned farmhouse now used by himself for storing wood and hay.

Cuenot was examining the valley intently, looking first to the right and then to the left.

"This is the moment," he whispered. "The Germans patrol the valley incessantly. Look——" he pointed to another farmhouse built on some high ground farther down the valley and on the opposite side of the stream, "that's one of their observation posts, and they use my place too. But it's all clear now and you should have time to get across. When do you expect to return?"

"To-morrow with any luck. At about the same time."

"Good. If it's safe I'll leave the door of the barn open. You can see it easily from the other side. If it's closed don't try."

"Agreed. And thanks—for everything."

"Don't rush it. Just walk steadily as though you knew the way. And good luck."

As Michel emerged into the open, he experienced for the first time since the start of his expedition a sensation of fear. After the protective shelter of the forest, to appear in full view of anyone in the valley was like entering a public place stark naked.

The Germans, Cuenot had told him, didn't hesitate to shoot; and as they were usually accompanied by their police dogs, the chances of escape if he ran into a patrol were negligible. Nor was it conceivable, if he was caught now, that any explanation would be accepted.

Without glancing to right or left he began the descent to the stream. Except for some cows grazing on the pasture there was no sign of life.

Not hurrying, and trying to look unconcerned, he reached the stream, crossed it and started to ascend the far side. A hundred yards brought him to the cover of the wood, but there was still a long steep climb, picking his way through fallen branches, waist-high scrub and rocks, before he came in sight of the boundary—a low wall loosely built of flat stones laid one on top of the other. A hundred metres... fifty... twenty-five... five... With a bound he was over the obstacle and standing on the free soil of Switzerland. As he paused to collect himself his heart was beating wildly.

It was a moment to remember but not to prolong. Without even glancing round, he hurried on; not until he was safely out of sight from the wall did he turn to look back in the direction of his beloved France.

The date was the 21st May, 1941.

He soon struck a path, and on the principle that all paths lead somewhere, followed it and eventually came out on a road.

In the distance was a house. As Michel approached he spelled out the name painted large on its side: LA BREVINE.

By its look it was the customs post and, sure enough, as Michel drew level, the customs guard came out on his porch. Michel went straight up to him and showed his identity card.

"I've just crossed the frontier. I've urgent business in Switzerland and I had no time to get a passport."

The customs guard took the card and examined it.

"What sort of business?"

"Family business."

In fact, Michel did have a sister living in Switzerland, who was married to a nephew of General Guisan, commander-in-chief of the Swiss Army. But except as a last resort he preferred not to drag her into it.

"How long are you staying?"

"Twenty-four hours."

"Returning the same way?"

Michel nodded.

"All right. You can carry on. But I'll keep this. You can pick it up on your way back."

"Supposing I'm stopped and asked for it?"

"Just say I'm holding it and have let you pass."

"Thanks a lot. I'll be here to-morrow."

"I'll be waiting," said the customs guard and returned to his house. Michel continued his journey.

It was a three-hour walk to Le Locle, where he hoped to find a train for Berne. But the sun was shining and he marched along jauntily, revelling in the sense of freedom.

In the villages through which he passed the people were dressed in their Sunday best. The sight of them going peacefully about their business, without the shadow of fear and want which hung over his compatriots, filled Michel with happiness. It was a foretaste of what they too would one day enjoy again; and the thought that by his action he might bring the day closer gave a new zest to his mission.

At Col des Roches, the last village before Le Locle, the congregation were just emerging from church. They looked so placid and contented in their solid Swiss way, standing about in their neat clothes and exchanging greetings, that he felt himself drawn towards them. He turned off the road and entered the cemetery, where various family groups were inspecting the graves.

While he mingled with them a Swiss gendarme approached and asked to see his papers. Michel explained his situation. The Swiss was polite but unconvinced. Michel then suggested they should go together to the police station and telephone the customs guard. This was agreed to.

Michel's story duly confirmed, the friendly Swiss invited him to lunch and afterwards arranged for a colleague to conduct him by bicycle to Le Locle.

The colleague, a sergeant, was full of enthusiasm for Michel's exploit. He was sure his lieutenant, who was always anxious to meet visitors from France, would like to hear of it first-hand. Would Michel do him the favour of stopping at the office and allowing himself to be presented to the lieutenant?

All this was a great bore as he had already lost valuable time. However, it seemed advisable to keep in with the Swiss, so he reluctantly gave his consent.

The sergeant had not exaggerated the lieutenant's interest in Michel. As local Intelligence Officer, one of his duties was to collect information brought across the frontier. Michel, coming from Paris, represented a windfall. Placing a large sheet of paper on his desk, he waited, with fountain pen poised, for the pearls about to drop from his visitor's mouth.

Michel was somewhat embarrassed. He had come to offer his services to the British, not to supply information to the Swiss. Anyhow, he was quite incapable of answering detailed questions on German military dispositions. He had never done any spying and had as yet no idea of the sort of things that spies are expected to discover. All he could do was to describe his journey, while mentioning such Germans as he had met on the way.

Fortunately this appeared of the highest interest to the lieutenant, who scribbled away happily as Michel told his story. The lieutenant, of course, knew much more than he did of what was going on along the frontier; but the fact, for example, that the 2nd Company of the 3rd Regiment of *Feldgendarmerie* was now stationed at Morteau—which Michel was able to confirm—evidently afforded him the liveliest satisfaction.

Getting up from his chair he went to the large-scale map which covered the whole of one wall, carefully selected one of the innumerable little flags with which it was dotted, and moved it to its new position a few centimetres away. Those who have worked in Intelligence will understand the pleasure this gave the lieutenant and the gratitude he felt towards Michel.

Conscious that he had hardly earned it, Michel next produced the only document he was carrying. It was the report on French production of military vehicles which he had already used to prove his *bona fides* to the Germans. This also was highly appreciated by the Swiss.

At last the interview ended. Michel had lost two hours. But he had made a friend, and one who might be useful in future.

As for the lieutenant, he was so pleased with the day's work that he escorted Michel to the station himself, and, since it was Sunday and impossible to change French money, insisted on buying his ticket to Berne.

Sunday afternoon was not the best time to call at a British Embassy, especially for a complete stranger. Nor did Michel's appearance help him. He had been travelling four days and nights, mostly on foot or on bicycle, and had spent two of the nights in custody. Since leaving his last resting place early that morning, he had walked twenty miles, partly across country. He was dusty and dishevelled and had lost the sole off one of his shoes. In short, he looked, and felt, like a tramp.

This was doubtless also the impression he made on the Embassy porter when he asked to see the Ambassador. The porter looked at him dubiously, then coldly directed him to an annexe, where he was shown by a clerk into a waiting-room.

Michel will always remember that waiting-room: not because of the furniture, which was what one might expect; or the ancient and dog-eared numbers of *Picture Post*; but for the solitary picture which adorned the walls.

It was not strictly a picture, but rather a framed strip of parchment inscribed with the following lines:

IN WAR: RESOLUTION
IN DEFEAT: DEFIANCE
IN VICTORY: MAGNANIMITY
IN PEACE: GOODWILL

Michel knew scarcely any English but during his two hours' wait, before anybody came to see him, he had ample time first to translate (with the help of a dictionary conveniently left in the waiting-room), then to copy out, and finally and laboriously to commit to memory these characteristically Churchillian sentences.

He has never forgotten them and until this day they have remained almost the only English phrases he can repeat without prompting. During the next four years they were to be a constant inspiration—especially the second line.

At last the door opened and there appeared a tall, fair Englishman dressed in a grey tweed suit. He looked Michel over quickly, then without sitting down or inviting his visitor to be seated, coldly inquired his business. He did not introduce himself and it was only later Michel learnt that he was Major B——, assistant military attaché.

Aloof in expression and glacial in manner, he listened to Michel's story and the offer of his services to the Allies with the air of one receiving, much against his will, a most distasteful confidence.

His response to the offer was entirely negative. He regretted it was quite impossible to take advantage of it. Michel should know that since the fall of France all direct communication with the United Kingdom had ceased. In any case, Switzerland was a neutral country and it would be quite improper for the British Embassy to engage in espionage against a power with whom the Swiss were in friendly relation.

That he should not be welcomed exactly with open arms was, of course, to some extent understandable. Michel's appearance, as we have seen, was against him, and he carried no credentials. There was no means of proving his *bona fides*; he could have been a double agent employed by the Germans or an *agent provocateur* sent by the Swiss. Secret agents are not thus recruited and B—— was justified in proceeding cautiously, although he might, perhaps, have used more tact.

Anyhow, Michel was furious. Barely able to control his anger, he wrote on a piece of paper and handed it to B——.

"Here are the names and addresses of two Englishmen. My brother-in-law, Mr. Robert Best, has an important business in Birmingham. The other, Mr. Sturge Moore, the poet and critic, is probably known to you by name. If you will be good enough to refer to them they will answer any questions about myself."

B—— glanced at the paper without any sign of interest, then laid it on the table as though he feared that the mere possession of such a document might compromise him.

"I shall return in a month," Michel continued. "Meanwhile, as I wouldn't like to have wasted my journey entirely, I will leave you this. You can rely on the accuracy of the information."

He then produced for the third and last time the famous document about the French factories. It had come in useful twice and, who knows, might be of some service to the British. Anyhow, he knew the contents off by heart by now and was tired of carrying the thing about with him.

Actually, the information proved quite useful to the British Government, and after being forwarded by B—— to London was broadcast by the B.B.C. as part of its anti-Vichy propaganda. This was heard by Michel's informant in the Ministry, who was greatly annoyed, since it placed him in danger and might easily have compromised Michel himself. Its publication was, in fact, a first class blunder on the part of the British.

At the moment, however, B—— scarcely deigned to glance at it.

Seeing no point in prolonging the interview any further, Michel bowed formally, snapped "*Au revoir*, Monsieur," and showed himself out, slamming the door behind him.

It wasn't till he reached the station that his temper started to cool.

Looking across the valley from his hiding-place in the trees, Michel saw that the barn door was open. So Cuenot had kept his promise.

He observed the prospect carefully. The same cows were munching on the same patch of grass! Otherwise the landscape was deserted. This, of course, did not prove that nobody was watching.

However, there was Cuenot's signal, giving him the "all clear." Nothing was to be gained by waiting; he must take the plunge.

This time, instead of going straight across the valley, he decided to steer a diagonal course. Though it would take a little longer, he would avoid going close to Cuenot's place. Thus, if by any chance the Germans *were* watching, at least he would not incriminate his accomplice.

To emerge from his hiding-place, descend the grassy slope, and cross the stream was the matter of a few minutes; another four at his ordinary pace brought him to the shelter of the French forest . . . and he had done it; crossed the frontier in both directions without being caught.

After proceeding a little farther to make his concealment more certain, he stopped . . . not to rest, but, in a silent prayer, to offer up thanks to God.

He was not, of course, yet out of danger; his presence so near the frontier would still be a matter for suspicion if he encountered a German patrol. Veering to the left he soon found the path, which he had climbed with Cuenot the previous day, and followed it down till it brought him back at Derrière-le-Mont.

He had arranged to call at Cuenot's house on his return and

found the carter and his family waiting to welcome him with a meal.

Although the worst was over, there was no safety while he remained in the forbidden zone. So as soon as he had eaten he said good-bye to the hospitable Cuenots and set off once more on foot.

His next destination was Le Cernois, some thirty or forty miles away, and he hoped to reach it that day. But before he had gone half-way exhaustion overcame him and he decided to spend the night at Pontarlier.

For once he slept late and it was noon when he came in sight of Le Cernois. This was the hamlet, it will be remembered, where he had left his bicycle shortly before meeting the German patrol; and although he risked meeting Germans again, since they occupied the customs house where the bicycle was held, he was determined not to return to Paris without it. For one thing, he needed it to cross the *Zone Rouge*; for another, bicycles were extremely precious.

By this time Michel was in poor shape. During the last thirty hours he had walked over sixty miles, and in spite of a night spent in a hotel in Pontarlier, where he had bathed and rested his blistered and bleeding feet, he was weary, footsore and nervously exhausted.

It was the hour of the midday meal and the dusty road was deserted. As he approached the customs house, however, a German soldier came into sight. Michel was prepared for this, but he was not prepared for what happened next, which was a mutual and simultaneous recognition by them both that they had met somewhere before. The soldier was, in fact, the same one that had arrested him a few days previously.

Michel stopped and said politely: "Good morning. You see, the French have released me. I have come to ask your commandant for permission to take my bicycle."

The German eyed him sceptically and without much friendliness, then jerked his head in the direction of the customs house.

"You'll find him there," he said surlily and walked on.

It was now too late for Michel to turn back; he could only continue on his way and trust to bluff to see him through.

On arrival at the customs house he found it deserted. In the courtyard where he had left it there was no sign of his bicycle, but after opening several out-houses he found it stowed away.

It seemed rather rude to remove his property stealthily—also, perhaps, suspicious. So he returned to the empty building, borrowed a sheet of paper and wrote a note to the German officer thanking him for keeping the bicycle and for leaving the shed unlocked. Then he mounted and rode away.

There was no way out of the hamlet except by the road by which he had come, so it seemed very likely he would meet his old friend again. And there, in fact, when he turned the corner was the German soldier coming towards him once more. As they passed Michel waved gaily and the soldier nodded back.

The remainder of his return journey was uneventful. After leaving Le Cernois he followed his previous route in reverse; sleeping again at Dole, drinking another glass of wine with his friend the lock-keeper, and duly reporting to the firm in Dijon on the charcoal resources of the Jura. Seventy-two hours after recrossing the frontier he was back in his flat in Paris.

He had not achieved his object, he was not yet accepted as an ally by the British. But he had done something perhaps more important. He had proved to his own satisfaction that his long-matured plan was a practical possibility. He had discovered a means of leaving and re-entering France with a reasonable chance of escaping detection, and he had made initial contact with France's friends abroad.

And this, in spite of his reception by B——, and a certain irritation with the English manner, filled him with a secret exultation and an iron determination to persevere in his project.

3. Second Attempt

Michel had promised to return to Berne in a month's time, and on the morning of the 16th June he boarded the train once more for Dijon.

His previous journey had been started in a mood of light-heartedness. This time he was both impatient and apprehensive. He knew now the dangers of the enterprise—not the least of which was another rebuff from the British. In that case all the trouble and the risk he was taking would be for nothing.

For three weeks he had been carrying his secret inside him. His escapade had taken him away for a week, and so long an absence needed some explaining to his wife and secretary. In the end they accepted his story about the difficult of finding charcoal, bad transport, etc.

Meanwhile his normal life was resumed. Dividing his time between his flat in the Rue des Arènes and his office in the Avenue Parmentier, he appeared entirely concerned with his family and his business. But always uppermost in his thoughts was the PLAN.

To go between his flat and the office he had to cross the Seine four times a day. Each time as he reached the bridge his eye was caught by the gaunt silhouette of a gigantic crane rising above the roofs of the city. Far away on the south-eastern horizon, it was a landmark visible for miles around.

This object became a symbol, at once inviting and menacing, which he found more disturbing with every day that passed. South-east was the direction of Berne, and to Michel it was as if a hand were pointing and a voice saying: "That is the road you have to take." Like some fateful decision from which there is no escape, and which is both a challenge and a temptation, the crane came to exert on Michel an almost hypnotic power and he could never see it without a sort of tightening inside.

It was therefore a relief to be sitting in the Dijon train, knowing that now there could be no turning back. Satisfactory also that out of the profits of his business he had succeeded once again in putting by sufficient money to finance the expedition without denuding his family; and this while continuing to refuse orders from the Germans, who could have been his best customers.

He had already informed the proprietor of the *Gazogène* factory that he was taking another trip to look for charcoal, so his arrival at the works occasioned no surprise. The afternoon was spent discussing various business matters. This suited Michel, as he did not want to leave Dijon too early.

When all was settled he took his bicycle and set out on the familiar Langres road. Three hours' pedalling brought him to the vicinity of Cusey. As it was still daylight, he turned down a side road, found a small inn and stopped to eat and await the dusk.

When it was nearly dark he left the inn and set a course across fields to approach the canal. He had noticed before that all its bridges were guarded and had he approached along the road he could have been seen by a sentry.

The lock, when he came in sight of it, looked just as forbidding as ever, with its barricade of spiked railings and the warning of mines. But it no longer held any secrets for Michel. Going straight to the right spot, he pushed the hinged section, opened the passage and went through with his bicycle. Then he carefully replaced the barrier.

A light was still burning in the lock-keeper's house, and a discreet knock brought him to the door. The good M. Vrignon at once recognised his visitor.

"Ah, it's you," he said. "I wondered who could be calling at this hour."

"I said I would be coming back."

"I remember. We'd better go inside."

In the modest living-room glasses and a bottle were produced, as before, and mutual healths drunk.

"You had no difficulty?" M. Vrignon inquired.

"None at all. I came across the fields."

"Just as well. They change the sentries at dusk and you would have met the relief on the road."

"That's why I avoided it."

"You're playing a risky game. They've tightened up since you were here before."

"We have to take risks in my business."

The lock-keeper eyed him shrewdly.

"I don't know what your business is, but we have a notion, my wife and I, that you're not working for yourself."

"No," said Michel, "I'm working for France."

"I suspected it," said M. Vrignon, "and I wish you success. *Salut.*"

It was Michel's intention to continue his journey without pause, but the lock-keeper strongly advised against it. Both he and his wife were so pressing that Michel finally agreed to spend the night with them. A bed was made up and he was soon asleep.

Waking at dawn he dressed quickly and stole downstairs, meaning to leave without disturbing his hosts. But Mme. Vrignon was already in her kitchen preparing coffee, and insisted on his breakfasting first.

Once again no questions were asked. All the Vrignons ever knew about Michel was that he had his own good reasons for avoiding the Germans. To these simple people that appeared sufficient justification for risking punishment themselves by offering him shelter.

It was raining heavily when Michel left Cusey and the prospect of a hundred mile ride to the frontier was unattractive. By good luck, after cycling for two hours, he found a bus bound for Besançon. Putting his bicycle on the roof he got a seat inside and travelled the next forty miles in relative comfort.

The bus was full of country people, most of them carrying baskets of provisions, and there was the usual animated chatter as it slowly progressed, with frequent stops to put down and pick up passengers. The talk was of local matters: crops, markets, prices, families. Nobody mentioned the war or the German occupation. Compared with the Parisians, his fellow travellers struck Michel as well fed and contented. They had not yet felt the Nazi boot, they were minding their own business and would have been rather shocked, he suspected, if he had taken it into his head to confide in them.

At Besançon, where it was still raining, he remounted his bicycle and took to the road again. Following the valley of the River Doubs he rode through green and wooded country, climbing most of the way until he reached Avoudrey. Here he left the main road and headed south, passing Col du Tounet and La Grande Combe, and eventually arrived at Derrière-le-Mont.

The tiny hamlet was as deserted as ever. As he knocked at Cuenot's door he looked at his watch. It was six o'clock. He had been travelling for exactly twelve hours without a stop, was drenched to the skin and extremely hungry.

Although he had warned the carter that he might be returning, he had given no date and his arrival was a complete surprise. However, he was welcomed like an old friend and immediately invited to join the family meal which was just beginning.

The Cuenots had nine children, ranging from ten to twenty years old. As Michel entered they were all seated at a long table, in front of steaming bowls of soup and an enormous loaf of black bread. After his long, exhausting and illegal journey, it was a cheerful and reassuring sight and he needed no pressing to take the place prepared for him. As for the simple peasant fare, he thought he had never tasted anything more delicious.

The long low room, which served both as kitchen and living-room, was almost bare of furniture. Apart from a Madonna, its only decoration was a framed photograph of the head of the household as a soldier in the first war.

But what was lacking in comfort was made up for by the

friendliness of the whole family. Like the Vrignons the Cuenots knew nothing about Michel except that he was defying German regulations, but this was enough to make him an ally who should be afforded all help.

With his usual impatience at any delay, and although he had travelled nearly a hundred miles since morning, Michel was anxious to push on and cross the frontier that night. From this he was dissuaded by Cuenot on the grounds that it was too dangerous—in the dark anything could happen. A bed was vacated and, tired as he was, he gladly accepted it.

Rising again at dawn he found breakfast already prepared for him. After swallowing it quickly he thanked his hosts warmly, promised to return soon, and started off on foot up the mountain.

An hour's march brought him to the highest point of the forest. A little to the right was the deserted farm, and there stretched below him lay the valley he had to cross before reaching the frontier.

As on the two previous occasions, it appeared completely deserted. But this, as Cuenot had warned him, could be deceptive, since all along the frontier the Germans had observation posts from which they could watch without being seen. One could only pray and hope that the prayer would be answered.

Michel started the descent. As before, he walked slowly, pretending to look for mushrooms. Thus he reached and crossed the stream, climbed the farther slope, and ten minutes later had scaled the wall and was standing on Swiss soil. It was seven-thirty a.m.

This time he did not stop to look back, but hurried on through the woods until he struck the road and soon arrived at the customs house of La Brevine.

Here he met with his first check. The customs guard remembered him well, but was far from friendly. He must return immediately by the way he had come.

Suspecting what had happened, namely that the guard had been reproved for letting him through before, Michel played for time. It would be a pity, he suggested, to send him back, for then the Swiss would lose the benefit of the important military intelligence that he was bringing especially for them. He then told the story of his interview a month earlier with the Intelligence Officer at Le Locle.

This impressed the guard sufficiently for him to go inside and telephone his superior. On returning he informed Michel that he had instructions to detain him until an officer arrived to investigate.

Two hours later the officer appeared. Michel repeated his story, giving the name of the lieutenant who had interviewed him and suggesting he be asked to confirm it. A telephone call was put through to Le Locle, when it was discovered that the lieutenant was no longer serving.

Michel now remembered the latter telling him that in civilian life he was an architect with a practice at Colombier. The exchange was requested to try and trace him; and with admirable efficiency, after a few minutes, produced the former Intelligence Officer at the other end of the line. He then not only confirmed Michel's story, but urged that he should be received as an informant of proved value.

The end of it all was that, instead of being turned back, Michel was treated like a V.I.P. An appointment was made with the Intelligence Officer at La Chaux de Fonds, arrangements were made for his transport, and Swiss francs provided for his expenses.

It would mean, as before, a tiresome delay, but that was a price worth paying for free entry into Switzerland.

It was about nine the next morning when Michel's train reached Berne. He had lost a day, but in compensation had spent the night at the best hotel in La Chaux de Fonds as a guest of the Swiss Army. Furthermore, in return for the information he had given them, he was authorised to circulate freely for twenty-four hours.

As it was still rather early and a lovely day, he decided to walk from the station to the Embassy. The latter was situated on the outskirts of the city, in a luxurious residential quarter lavishly laid out with trees and gardens. As Michel strolled along he contrasted its air of well-being with the desperate and lawless business in which he was engaged. How could people living in such a respectable neighbourhood have anything to do with a man like himself? Would he not be shown the door again?

He glanced down at his suit. He had brushed it carefully that morning and his shoes were clean and in good repair. At least he no longer looked a bandit.

On arrival at the Chancellery he was shown into the same waiting-room and a few minutes later Major B—— appeared. The Assistant Military Attaché was still reserved in his manner, but his expression was not quite so forbidding.

He held out his hand, said, "I'm glad to see you," and then took Michel into another room, where they sat down facing each other across a table.

"I would first like to ask a few questions," B—— began. "What was your mother's maiden name and where and when was she born?"

Other questions followed of an equally personal nature. At what university had his father graduated? How many sisters did he have and to whom were they married?

Whilst Michel answered B—— would glance at a sheet of typescript lying on the table in front of him. When at last he was satisfied he smiled for the first time and pushed the sheet across to Michel.

"If the gentleman you are inquiring about," Michel read in French, "is called Michel Louis Hollard, born at Epinay-sur-Seine on the 10th July, 1898, son of Madame Hollard, *née* Monod, and of Monsieur Auguste Hollard, Doctor of Science, Professor of Chemistry, etc., then he is a genuine patriot who in 1916 at the age of seventeen engaged to fight againt the Germans."

"You see," said B——, "we have to take our precautions. When you first came to see me I knew nothing about you and it could easily have been a trap. Now that I know you are speaking the truth, I should be glad to accept your offer—that is, if you are still of the same mind."

"If I wasn't I wouldn't be here," replied Michel.

"Good. Then let's get down to business. First of all, how often do you think you can make the journey to Berne?"

Michel reflected. It wasn't going to be easy to find pretexts in future. The charcoal story was wearing rather thin. But he never took his fences till he met them, so after hesitating a moment he answered: "Every three weeks."

"Splendid," said B——. "That would be ideal. Next question: do you think you can obtain the information we need?"

"Well, I don't know yet what it is."

"First and foremost the exact position and description of all enemy units in the Occupied Zone."

Michel looked surprised. He wasn't expecting anything quite so simple.

"Is that all?" he said. "What about the aerodromes, and the petrol and munition dumps? And the defences, which the Germans are building everywhere? Doesn't that interest you too?"

"Of course," replied B——, "everything interests us, but your most important task is to locate and identify all German military formations, particularly armoured divisions."

"Don't you have that information already?"

B—— smiled. "Naturally we have a great deal of information, but another check is always useful."

Michel said nothing. He had a feeling of anticlimax. As an army officer he knew the rudiments of military intelligence; realised that it was not a matter of individual prowess, producing dramatic coups, but a painstaking labour, the result of team work piecing together an infinite number of small facts.

And yet the streak of naïvety in his make-up had led him to expect something . . . well, less humdrum than merely providing "another check."

However, he was a soldier. He had offered to serve, he had been accepted, and he was there to take orders.

"All right," he said, "I understand. I'll do my best."

With that the interview concluded.

As B—— was showing him out Michel made some reference to the charm of the Embassy's surroundings. B—— agreed and proceeded to expatiate on the beauties of Berne generally. It was then that Michel discovered that this coldly reserved Englishman was an enthusiast for the arts with a quick sense of humour. In addition, his French was impeccable.

After chatting in a friendly way for several minutes B—— held out his hand.

"Well, *au revoir*. And good luck to you."

As he walked away Michel's heart was light. He had attained his first objective, and if the assignment given him was not terribly inspiring, at any rate it should be easy. He had merely to keep his eyes open.

So little did he foresee what exactly he was undertaking, or where it would lead him in the end.

4. *Organisation of a Réseau*

The task set by B—— had sounded simple enough to Michel, sitting in the Embassy in Berne, but back in Paris he realised, as soon as he began to think about it, that it was not going to be easy at all.

Paris, for example, was full of German soldiers, but many of them were on leave from other parts of France, or other occupied countries, or even from Germany. In a single street one could meet men from a hundred different units, and even if one succeeded in interpreting their insignia—which was not by any means easy for a foreigner—one was not much further advanced.

There were known to be several divisions stationed in the Paris region, but which they were and where exactly they were located was another matter. How did you set about looking for them? Whom could you ask—knowing that merely to show curiosity on such a subject might well lead to your arrest?

Moreover, Paris was only one centre. B—— had given him a list of "strategical points," but it was simply a list of the principal towns in the Occupied Zone. Anyhow, the Germans seldom set up their headquarters in the town; they were usually in some remote and closely guarded château, which it was sufficient to approach to arouse suspicion.

After a week spent tramping the streets of Paris, travelling to the suburbs and frequenting the cafés where German troops were most often to be seen, Michel was not much wiser than before.

He soon reached the conclusion that he could do nothing alone. He needed helpers, plenty of them and quickly. But where to find them? Whom could he turn to without risk of being betrayed? It was June 1941, and if there already existed a French Resistance movement Michel had not yet been able to discover it.

The problem was still unsolved when one day there came to his office a little man dressed in worker's clothes, who asked if he could be supplied with a gas engine. Interviewed by Michel he gave his name as Louis Margot, ex-prisoner-of-war recently repatriated owing to wounds. He had acquired an old lorry and planned to equip it with a gas engine, with a view to starting a one-man haulage business.

Michel took the order, promised to expedite it, and made an appointment for Margot to return a few days later, when the engine would have arrived from the factory at Dijon.

It took several days to adapt the lorry and fit the engine, during which Michel had opportunities to talk to his new customer. Aged thirty-five, with a working-class background, Margot impressed him by his common sense, receptive mind, and firm character. He was also apparently a fervent patriot.

On the last day, when their business was finished, Michel invited him into his private office.

"I have been thinking that perhaps you could help me," he said.

Margot looked blank.

"You see," Michel went on, "I've gathered from our conversations that you don't like our new masters any more than I do."

"Surely I don't like them. How could any Frenchman like them?"

"I agree. And do you also believe in an Allied victory?"

Margot looked dubious. "That depends. If the English can hold out and the Americans come to their help . . ."

"The English *will* hold out. And the Americans *will* come in —not this year, perhaps, but sooner or later, as they did before. But we mustn't leave it all to our Allies. The French must help themselves. Otherwise we're finished—whoever wins."

Margot gave a shrug. "I think you're right. But what can we do?"

Michel hesitated. By now he was pretty sure of his man, but it was the first time he had gone as far with another Frenchman and he realised that the next step would be fateful. If he had made a mistake his whole plan might be ruined.

"I'll tell you," he said quietly. "But first are you sure you would like to help?"

Now it was Margot's turn to hesitate. He was beginning to perceive what Michel was driving at. He was being asked to take a serious decision, but under Michel's calm gaze, as he confessed to him later, he felt he had no choice.

"Yes, I would like to."

"You realise it could be dangerous?"

"I don't mind that."

"Good, then this is what I want you to do. You have your lorry and you will be plying between Paris and the suburbs. There are German troops stationed in various sectors of the perimeter. Without going out of your way, find out all about them: exactly where they are and what they consist of."

Margot showed no surprise: he had evidently guessed what was coming.

"That shouldn't be difficult," he said. "I saw a good deal of the German Army when I was a prisoner."

"You won't find it so easy, but it's not impossible. As you know, each division has its own symbol, which is painted on its vehicles and embroidered on the flag displayed outside its headquarters. By noticing where vehicles with the same markings converge, you will discover their point of concentration. Inquiries in the neighbourhood should then reveal the location of the command post. If you can discover the name of the commander so much the better."

"Is that all?"

"That's the most important. But of course anything else you can find out will be useful. For instance, petrol and ammunition dumps, defence works, air strips, A.A. installations, et cetera."

Margot nodded.

"Write down the least possible," Michel continued. "And if you have to make notes, don't carry them with you. Practise memorising. And be accurate. One precise detail is worth a dozen vague rumours. Do you understand?"

"I understand. You can count on me."

"Good. You can come and see me at the garage when you have anything to tell me. We can always find a pretext."

A few days later Margot reappeared with his lorry, ostensibly to have some small defect repaired. He brought with him his first report. It was all and more than Michel had hoped for. Disregarding the latter's injunction he had gone out of his way to obtain the required information. After supplying some additional details, he left with a promise to return with more in a few days' time.

Michel was delighted. At last something was happening. Further, the success of this first experiment gave him confidence in approaching others.

During the next few weeks he engaged several more accomplices, all in the Paris region, and set them to work in the same way. They came from all walks of life—one was a railway employee, another owned a café, a third drove a taxi—and they gathered the information Michel wanted in the course of their ordinary duties.

Later, others were recruited in the Seine Department, at Dijon and various other centres. By the end of the year he was getting reports from a dozen different sources, in addition to the information he gathered himself, and passing them on regularly to B—— in Berne.

Some of his best workers were those, like Margot, whom he had met in connection with his business. Margot himself was perhaps the best of all. Devoted and conscientious, he would go to endless trouble in following up a clue, or confirming some detail.

The system of voluntary helpers, who gathered information in the course of their ordinary duties, functioned reasonably well as far as it went, but Michel soon realised it was not enough. The results, though often valuable, were too erratic. A person would start with enthusiasm and then become discouraged or distracted, or perhaps move to another job where he could no longer be useful. Since their services were given free, Michel could not be too exacting.

He was, therefore, forced to the conclusion that the only solution was to employ full-time agents, paid by himself and working strictly under his orders.

It was soon after he had taken this decision—towards the end of 1941—that Olivier Giran first came to see him.

Olivier, son of a friend of Michel's father, was just twenty at the time, but seemed several years older. Of medium height, with broad shoulders and a deep voice, brimming over with confidence, he looked and acted as one capable of enjoying life to the full and ready for any adventure.

His one ambition, he told Michel, was to fight the Germans. He had already made an abortive attempt to reach England, had been arrested at Marseilles and imprisoned. Could Michel suggest anything?

As it happened the boy had passed his childhood in Switzerland, in a village near the frontier poetically named La Côte aux Fées, not very far from Pontarlier. He therefore knew the region well through which Michel travelled on his way to Berne. Who better to act as courier?

It was not what Olivier had hoped for; but after Michel had explained that the job he was offering was possibly no less dangerous than soldiering, and probably a lot more useful, he agreed to take it on. An additional incentive was the hope that once known to the British he might eventually be accepted as a combatant.

It was thus that Olivier Giran became the first and youngest of the permanent agents of the future *réseau* "*Agir*."[1]

Their pact concluded, Michel lost no time in initiating the new recruit in his duties. The first need was to provide him with a safe passage across the frontier. Since Michel was reluctant to compromise his own route, it was necessary to find a new one.

In this he was helped by the Swiss. The Swiss Intelligence Officer at La Chaux de Fonds who had interviewed him on his second visit had given him an introduction to his father, a Monsieur Grandi.

Monsieur Grandi, although a Swiss, lived in France, being the manager of a factory at Les Verrières de Joux, a small village in the region of Pontarlier. The factory was only five hundred yards from the frontier, and was therefore an excellent starting point for a clandestine crossing.

It was here that Olivier, thanks to M. Grandi, successfully made his first entry into Switzerland. Thanks also to the same connection he had no trouble with the Swiss guards, arrived safely in Berne and delivered his parcel to B——. He then returned by the same route without incident.

Thereafter he made the journey regularly in place of Michel.

[1] The name Michel eventually gave to his network.

In addition he was given the area round Dijon in which to collect information. He soon showed himself brave, resourceful and energetic, and if he had a fault it was excess of enthusiasm and over-readiness to accept risks.

This arrangement brought great relief to Michel. By saving him the journey to Berne, which took up several days every three weeks, it enabled him to devote more time both to the running of the *réseau* and to the conduct of his business. Since the latter was not only his sole means of livelihood, but also provided both the "cover" and the finance for his other activities, he could not afford to neglect it.

In his next choice Michel was equally fortunate. Joseph Brocard was a very different type from Olivier. Of the same age but small and slightly built, with pinched features and a voice which was little more than a whisper, he looked anything but robust, but had something in his expression which suggested unusual determination.

Michel first met him in Switzerland, where he had tried unsuccessfully to enlist with the Allies and was about to return in disgust to France. This was the spirit that Michel always looked for. He made an appointment to meet Brocard again in Paris and there and then engaged him as his second full-time agent.

A few days later, equipped with a false identity card and a labour certificate in the name of Joseph Bart, the new agent set off on his first mission. Its object was to identify German units in Brittany.

Bart, as he was henceforth known, was so successful that his area was soon extended to a large part of northern France, including the forbidden coastal zone. He was quite fearless, indefatigable, and meticulously accurate.

Only once did Michel have occasion to find fault with him. It was of the utmost importance that all rendezvous should be kept to the minute. Failure of either party to arrive at the appointed time was a sign to the other that something had gone wrong, and if he waited he might be risking arrest himself. Therefore precise punctuality was an absolute rule.

One day Bart, who was usually most punctual, arrived at the meeting place two minutes late. Michel made no comment, but simply handed over his watch and begged the other to keep it. Blushing like a girl Bart pocketed the watch. He was never late again.

By the beginning of 1942 Michel had recruited four more permanent agents, bringing the total to six, who were distributed throughout the Occupied Zone. All of them gave their full time and were paid their living and other expenses out of his own pocket. Their main task was keeping track of the occupying forces, which the British still insisted on as a priority.

Meanwhile he did not dispense with his voluntary informants, but these had the easier and less important job of reporting on the enemy's static installations, such as aerodromes, arms factories, stores, etc.

In addition there was a special category of volunteers, used exclusively to report *movements* of German troops and material. These were all railway employees and they played an essential part in disclosing changes in the enemy's dispositions.

For example, a station-master at X would report the departure of a certain German division for destination Y. This would set in train further inquiries by Michel's team, as a result of which it would be discovered, in addition to the original information: (a) which division had replaced the former one at X; (b) by whom *it* had been replaced; (c) where the division previously at Y had gone to; (d) which division it had replaced there; and (e) where the latter had gone to.

One could, in fact, extend inquiries in both directions indefinitely, and the further they went the more complete the picture which emerged.

This, then, was the organisation which, starting from scratch, Michel created in the second half of '41. With minor adjustments it remained unchanged until November, 1942, when the German occupation of the whole of France called for a great increase in its activities.

He built it piece by piece with no preconceived plan and nothing to aid him but common sense. Each move was an experiment and he learnt, as he went, by experience.

This, perhaps, was a blessing in disguise. With no advice from outside, no rules to observe—except those he made himself—he approached each problem unbiased and solved it by the light of his intelligence. In all his decisions the only influence was his own judgment.

Equally important as a factor in its success, the *réseau* was entirely self-sufficient. It drew its strength from its own resources and no extraneous aid was ever offered or made use of. There were no parachute drops, no wireless transmitters, no system of internal couriers or "post-boxes." All the impedimenta of the cloak and dagger business, which so often proved fatal to other networks—especially those controlled directly from London—were dispensed with. In fact, Michel never knew of their existence.

It might be argued that through not using wireless there was a loss of time in communicating with London. In fact, however, very few intelligence reports are urgent, unless they are concerned with some immediate operation. And what was gained in time by using wireless was more than outweighed by the disadvantages.

Radio messages which could be intercepted and their source detected were the most effective means at the disposal of the Gestapo for tracking down Allied agents. Moreover, having captured an agent with his transmitter, the Germans would send messages to London purporting to come from him and in this way laid traps for many of their victims.

Then again only the shortest messages could be sent by wireless, whereas Michel's reports, forwarded in code through the Swiss post office, could be sent in full; while documents, plans, photographs, etc., which it would have been impossible to transmit by wireless, could be safely dispatched to London through neutral countries.

Finally, Michel's was a "one-man show," and this was its greatest safeguard. In the whole of the *réseau*—and by the end it numbered over a hundred persons—the sole connecting link was Michel himself, and he was the only member of whose existence any of the others knew. Thus he alone risked being betrayed if one of them was caught and questioned. It was only much later, and in case something should happen to himself, that he appointed three deputies and took them partly into his confidence.

All reports were delivered to him personally; either the agent came to Paris or he visited him in the provinces. These direct contacts, made at regular intervals, were invaluable. They enabled him to control the work at first-hand, without any danger of misunderstanding. They were also essential for maintaining the morale of his team.

The only drawback of the sytem was that it involved a lot of travelling. Fortunately his business was a perfect excuse for this, while it also provided cover for most of the permanent agents, whose labour certificates showed them as salesmen for the *Société Gazogène Autobloc de Dijon.*

5. *Arrest of Olivier*

Olivier Giran, having been engaged by Michel as his courier, made his first journey into Switzerland in January, 1942; and for the next six months he made the journey to and from Berne every three weeks.

This arrangement worked admirably. Olivier knew the country, he got on well with B—— and there was no difficulty with the Swiss, who had agreed, in exchange for the information they brought, to allow Michel or his courier free passage whenever they wished.

But in June a disaster occurred.

Olivier had a friend, a young Dutchman, whom he had met at the Netherlands Chamber of Commerce in Paris. Early in the spring this friend asked him if he could arrange for a group of Dutchmen, recently escaped from Holland, to be smuggled out of France into Switzerland.

Olivier, always looking for some new adventure, jumped at the proposal, and it was agreed that he should leave Paris with the party the same night.

By good luck there was no control at Auxonne, where the railway entered the *Zone Rouge*, and the train reached Pontarlier without incident. From there the party proceeded on foot across country, crossed the frontier undetected in spite of one alarm, and arrived safely at La Côte aux Fées.

Delighted with his success, Olivier returned to Paris, to receive an ovation from his friends at the Netherlands Chamber of Commerce.

It was only some weeks later that Michel heard of the escapade. Realising the risk he asked Olivier not to repeat it. Unfortunately in the meantime the latter had already promised to escort another party of nine: and on the understanding that this should be the last Michel reluctantly gave his consent.

At eleven a.m. on the 30th June, having arrived in Dijon the previous evening, Olivier went to the station to meet the train bringing the Dutchmen from Paris. He was accompanied by a youthful friend of his schooldays, Jean Bouhey.

They waited outside the exit as the passengers came off the train, but there was no sign of the party. Olivier then decided to look for them on the platform, leaving Jean to keep watch outside.

Five or ten minutes passed while Jean waited anxiously. Then he saw an armed German soldier emerge. Others followed escorting a group of civilians, handcuffed two by two. In the middle of them, handcuffed to a guard, was Olivier. As he passed he glanced at Jean and made a sign of discouragement. Jean was about to reply when he saw that the guard was looking at him. Turning away he discreetly made his escape.

Michel heard the news three days later, on his return from a journey. It came from Olivier's parents, whom he knew, and who had been informed by Jean Bouhey.

He was shocked. Not only was it the first serious set-back, but he was closely attached to Olivier—the earliest and the youngest of his full-time agents. While the young man had brought it on himself, he felt personally responsible for the disaster.[1]

Although for all he knew he was now in danger himself, his first thought was for Olivier. It was essential to discover where he was imprisoned, so that arrangements might be made for sending food parcels and messages and, if possible, organising an escape.

He decided to investigate himself, and after informing the Girans took the first train to Dijon.

The Departmental Prison, which the Germans had taken over, was a massive grey building standing at the end of a wide boulevard. Its grim façade, only broken by the rows of iron bars guarding windows of frosted glass that were never opened, formed a sinister contrast to the gaily flowering chestnuts which lined each side of the boulevard.

Some of the windows, Michel noticed, were covered with sheet iron. They were those of the punishment cells.

Michel had no plan, but he thought it unlikely that Olivier would already have been removed from Dijon. It was a question of making certain he was still in the prison.

As he approached the building he saw that the main entrance, flanked by a massive iron gate, was open; and decided on the spot to beard the lion in his den.

Just inside the entrance was a small lodge, where a German N.C.O. was seated at a table. At a smaller table next to it sat a

[1] In fact, Olivier was betrayed by a German agent called Engbert, posing as a Dutchman. The latter was eventually detected by the Dutch and executed.

young woman: blonde, pretty, but with an insolent expression, and speaking French perfectly.

Michel approached the lodge, knocked on the open door, and as the German looked up said in French: "Excuse me, Monsieur, but I am inquiring after a certain Olivier Giran. Can you tell me, please, if he is here?"

While the girl translated into German, the N.C.O. looked Michel over. Then, turning to the interpreter and speaking in German, he told her to ask the gentleman why he was interested in Giran.

Michel, who had learnt German as a child, knew enough to understand. He had his answer—and his warning—and did not wait for the translation. As a precaution he had already started edging away. Mumbling some excuse he moved swiftly towards the gate and a second later was outside in the street, where he was soon lost in the crowd.

Back in Paris Michel informed the Girans. Olivier's mother immediately left for Dijon and the next day, accompanied by a friend, visited the prison. Thanks to a humane guard, an Austrian, she was able to send not only food but a message to her son. A few days later a reply was smuggled out to her, and thereafter communication was regularly maintained.

By this means Michel learned that in spite of repeated interrogations Olivier had kept his mouth shut. All he had confessed to was smuggling for money. This was not regarded by the Germans as a very serious offence and there thus seemed some hope of his eventual release.

But in October a new blow fell. M. and Mme. Giran were both arrested in Paris and taken to Fresnes prison. Soon after, Olivier himself was transferred to Fresnes. Thanks to the charity of the German chaplain, a Lutheran pastor, Mme. Giran was able to communicate with her son; and when she and her husband were released for lack of evidence against them, they continued to exchange messages through the same intermediary.

Early in 1943 Olivier was again removed, this time to Angers. There he was subjected to a new series of interrogations. Once again and thanks to another German chaplain, who showed the same compassion as the one at Fresnes, Mme. Giran succeeded in keeping in touch with her son; and it was through this clergyman that she learnt of his death and the manner of it.

On the morning of the 16th April, 1943, Olivier and two other young men were taken from their cells to the place of execution and shot by a German firing squad.

6. Illegal Passage

After the arrest of Olivier Giran, Michel resumed his rôle of courier himself.

He was not entirely sorry to do so. He had missed the periodical contact with B——, with the chance, once in a while, to breathe free air and to hear news of the world outside the prison that France was rapidly becoming.

During the summer and autumn his arrangements for leaving and returning to France worked without a serious hitch. The two critical obstacles were the line of demarcation of the *Zone Rouge* and the immediate vicinity of the frontier, and for both he had evolved an improved technique.

When he arrived from Dijon at the Cusey lock, always at a pre-arranged time, M. Vrignon would be waiting and if Germans were about would make a warning signal. On the return journey he cycled straight to the lock-keeper's house, which, being inside the zone, could be approached openly.

From the windows of the house the German sentries could be seen. If one of them came too close, a diversionary operation might be necessary. In this case, Mme. Vrignon would stroll out, engage the soldier in conversation and manœuvre until his back was turned to the lock. Michel would then slip out of the house, pass through the barrier and disappear in the dusk.

For the frontier he always telephoned Cuenot the day before, to inform him at what time he would be arriving "to collect the load of charcoal." Cuenot then arranged to go on ahead, and if the valley was clear of Germans he opened a window of the farmhouse. On the return journey the "green light" was the open barn door.

Thus all went well until the coming of winter. Then one day Michel arrived at Derrière-le-Mont to find snow covering the ground. Since this was a new hazard he decided to wait for nightfall when his tracks were less likely to be seen.

Setting out after dark he climbed the familiar path until it brought him to the edge of the forest. Below him the valley gleamed white in the starlight, making every dark object more conspicuous. Worse, the snow had stopped falling, so that his footsteps remained visible should a German patrol pass. In that case he would be in danger from an ambush on his return.

While he was considering what to do, he noticed that there was a barbed wire fence extending right across the valley. It ran from a point near where he was standing, down to the stream, and up the slope on the farther side, to end where the forest began again. This gave him an idea.

Placing his feet on the bottom wire and holding on to the top one, he began to walk sideways along the fence. As anyone knows who has tried, this is a tedious process at the best of times; in Michel's circumstances it was excruciating. While the stillness of the night was shattered by the twanging of the wire, he was horribly conscious of his black form vividly silhouetted by its white background.

Half a dozen times, as he hooked himself on a barb, or struggled to keep his balance when the wire sagged, he was almost in a mind to give up; but telling himself this would be illogical, he continued his crab-like progress and eventually arrived safely at the edge of the wood.

Determined never to repeat this experience, the next time he tried attaching his boots back to front. He also made the same experiment with snow shoes. But apart from their discomfort these ruses were dangerous; they might mislead the enemy as to the direction he had taken, but could not conceal his passage of the frontier.

Reluctantly he decided he must find another route, below the snow line; and after careful investigation of various localities selected two alternatives.

The first was a good way farther north, at a place called Villars-les-Blamont. This was a small village on the main road between Pont-de-Ronde, in France, and Porrentruy, in Switzerland. Here Michel discovered two valuable accomplices, Emile Mathiot and his wife Geneviève.

Their home was a two-room bungalow, built on a steep bank overlooking the main road. Behind it the ground rose gently to a plateau, beyond which was a wood. The edge of the wood marked the frontier. It was about four hundred yards away.

As soon as Michel arrived at the bungalow, Geneviève would leave, driving her goat, and let it graze along the fringe of the wood. On reaching the highest point she took a good look round, then turned and faced the bungalow. This was the signal for Michel to start.

Half-way to the wood was a patch of bushes. Here he remained in hiding to await a further signal. This was a red handkerchief which Geneviève dropped if the coast was still clear. He then made a dash and gained the shelter of the wood, where he was safe on Swiss soil. For the return journey, always at a pre-arranged time, the process was reversed, except that he avoided the bungalow. This was so as not to compromise the Mathiots should he be seen by a German.

Apart from the assistance of the Mathiots, this route had the advantage of being close to the village of Glay, where Michel had a son at school. In consequence there was always a good excuse for his presence.

The second alternative route, and the one he eventually came to use most often, crossed the frontier at a point south of the Lake of Geneva, and about ten miles from Geneva itself, between Machilly (France) and Jussy (Switzerland). A side road, little used, connected the two villages and the whole district was thickly wooded.

This made the approach to the frontier relatively safe, but the actual crossing was not so easy, as it was obstructed by a barbed wire entanglement three feet high and six feet across. Beyond this obstacle was a stream, which marked the boundary.

On all his expeditions Michel dressed like a peasant, in blue canvas jacket, brown corduroys and beret. In his hand he carried a spade, a hoe, or an axe, and on his back a sack partly filled with potatoes under which were hidden any compromising documents. Thus if he ran into a patrol they would suppose he was a farmer or a forester engaged on legitimate business.

For the Machilly-Jussy route he took the train from Annecy, and got off at the station of La Roches Foron, where there was a wait of fifteen minutes. This gave him time to go to the buffet and collect a parcel, which he left there permanently. It contained, besides his peasant's clothes, a disguise as a railwayman: cap, armlet, leather pouch, lantern and the symbolic piece of cotton waste.

As soon as the train started he locked himself in the lavatory . . . to emerge a few minutes later looking the typical *cheminot*. Over his city suit he was wearing the blue jacket and corduroys—the common uniform of all workmen in France—and on top of this again the accoutrements of the railwayman. The sack of potatoes and the beret remained for the time being in the parcel.

When the train stopped at Machilly he opened the door away from the platform, jumped down on the track and started walking back along it, while stopping occasionally as though to inspect the line. Naturally nobody took any notice.

After going about five hundred yards he arrived at a culvert. Here he left the track, disappeared under the arch and retrieved a woodsman's axe from its hiding-place. In its place he hid the parcel, after removing the sack of potatoes and repacking the railwayman's insignia. Then, dressed as a peasant, he shouldered the sack and the axe and set off across the fields.

Ten minutes' walk brought him to a farm, whose occupant,

a M. Paccot, was his friend. From him he learnt if any Germans were in the vicinity. When the coast was clear he crossed a couple more fields, entered the wood and soon reached the frontier.

Once on Swiss territory he went straight to the nearest customs post, where by arrangement with the Swiss Military Intelligence he was by now an accepted visitor. There he removed his peasant's clothes, and with his axe and his sack locked them in a cupboard which was specially reserved for him. Shortly after, he was on his way to the station looking like any other business man.

In three years Michel crossed the frontier forty-nine times in both directions without being caught. He never missed an appointment in Switzerland and was never more than a day late. This remarkable achievement was due partly to the pains he took in planning each expedition and partly to the help he received on each side of the frontier. In particular the devotion of his compatriots—the friendly farmers who gave him shelter and reconnoitred the ground—did most to ensure his safety.

7. *The Lighting of the Torch*

On the 8th November, 1942, Michel, on a visit to Switzerland, was told of the success of Operation Torch, the landing of Anglo-American forces in North Africa, and was asked to redouble his surveillance of German troop movements, particularly towards the south.

As far as Michel was concerned, and for most Frenchmen, this was the turning point of the war. They had not heard of the battle of El Alamein, fought only a fortnight previously; or if they had it was only as an event of little significance. But now the war had returned to French territory, which could only be a stepping stone to France itself. It showed that the Allies were determined to drive the invader from their soil.

Three days later this impression was confirmed by the German occupation of the Free Zone. That in the eyes of the French could only mean that the Allies planned to land in the south of France.

The effect was to encourage the patriots, shake the confidence of the Vichyites, and help the undecided to make up their minds. Most of the last category lived in the *Midi* and it only needed the presence of German troops to topple them off their fence and on to the right side. If prior to the 11th November, 1942, there were perhaps twenty per cent of "collabos," fifteen per cent undecided, and sixty-five per cent pro-Ally, subsequent to it the proportion was more like fifteen per cent of "collabos" and eighty-five per cent pro-Ally. In other words, France henceforth was overwhelmingly pro-Ally, with a hard core of Vichyites forming the minority. For Michel this shift in opinion was of capital importance. It meant that he could now depend, in a greater measure than ever, on the tacit or active assistance of the honest citizen when and wherever he needed it.

The occupation of the Free Zone had resulted in a major redeployment of German forces. While some divisions were being moved south, others were arriving to replace them. On the roads and railways there was an incessant movement of troops and material.

As had been impressed on Michel, it was vital to the Allies to be informed of these changes quickly. Axis troops had already landed in Tunisia. Nobody knew what Hitler's next counterstroke would be.

Since Michel had no agents working in the Free Zone, the urgent need was to recruit suitable observers on the roads and railways which the Germans were using.

For road transport the main artery to the south was *Route Nationale* 7, which goes from Lyons to Nice via Valence, Avignon and Aix-en-Provence. It was essential to have at least one agent posted on it.

One of the best hotels on this road was the Hôtellerie de Pierrelatte, about half-way between Valence and Avignon. Built in Provençal style, with white walls and a red roof, and famous for its cuisine, it was the favourite stopping place for high-ranking German officers looking for a meal or a bed.

Michel had known the place before the war and had a slight acquaintance with the proprietress, Madame Simone Boirel. A woman of thirty-five, with lively brown eyes and the features and accent of a Provençale, she had inherited the hotel from her father and ran it with her husband, who was also the chef. Vivacious and energetic, always smiling, she was the perfect *patronne* who makes her customers feel welcome and takes a personal interest in the needs of each.

A few days after his return from Switzerland Michel arrived at the hotel. He had already followed the movement of one panzer division from Lyons to Marseilles and had observed the installation of its H.Q. at the Hotel de Noailles. He now invited Mme. Boirel to join the *réseau* with the special mission of keeping him informed of all military traffic passing on *Route Nationale* 7, and of all important German officers who stopped at the hotel. She accepted at once.

This was the beginning of an association which, although it was to end in disaster, proved highly fruitful during the next two years. While her devotion to the cause was never in doubt, Simone Boirel was in the happy position of being able to combine patriotism with business. The more popular she became with the German Army, and the higher the reputation of her hotel with its General Staff, the more successful she was as Michel's agent.

Having provided for a watch to be kept on the road, Michel next turned his attention to the railways. There were two main lines from Lyons to the south and they followed the left and right banks of the Rhone respectively. South of Avignon they united and then continued as one line through Tarascon to Marseilles, Toulon and the Riviera. Tarascon was thus a point of convergence for all traffic in transit for the Mediterranean whether from north, east, or west.

From discreet inquiries among the station employees Michel had discovered that the *sous-chef de gare* (deputy station-master), by name Lemeau, was very anti-German; and had persuaded him to act as his agent. When, however, a few days later he arrived to collect the first report, Lemeau was not at the rendezvous. He would probably be found at a signal box, a porter informed Michel, about a mile down the line. Michel at once set off in pursuit.

When he arrived at the box Lemeau was talking to the signalman. At the sight of Michel he looked embarrassed but agreed to accompany him outside. It was obvious that he had changed his mind and was trying to avoid a second encounter.

After walking a little way along the track, they left it at Michel's suggestion and scrambled down the embankment to a place where they were hidden by a clump of trees.

Michel so far had said nothing. He was considering how to tackle his man. The interview, he realised, was crucial. As *sous-chef* Lemeau was responsible for the service on that sector, and probably the only person in a position to obtain the detailed information Michel needed.

If he refused his help, all would be to start again, but with the outcome prejudiced by an initial setback. Indeed, for all Michel knew, Lemeau might have denounced him already—although he thought this unlikely.

As always when the situation was critical, Michel's awareness of his surroundings was heightened. It was late afternoon and the countryside stretched in undisturbed peace to the horizon. It was a flat landscape of ploughed fields, enclosed by hawthorn hedges, only relieved by an occasional farmhouse. A few miles away a level line of poplars marked the left bank of the Rhone, while to the east the sharp spire of a church rose above the distant sky-line. Although it was winter this was the *Midi* and there was a scent of flowering rushes in the air.

Making no reference to their broken appointment, Michel pretended that he himself had been reconsidering the matter. Perhaps, he suggested, he had not sufficiently emphasised the danger. Many Frenchmen had already lost their lives doing such work, and he would not like Lemeau to take it on under any illusion as to the risk he would be running. On the other hand it was of vital importance that Frenchmen should play their part in the liberation of France.

He talked for quite a time on these lines, while Lemeau listened in silence without betraying his thoughts. He seemed to be struggling with some emotion which inhibited him from speaking.

At last Michel judged that the moment was ripe. Looking the *sous-chef* in the face, with a smile he said: "Well, now you know the worst, are you prepared to work with me?"

Lemeau made no reply, but lowering his head as though in shame gave a nod of assent. This time Michel knew that he meant it.

Without exchanging another word they shook hands and separated; Lemeau to return to the station, while Michel made his way across country to the town.

The *sous-chef* kept his promise. When Michel returned a week later he was handed a complete account of every German convoy that had gone through in the interval.

From then on there was no more conscientious member of the *réseau* than Lemeau. It was as if he were determined to atone for his moment of hesitation. This, as he later confessed to Michel, had been the result of a circular sent out by Vichy, and received on the very morning after their first meeting, instructing all railway officials, under pain of severe penalties, to co-operate to their utmost in the transport of the *Wehrmacht*.

At Lemeau's suggestion Michel shortly afterwards recruited two other key railwaymen, employed at Le Teil and Porte-lès-Valance respectively. These were strategically important goods stations and between them controlled all traffic proceeding south on either side of the Rhone.

Thanks to these four new agents Michel obtained each week a complete picture of the German trek southwards and punctually passed it on to Berne.

One further and important change, which must be recorded here, followed the events of November, 1942. This was B——'s introduction to another Englishman who arranged that in future Michel should report to an address in Lausanne.

The new arrangement was a great improvement. As representatives of the War Office the Military Attaché and his assistant were primarily concerned with military matters. Henceforth, Michel would work for the S.I.S.—Secret Intelligence Service—which served all Departments from the Cabinet downwards and was in consequence interested in everything.

Although their personal relations had always been friendly, B—— had never unbent officially and always received Michel's reports with a kind of distant acknowledgment. He studiously avoided committing himself on their value, and, apart from his original directive, never made a request or even offered a suggestion which might have assisted Michel in the work.

This reserve was quite normal, since the utmost caution needed to be exercised to avoid being duped by a "double agent" —that is, one who works for both sides, or pretends to work for one when his loyalty is to the other. An agent had to prove himself before he was taken into confidence. Until then one received whatever he had to offer, while giving nothing away. It was only when the British were convinced that Michel was entirely devoted to the Allied cause and could make a valuable contribution thereto that they were prepared really to co-operate with him.

Thus the significance of the change was that, having served his apprenticeship with the amateurs, he was now considered fit to be handed over to the professionals. At the same time he was promoted from being a casual informant to the status of a trusted ally.

His new contact—always known as "O.P."—was a charming

person. In civilian life a successful business man, with a great knowledge of the Continent and a wide culture, he took to Michel at once, appreciated his worth, and laid himself out to be as helpful as possible.

After this Michel was never left in doubt as to what was wanted of him and how far he had succeeded. He received useful advice as well as precise instructions, and at last had the feeling that in his skilled and dangerous work he was fully backed by the British.

Nor was the encouragement given to him only moral. Until almost his last visit to Berne he had never asked a penny of the British and had borne all expenses of his organisation out of his own pocket. These had greatly increased with the expansion of the *réseau*, while he no longer had any time to give to earning a living.

It was impossible, therefore, to continue without financial assistance. This was now willingly offered and henceforth he received ample funds for his work.

8. *Traveller in Trouble*

With sixty agents operating in as many different areas, who had to be regularly visited, briefed and in some cases paid, Michel was now almost incessantly on the move. Because of the great increase both in the volume and the urgency of his information, he had stepped up the frequency of his visits to Switzerland to once a fortnight; and in the twelve days that elapsed between his return from one visit and departure on the next he had barely time to make his round and collect his agents' reports before setting out once again.

Those in the northern and eastern sectors came to meet him

in Paris, but this still left forty to be contacted in the centre and south. His usual itinerary included Dijon, Chalons-sur-Saône, Lyons, Valence, Le Teil, Pierrelatte, Avignon, Tarascon, Arles, Aix-en-Provence, Nice, Toulon, Marseilles, Nîmes, Montpellier, Sète, Béziers, Narbonne, Carcassonne, Castelnaudary and Toulouse. He travelled by train, using a "sleeper" when possible, so as to store up energy for an emergency and for the gruelling walk across the frontier.

It might be asked how he was able to travel so freely; for although the Germans now occupied the whole of France they still retained the old line of demarcation between the northern and southern zones, and to cross this a permit was needed.

As the representative of the *Office Téchnique du Gazogène de France*, whose business took him all over the country, Michel had no difficulty in obtaining his *Ausweis*. But once he had crossed the line from north to south, he travelled under a false name with a false identity card in order to leave no tracks of his real self.

Train journeys, of course, were always liable to be dangerous. Apart from their regular control points, the Germans made frequent searches *en route*, when the passengers had to show their documents and be prepared to open their luggage.

That was why Michel, in the early days, always left the train at Dijon and used his bicycle for entering the *Zone Rouge*. Early in 1942, however, the Germans relaxed their control to the extent of only exercising it intermittently. Through friends on either side of the line Michel received warning of the date on which it was to operate and had merely to avoid travelling on that day.

The operation of the *réseau* and liaison with the British, which might have been considered the administrative side of Michel's work, was not by any means the end of it. On the contrary, he never hesitated to undertake a mission himself if the situation demanded it.

After the Allied landing in North Africa, for example, it was important to find out what was happening in Toulon. Through Admiral Darlan at Algiers the Allies were making desperate efforts to persuade the French fleet, if not to join them, at least to place itself out of reach of the Germans. The latter were equally determined to gain control of it.

Finally the question was settled by the French sailors. On 27th November, 1942, while the German troops were closing in, they scuttled their ships in the harbour.

As it happened, Michel was in Switzerland at the time. No sooner had the news come through than he was requested by his British contact to go to Toulon immediately, in order to find out the exact extent of the damage and what chances there were of any of the ships being salvaged.

This, he knew, was not going to be easy. Immediately after their invasion of the Free Zone the Germans had put a cordon round Toulon and all traffic in and out was rigorously controlled. Following the scuttling of the fleet, these measures were tightened up. Annoyed by the loss of such a valuable prize, the Germans reacted by making life still harder for the Toulonese.

When Michel arrived on the evening of the 28th—having walked in from the country through lanes and side streets—the atmosphere was tense and oppressive. Germans were everywhere and the few Frenchmen to be seen had the cowed look of people who have suffered a disaster. Like Portsmouth or Plymouth, Toulon existed for the navy and its destruction was a tragedy that touched every inhabitant. Even the waterfront, normally the centre of attraction, was deserted.

As he debouched on the quay Michel could see on all sides the tops of masts and funnels marking the grave of the fleet. From the partly submerged hulk of a beached cruiser thick columns of smoke were still rising. A film of fuel and grease covered the waters of the port, in which the last light of the dying day was reflected in lurid colours.

It being too dark to investigate further, Michel started to look for a bed. He soon discovered that every hotel had been requisitioned either by the *Wehrmacht* or the *Kriegsmarine*. After trying a dozen unsuccessfully he decided to adopt a bold policy. Ignoring the large swastika hung outside, he entered the Terminus, the big hotel near the railway station, marched up to the reception desk and asked for a room.

Before the receptionist could reply a German N.C.O., who had overheard his request, brusquely demanded his business.

"I'm a mechanic," Michel replied. "I'm in Toulon to repair some machinery."

The German looked slightly less hostile.

"Could you repair a radio set?"

"Certainly."

"Then follow me."

The German led the way to a reception room, in the corner of which stood the defective set. Michel made a brief inspection, saw what was wrong and turned to the German.

"Supposing I do mend it, what will you give me?"

"I'll pay you a good fee."

"I don't need that."

"What do you want, then?"

"A room for the night in this hotel."

"I promise you shall have it."

"Which one?"

"I'll show you."

Thereupon the German summoned the manager and demanded the best room that was vacant for Michel. The manager having proposed "*Appartement No. 2*"—a self-contained suite on the first floor—the German gave his approval and Michel set to work.

An hour later he had repaired the set and tuned in to London to test it. The news bulletin in French had just finished and was being followed by the usual innocent-sounding messages, which in fact were signals in code.

With the N.C.O. standing beside him Michel was listening without much interest when his attention was riveted by a phrase which was somehow familiar. "The beer is good," the announcer repeated, and then repeated it again.

There was no longer any doubt. By an extraordinary coincidence he had been listening to a code message put out at his own request. It was the message giving warning of the bombing of Abbeville aerodrome that one of his agents had asked him to arrange.

Thinking of the "plastering" the German airfield would soon be receiving—possibly that very night—and of the pleasure this would give his agent, Michel could hardly contain his joy. He longed to impart the news to his stolid German friend, to slap him on the back, and tell him to cheer up. Instead he started humming his war song: *Tout va très bien, Madame la Marquise.*

He switched off the set.

"That was London," he informed the German, "and the fact that we heard it so well in spite of your jamming shows what a good job I've made of it."

Pleased and grateful, the German offered to stand him a drink and would have taken him off to the bar. But Michel was exhausted and only wanted to sleep. He therefore excused himself; whereupon the German insisted on showing him to his room, unlocked the door and himself drew the curtains before bidding his guest good night.

The room with its private bath was luxurious, the bed magnificent and there were even towels—which had practically disappeared from French hotels since the war. It was the fact, however, that he was enjoying it at the expense of the *Wehrmacht* that gave such unwonted comfort its particular relish.

When he left the next morning, bowed out by the hotel staff, and without having even filled in the usual form, he was repeating to himself one of his favourite slogans: *De l'audace, encore de l'audace, toujours de l'audace.* It had certainly paid off on this occasion.

As he approached the naval dockyard Michel saw that the entrance was guarded by a German sentry. He was unprepared for this and was considering what pretext he could use when the soldier came to attention and saluted. Too astonished to react, Michel smiled feebly and passed through.

(Later it occurred to him that there was a possible explanation: if the soldier was billeted at the Terminus he might have recognised Michel as the honoured guest of his *Feldwebel.*)

In broad daylight the spectacle of the sunken fleet was heart-rending. One battleship, two battle cruisers, seven cruisers, twenty-nine destroyers and sixteen submarines had been scuttled, as well as many smaller craft; but since only the upper works were showing it was difficult to identify the wrecks.

Over all there was an air of desolation. The dockyard, usually a hive of activity, was silent: the jetties deserted, the ferry and pilot boats abandoned, the cranes idle and even the power station stilled.

Some distance away two solitary individuals were standing by the statue to the "Genius of Navigation," gloomily contemplating the scene of devastation.

As Michel approached he saw that one was an elderly man, the other quite young. He went up to them and in reply to his inquiry the younger man started to point out the wrecks, giving each ship its name. The partly submerged ship, he explained, which was still on fire, had engaged the Germans on shore to keep them at bay while the scuttling of the fleet was completed. They had replied with shells, killing many French sailors.

While this conversation was going on the older man said nothing, only nodding from time to time to confirm some remark of his companion. There was something in his bearing, however, that impressed Michel favourably. Tall and lean and rather grizzled, dressed as a workman, he possessed both dignity and authority.

After a time Michel invited them both to a café. He then asked the older man, a foreman artificer employed in the dockyard, to do him a small favour. He had, he explained, some occasional business in Toulon, but it was difficult to obtain the necessary authorisation. An inter-zone postcard, posted in Toulon and requesting his presence to repair a gas engine, would enable him to obtain a permit to return. Would his new acquaintance oblige by dispatching such a card—which Michel then produced already written and addressed—a fortnight from that day?

The foreman artificer having agreed and pocketed the card, Michel shook hands and left. He was well satisfied with the morning's work. He had got the information he wanted, knew what ships had been sunk and which could be salvaged, and in addition had established contact with a likely new recruit, well placed for acting as his agent in Toulon.

Following the same route in reverse, he slipped out of the town without being stopped and an hour later was safely in the train.

Punctually on the agreed date the card arrived in Paris. Armed with it Michel obtained his permit, and the following day was back in Toulon. Going straight to the address of the foreman artificer, he was lucky enough to find his man at home and alone. The latter had already guessed what Michel was up to, and in a very short time they reached an understanding. It was thus that Alexandre Roman became a member of the *réseau* "*Agir*."

Married, with two children, devoted to his family (for whose sake he often went hungry himself), and showing signs of the hardships imposed by the Germans as a reprisal, Roman was the best type of skilled artisan. As a senior foreman employed in the armaments section of the dockyard, which had started to function again under German supervision, he was also the ideal person for Michel's purpose. From now on, thanks to his vigilance, nothing of importance that occurred at Toulon failed to reach the British Intelligence Service.

One of his earliest and most important reports concerned a new type of torpedo, invented by the French, plans of which had been seized by the Germans on taking possession of the arsenal. By a lucky chance Roman had worked immediately under the inventor and was able to produce a complete description of the torpedo—it ran on hydrogen peroxide—and send it through Michel to the Admiralty in London.

In the summer of 1943, when the battle for Sicily was raging, the Axis patrol boats damaged in the campaign docked at Toulon for repairs. By virtue of his functions Roman always knew the date they were to sail, and included the information in the fortnightly report which Michel took to Switzerland. This was passed on to London and as a result the enemy craft were usually attacked as soon as they left port. Their losses were known immediately in the arsenal and included by Roman in his next report.

One day when he was lying on his stomach on a cliff, sketching a new naval supply base constructed by the Germans near La Seyne, a German soldier who had been watching him from the branches of a tree jumped down and demanded what he was drawing.

Roman had his explanation ready. He was planning, he said, to build a house on the waterfront, and was making a sketch to assist him in choosing the site.

This incredible story was not accepted by the soldier, and he hauled Roman off to the guard-room. Fortunately the N.C.O. was more credulous; and after the prisoner had produced proof that he was an inhabitant of Toulon he was released with a caution.

He continued his valuable work for a year. Then something happened to place him in danger.

Michel had an agent called Louis Maiffret, who was employed as a surveyor by the municipality of Nice. Maiffret had been introduced to Roman by a third agent, who was occasionally used by Michel to collect their reports on his behalf. This agent thought it useful that Maiffret and Roman should meet, so that in the event of his being unable to visit Nice, Maiffret could come to Toulon and hand his report to Roman.

As soon as Michel heard of the arrangement, he realised that it was undesirable, since if either of the two was arrested the other would probably be compromised. He therefore left at once for Toulon with the object of putting an end to it.

When he arrived at the Romans' house Mme. Roman let him in and he saw at once that he had come too late. In a distraught voice the poor woman told him what had happened. Two days before, early in the morning, some Germans in plain clothes had called at the house and removed her husband in a car. Since then no more had been seen or heard of him.

Both for his sake and hers Michel did not prolong the interview. After making certain that she had enough money for immediate needs, and promising to do what he could to discover her husband's whereabouts, he took his departure with a heavy heart.

Weighed down by a presentiment of worse to come, he took the first train to Nice. There, without going farther than the station, he learnt the full extent of the disaster. Louis Maiffret's father, Jean, chief controller of traffic at Nice station, who also worked for Michel, had been found with a list of military movements which could not be explained by his official functions. He and his son had both been arrested and had been seen as they were put on the train for Marseilles. Inevitably the arrest of Roman had followed.

His disappearance was a bitter blow to Michel. Utterly loyal, disinterested, fearless and conscientious, and hiding those qualities under the same unassuming manner that had taken Michel's fancy at their first encounter, he was one of the most effective members of the *réseau* and the value of his information had been proved time and again.

As always when he lost an agent, especially if the latter was a family man, an agonising question arose in Michel's mind. Was he justified in exposing another to mortal danger? Could the victim's dependants ever forgive him?

The question was never answered to his satisfaction; but when his own turn came it was a consoling thought that he was sharing to some extent the martyrdom of those for whose fate, as their chief, he felt responsible. In the darkest days of Neuengamme it was this thought that sustained him more than anything else.

One day in the summer of 1943, during a meeting between Michel and his new British contact, the sympathetic "O.P.," the question came up of the whereabouts of Von Rundstedt.

"O.P." declared firmly that he was still commanding the Mediterranean section of the German Army of Occupation. This was the Army Group whose headquarters were at Avignon and it controlled all German troops in the south of France.

Michel was not so certain. He had heard rumours of changes and since he had no agent at Avignon he volunteered to go and find out himself.

"No point," said "O.P.," "since we know it's Rundstedt."

Michel was still not happy about it and after leaving Lausanne decided to investigate. A few days later, having completed his tour of the *Midi*, he arrived at Avignon station.

It was some time since he had been there and he was struck once again by the charm of the ancient city. In the late afternoon the air was pleasantly cool and charged with the scent peculiar to Provence: a mixture of thyme and fig-tree, vines and olives. Plane trees in full foliage spread their shade over the street and there was an atmosphere of relaxation after the heat of the day.

There was, however, one jarring note. As he strolled across the square adjoining the station, he glanced at the twin turrets which formerly guarded the walled town and saw that the Germans had mounted A.A. guns on top of them!

A few minutes' walk brought him to the Hotel Terminus, where the German commander had installed his headquarters. Planted in front of the entrance was the flag—a black and white centre surrounded by red—denoting an Army Group. A wooden barrier, extending to the middle of the road, prevented any approach. This was guarded by three French policemen, while the space inside was patrolled by German soldiers under the command of an N.C.O.

Immediately opposite the hotel was a café. Michel went to the counter, ordered a coffee, and, after engaging the patron in conversation, lowered his voice and said, "Tell me, your neighbour across the way . . . is it still the same one?"

The patron did not reply, but moved away and busied himself with the crockery. Taking the hint, Michel left the café.

The three French policemen were still lounging by the barrier. Michel observed them, undecided on his next move. Then he told himself that after all they were Frenchmen. Anyhow he had no time to waste. In an hour his train would be leaving.

He approached the nearest of the three and repeated the question he had put to the patron of the café.

"No," replied the policeman without showing any surprise, "there's been a change in the last two weeks."

"Do you know the name of the new one?"

"No," said the policeman and turning to his colleagues he asked if either of them knew it. Both shook their heads.

Then one of them said: "Why don't you ask the proprietor of the hotel? He's still living there and he's a very good chap."

"What's his name?" Michel asked.

"Pamard. Monsieur Pierre Pamard."

Michel thanked his informant, the barrier was lifted and he passed inside.

As he approached the entrance a German sentry stopped him and asked for his pass. He replied by requesting to see the N.C.O.; and when the latter arrived explained in German that he only wanted to see M. Pamard, for whom he had an urgent message.

"I'm sorry," said the N.C.O. politely, "but nobody is allowed to enter without a pass and if I let you through I shall get myself in trouble."

"But nobody will see me," protested Michel. "M. Pamard is an old friend and I know the hotel well. I shall see him in his private office."

He produced some American cigarettes and pressed them into the hand of the sergeant. The German gave a shrug and he hurried through the door.

He had never been in the hotel before, but assuming the confident air of one who knows his way about, he marched straight ahead. The hall was full of German and Italian officers, to whom he smiled and made a slight inclination as he passed. When he had almost reached the point where he could go no farther without stopping to inquire the way, a young woman appeared in his path.

Michel stopped and asked for M. Pamard.

"Who shall I say?" the girl demanded.

"My name will mean nothing to him," replied Michel. "Just say it's an old comrade from the regiment."

The girl disappeared and a few moments later Michel saw approaching him a tall dark man of about thirty-five, dressed in the conventional black coat and striped trousers of the high-class hôtelier.

Before he had time to speak Michel seized his hand and shook it vigorously. At the same time he whispered: "I'll explain everything—but not here." He then led the way to a place where they could not be seen from the hall, and after apologising for his subterfuge explained that for private reasons it was essential for him to know the name of the general who had succeeded Von Rundstedt.

"General Von Felber," replied M. Pamard. "But that was some time ago. Since then Von Felber has been replaced. I don't know the name of his successor but my wife will know and if you'll excuse me a moment I'll ask her immediately."

A few minutes later he returned and handed Michel his card. On it was written the name: Von Sonnenstern.

"Thanks," said Michel. "Now there's something else. I want to know where Von Rundstedt and Felber were moved to and where Von Sonnenstern came from. Also the towns where his subordinate commands have their headquarters—and anything else you can find out."

As though this was the most natural request in the world, M. Pamard nodded understandingly. Some of the information, he thought, was already available. The German generals who had left the hotel nearly always wrote to his wife to say how comfortable they had been. It was a question of checking up and might take a little time.

"Good," said Michel. "Then I'll return in a few days. Choose a rendezvous and give me a number where I can leave a message in safety."

After arranging to meet at the bar of another hotel—which being kept by a *milicien*[1] was above suspicion—and to telephone to fix a day and a time, Michel took his departure.

While Pamard was seeing him out with all the marks of the warmest friendship, the German N.C.O. looked on with approval, as though to show his pleasure that Michel had succeeded in finding his old friend.

A few days later Michel collected Pamard's report and took it straight to Switzerland. "O.P." accepted his defeat with a good grace.

"But," he added, "*somebody* is going to look pretty silly."

There is a tragic epilogue to this story. Pamard continued to work for Michel and provided some useful information; but after the latter's arrest he was approached by another resistance group with a request to work for them. For fear of compromising the *réseau* "*Agir*" he declined. He was in consequence labelled as a "collabo" and after the liberation of France shot by his compatriots as a traitor without being given the opportunity of vindicating himself.

[1] Member of the hated Vichy militia, largely employed to suppress opposition.

9. *The Expert Comes To-morrow*

In the summer of 1943 Michel was requested by his British contact to investigate the aerodrome at Cormeilles-en-Vexin. This was a very large airfield not far from Paris used by the *Luftwaffe*. It had twenty miles of runway and was believed to be divided into three sections. One of them, skilfully camouflaged, was used for operations; a second appeared to be out of service; while a third, surrounded by fencing, was equipped with searchlights and A.A. The directive given to Michel was to plot the limits of the three sectors, and to discover the exact function of each.

He decided to entrust the job to Bart. The latter had distinguished himself by his work, particularly on the Channel coast, and was now based on Paris and available to be sent on special missions.

Although partly enclosed, the aerodrome was too vast to guard, and Bart had no difficulty in approaching its perimeter. Carrying a large-scale map in one hand and a pair of field glasses in the other, he proceeded methodically, noting the various features.

After fixing the boundaries of the neutral sector and shading it in on his map, he reached a part of the ground where there were some curious buildings. Nobody being in sight he decided to explore it. The results were interesting. For example, a church steeple made of wood surmounted a large storage tank, while what looked like a row of cottages were in reality repair shops.

A little farther on two haystacks next aroused Bart's curiosity. Scraping away the soil he discovered at first a layer of concrete and then a padlocked manhole. He guessed these were ammunition lockers and was just proceeding to mark the position on his map, when suddenly a German soldier concealed in a silo landed on the ground and covered him with his rifle.

There was no question of flight. The German was only a few yards away and must have been watching him for some time. With his hands above his head he was marched off to the guard-room; and from there taken before an officer wearing air force uniform.

Bart had already prepared his story. He was cycling past the airfield when he noticed a church and some cottages that had not been there when he was last in the neighbourhood. Obeying a natural curiosity he had stopped to investigate.

What about the map—and the glasses?

Well, the glasses had been given him by a friend in the neighbourhood whom he was visiting (this was true, he had borrowed them for the occasion from the curé of the next village), and he was taking them back to Paris.

As for the map, why, he had picked it up off a bench on arriving at the station. It was already marked—in fact it was that which had aroused his curiosity in the first place.

During an hour's interrogation, accompanied by some knocking about, Bart stuck to this story. Finally he was informed that the explanation was not accepted and that he was to be sent to Maisons-Laffitte for questioning by the Sicherheits-Dienst.[1]

That night he spent in a police post at Pontoise. Towards dawn, seeing that his escort were asleep, he rose and crept towards the door. He had stepped across two of the men without disturbing them when the third sat up. All he could do then was to request to be taken to the lavatory.

At Maisons-Laffitte he was mercilessly "grilled" all day. Different interrogating officers succeeded one another with progressive brutality: at first face slapping and blows of the fist,

[1] Security Police to be distinguished from the Gestapo (*Geheimnis Staats Polizei*) or Secret State Police. The latter however worked with the Security Police and were always called in for cases of espionage or subversive action.

then beating with various implements. With desperate courage, Bart stuck to his story. He had found the map at the station; the writing on it was not his.

Paper and pencil were put before him and he was ordered to write down some sentences which his interrogator dictated. Guessing the purpose of this he wrote in a faked hand, but weak as he was with pain and exhaustion the effort was not very successful.

"Right," said the German. "Now we'll send for the handwriting expert. He'll soon tell us if you're speaking the truth."

As it happened the expert could not be found. He would not be available, apparently, until the next day; but if the writing on the map was identified as his, Bart was informed, he would be shot immediately as a spy. He was then conducted to Houilles, a small town just outside Paris, and locked up for the night.

His cell was on the third floor of the building, about fifty feet above ground. High up in the wall there was a small rectangular window protected by a network of wire. The wire was stretched taut across a wooden frame which was secured by wire lashings to bolts in the wall. In the door was the usual spy-hole enabling the guard to look in.

All thought of escape seemed hopeless. And yet one phrase spoken by his interrogator kept recurring in his head: "The expert comes to-morrow." He was convinced his faked handwriting would not delude the expert. Unless he got away, there could be only one end to it.

He looked at the window again. It appeared inaccessible—and yet perhaps not quite. The guard had just looked through the judas, and Bart had heard his retreating footsteps. Presumably he would hear them coming back. He had the impression that he was the only prisoner on that floor, so visits to it might not be very frequent.

Placing the truckle bed on its side, he stood on it and just managed to reach the window. He started to unravel, strand by strand, the wire lashings which attached the frame to the opening. With only his hands to help him it was a slow and painful business and soon his nails were ripped and his fingertips bleeding. But he worked on steadily, only pausing to listen for footsteps outside. Once the guard returned and he just had time to drop on the bed and feign sleep before the judas was opened. By midnight he had the frame dismounted.

The opening measured about sixteen inches by twenty inches—large enough for the slight form of Bart to pass through. But what then? A drop of fifty feet—in the dark—on to what—not to mention the noise of the fall?

At that moment the sound of a train could be heard in the distance. This gave Bart an idea. He had already heard several pass quite close, making the night hideous with their clatter. If he could time his leap to freedom when this one approached, the noise of it would deaden that of his fall.

It might be suicide, but the alternative was to face the expert—and it was not as though the Germans would shoot him at once, either. Convinced of his guilt they would want some more out of him, and by now he knew enough of their methods to feel that death was preferable to another "grilling."

Anyhow, there was no time to calculate the risk. The noise of the train was growing louder every moment. In a few seconds it would have passed. Without a clear idea of what he meant to do with it, Bart seized his blanket and pulled himself up to the window. He squeezed through the opening feet first until he was sitting on the ledge outside. Then he spread the blanket above his head to act as a parachute, kicked with his heels to take him clear of any obstructions . . . and jumped.

By a miracle he was not killed—nor even knocked unconscious. He had fallen into a garden on to soft ground. As he lay on his back in an agony of pain, groaning audibly, he heard the train go by in a shattering inferno of sound.

Soon after he heard footsteps approaching. Pushing inside his mouth a corner of the blanket which he was still holding, Bart succeeded in rolling to a hedge. The sentry, as he guessed it must be, was patrolling on the other side.

By a supreme effort Bart managed to get on all fours, and,

sometimes crawling and sometimes dragging himself on his stomach, reached the end of the hedge, where there was an opening. This led to another garden at the end of which was a small house.

How he got there Bart never knew, but he eventually arrived at a door, under which he could see light. He had just sufficient strength to knock feebly before collapsing; and as the door opened his unconscious form fell across the threshold.

When he came to he was lying on a couch in a sitting-room. Two elderly people, a man and a woman, were standing over him. The woman had a cup of coffee ready and raised his head to help him drink. His back hurt atrociously—although he did not know it yet, he had broken his spine in three places—but it got some support from the rough bandages made of sheets with which the occupants of the house had bound up his torso.

Bart's first question was to ask the time.

His hosts tried to calm him. There was nothing to worry about. They would look after him, and he must just lie still until they could send for an ambulance.

"Impossible," said Bart, "I've just escaped from the *boches*. They will be looking for me now. Unless I can get to the station I shall be caught and shot."

"But you can't move," the man objected. "We think your back is broken."

"Yes I can if you'll support me. I feel stronger now. Anyhow, it's my only chance."

After some more argument it was agreed to try. It was about 5.30 a.m. and there was a workers' train from Houilles at 6.45.

With one arm round the neck of his Good Samaritan, and the other leaning on a stick, Bart set off for the station. To avoid passing in front of his recent prison it was necessary to make a wide detour; and although the station was only a short distance away it took them nearly an hour to reach it.

But they caught the train—Bart's companion buying the tickets—arrived in Paris, took the *métro* to the Gare de Lyons, and eventually reached a small hotel near the terminus where Michel had a room permanently reserved.

He used it occasionally to sleep in, and also to keep the reports brought to Paris by his agents in northern and eastern France. These were hidden on top of the wardrobe and he only collected them just before leaving for Switzerland.

It was here that he found Bart later in the day, stretched on the bed and exhausted with pain.

By this time the injured man was not making much sense, but his speech was sufficiently coherent to convey roughly to Michel what had happened to him. When he had finished his story Michel looked at him sternly and said: "Did you tell them anything?"

"Of course not."

"Are you quite sure?"

"Nothing. I swear."

"Good," said Michel. "In that case we'll attend to your affair."

Fortunately he knew of a nursing home whose surgeon, Raoul Monod, was a cousin and friend of his. It was run by the Protestant *Association Diaconnesses*, and was not far away, at 18 Rue du Sergent Bauchat.

There Bart was taken the same evening and operated on immediately. An X-ray revealed three broken vertebræ. These were set by the surgeon and the injured man encased in plaster.

By what seemed not one miracle, but a succession of miracles —the second being the failure of the Germans to discover his escape, and the third his getting to Paris with no spinal column— Bart had so far survived.

But his escape was not yet assured, and every day he lay in the nursing home the risk of discovery increased. The problem was first to find a safe place for him, and then to move him to it.

One of the difficulties was that he would take months to recover and meanwhile would need to be nursed. For this reason he could not be sent to the "parking place," where there were no facilities for the injured. On the other hand, an invalid always attracted attention and this made Michel's friends reluctant to harbour him. To complicate matters further, Bart was liable for conscription in the labour force.

After considering various alternatives—including a hiding-place in the country—Michel decided that the only solution was to remove Bart to Switzerland, and proceeded to make his plans accordingly. Fortunately it was summer, so he could use the original route across the frontier, where there was no barbed wire to negotiate.

After a week in bed the patient was considered well enough to be moved. It was arranged that his mother should collect him at the clinic and conduct him to the Gare de Lyon where Michel was to meet them. All went well until they were passing the barrier, when the ticket inspector demanded their *fiches d'admission.* These were special passes with which passengers had to provide themselves to gain admission to a particular train. Michel had not had time to obtain them.

"This young man is seriously injured," he explained. "He has to leave Paris for urgent treatment."

"Then you should have brought a medical certificate," the inspector replied.

At this Bart, who had overheard, pulled up his shirt and displayed his plaster cast. The effect was sensational. Drawn on the white surface with a violet pencil and covering it from neck to waist line was a large Cross of Lorraine—the emblem of the Free French. Below was printed a title: 1ST REGIMENT OF PARACHUTISTS.

The drawing was the work of Bart's neighbour at the clinic, who had waggishly added the title as a tribute to his original method of descent from a third story window. Michel, who had not seen this artistic effort before, was horrified; but the inspector took one glance, discreetly looked away, and motioned the three to pass through.

Thanks to a friendly guard a corner seat was secured for Bart and he passed a reasonably comfortable night in the train. There was no longer any control at the line of demarcation and the journey passed off without incident.

At Besançon, where they arrived early the next morning, Bart's mother said good-bye to him. He and Michel then continued on the single line railway which runs between Besançon and Morteau.

At La Grande Combe, five miles from the terminus, they left the train to continue the journey on foot. Bart could walk, but only slowly, and the plaster cast weighed painfully on his hip-bones. Michel usually travelled by paths and across country, but this was too difficult for Bart, so they had to keep to the road where the risk increased of meeting a German patrol.

After walking for two hours they arrived at Derrière-le-Mont. Cuenot had been warned and his wife was waiting for them with a meal. Bart had so far stood the journey well, and after the meal and a short rest he was ready to go on.

Now began the real test. The mountain path, which Michel had travelled so often, became progressively steeper and narrower. After a time there was no room for two people and Michel, who had been helping his companion, had to abandon him to his own devices.

The pain caused by the plaster pressing on Bart's hips soon became unbearable. To ease it he took the weight with his hands. This meant abandoning his stick and he had difficulty in keeping his balance. Step by step, sometimes inch by inch, Bart struggled forward, while Michel looked on helpless in an agony of doubt whether his plucky comrade would ever make it.

At last the climb eased as they reached the plateau and hit the track which led to Cuenot's farm. The carter had gone ahead to reconnoitre and Michel saw with dismay that the door and window were closed. This meant that it was not safe to cross the valley.

He looked at his watch. There were five minutes still to go till the agreed time. He watched the farm anxiously, while Bart lay on the ground desperately trying to recuperate his forces.

At last the door opened. Inside he could see Cuenot looking out. It was the "all clear" sign.

Revived by the news, Bart struggled to his feet and with Michel again supporting him they resumed the march.

From the edge of the forest there was an easy descent of about a hundred yards to the stream at the bottom of the valley, and this was accomplished without too much difficulty. But when they started to climb the farther slope Bart soon began to show signs of distress. For a little way he struggled on and succeeded in reaching the shelter of the trees. Then he stopped. For the time being his strength was finished.

The worst was still ahead—a quarter of a mile at least of stiff climbing through scrub and rock. Dropping on his knees Michel took his companion on his back; then advancing on all fours, a foot at a time, half carried, half dragged him the rest of the way. By the time they reached the wall which marked the frontier, he had just enough strength to lift Bart over and pull him under cover of some trees before he himself sank down completely exhausted.

There they lay together, without an ounce of strength left but savouring the sweet taste of another victory, gained by sheer "guts" over an all-powerful enemy.

When they had recovered their strength sufficiently, they resumed their walk and eventually arrived at La Brevine. From there Michel telephoned one of his friends in the Swiss Army, who immediately left by car to meet him. A few hours later he and Bart were both installed comfortably at a hotel in Neûchatel.

The next day Bart was admitted to hospital, while Michel returned to Paris. He had made many secret and dangerous journeys to Switzerland, but none had taken more out of him than this. nor afforded him so deep a satisfaction.

PART TWO

10. *A Warm Scent*

Shortly after his return from escorting Bart to safety, Michel received an intriguing message. One of his agents, a railway engineer at Rouen called Daudemard, had overheard a conversation in a café between two building contractors. They were discussing some new and unusual constructions which were being carried out on German orders at various points in the *Seine Inférieure* Department. What made them unusual was the amount of material required and the extreme accuracy demanded for the siting of certain buildings.

As always when it seemed that the matter was important, Michel decided to investigate himself.

Arriving at Rouen one day in August, he went straight to the local Labour Office and asked for the welfare section. To the official who received him he explained that he was the representative of a Protestant welfare organisation and was anxious to get in touch with some of the workers recently engaged for the Occupying Authority.

He then produced from his brief-case several bibles and a number of religious and moral tracts. The official glanced at the titles—*Christian Marriage*, *The Scourge of Disease*—and appeared to be favourably impressed. It was an excellent thing, he thought, that someone should be concerned with the spiritual life of the workers. Uprooted from their families, living in conditions that left much to be desired, but with plenty of money in their pockets, they were obviously exposed to grave moral dangers. He would therefore be glad to assist in any way he could. What did Michel want?

"If you can tell me the names of the places where the construction is proceeding, I will visit them. It is always best to get at the men when they are working."

"Well, I don't know them all, but here are one or two you could start with," said the official.

He wrote some names on a slip of paper and handed it to Michel, who thanked him warmly, repacked his brief-case, and withdrew.

An hour later he got off the train at Auffay, a small place about twenty miles north of Rouen. He had changed *en route* and when he emerged from the station was wearing his working-man's clothes over his city suit, and a black beret on his head. He had left his brief-case behind and carried on his shoulder a well-worn haversack containing his maps.

He had chosen Auffay from among the places whose names had been given him because it seemed the most accessible; but inquiries in the village produced no result. Nobody seemed to have heard of any important construction being carried out in the neighbourhood.

There were four principal roads leading out of Auffay. In his usual methodical way Michel decided to explore each of them for a distance of five kilometres.

After drawing three blanks he tried as a last resort the road which led westward towards Bonnetot le Faubourg. It took him through gently undulating country, with hedged fields, occasional copses and green meadows in which cattle were peacefully grazing.

He had gone about three miles and reached a point where the land flattened, when he came on what he was looking for. On a large open space immediately adjoining the road several hundred labourers were busily employed. While some of them were erecting buildings of various shapes and sizes, others were laying roads or putting down concrete. The din of bulldozers, mechanical mixers and pneumatic drills was incessant.

The site was about four hundred yards square, but looking at it from the road told him nothing. Somehow or other he had to gain admittance and inspect it at closer range. Except on the north-east, where it was bounded by a copse running at right angles to the road, the site was open on each side, and sentries were posted all round at short intervals. Other Germans in uniform could be seen on the ground; presumably they were engineers supervising the work.

Clearly there was no hope of sneaking in unobserved. He had to find a plausible pretext for entering the site.

Looking round for some tool to give him countenance, he noticed a wheelbarrow lying in the ditch beside the road. After hiding his haversack under a tree, he pulled the barrow out, wheeled it to the entrance of the site, and marched boldly in under the unsuspecting gaze of the guards.

He had already marked down a group of labourers, who were working on one of the buildings in the middle of the ground, and he now directed his wheelbarrow towards them. Arrived in their midst he dropped the barrow, and busied himself, as they were, shovelling sand and cement.

Nobody questioned his presence and he was soon in conversation with one of his mates.

"What's all this for?" he asked after a while.

"We don't know exactly," the man replied, "but they say the buildings will be used as garages, for their transport."

This struck Michel as fantastic. The building they were erecting was much too small to shelter vehicles, and none of the others, as far as he could judge in their unfinished state, was any larger. It was obvious that the garage story was invented by the Germans to conceal their real intentions.

Making some excuse to his mate, Michel retrieved his barrow and after half filling it with bricks set out on a tour of exploration. As far as he could make out without appearing too curious, there were ten separate constructions, none more than one story high. Concrete paths and roadways were being made to connect them.

What particularly intrigued him was a wider strip of concrete, about fifty yards long, which had been laid along the edge of the site nearest the wood and at the corner farthest from the road.

Still more intriguing, there extended down the middle a row of wooden posts on which was stretched, a few feet above the ground, a single length of blue string. This continued beyond the strip for another hundred yards, and to make it easier to sight against the landscape there was a metal disc attached to the top of each post and a strip of white sand running across the grass.

The more Michel looked at the concrete strip, and especially the length of string stretching away into the distance, the more convinced he was that it held the key to the mystery. But what was it?

The string did not seem to serve any purpose. It was too light to carry a weight or stand any strain. Where had he seen anything similar before? Bricklayers used a line when building a wall. It was not that. What about the metal discs? They reminded him of something he had seen used by surveyors when lining up the direction of a new road. But, of course, that was it: a line of direction. Otherwise why prolong it so far beyond the site?

With a sudden intuition he walked back to the concrete strip and placed himself so that he was in line with the direction of the string. There were some men working nearby, but they weren't taking any notice of him, and the nearest German was some way distant.

He always carried a pocket compass, and it had often helped him to find his way when crossing the frontier. Bending down and pretending to do up his bootlaces, he placed the compass on the ground and read off the magnetic bearing of the string—which was also that of the axis of the concrete strip.

As he stood up he noticed one of the workers looking at him. Michel went up to the man and said: "Tell me, what's this emplacement in aid of?"

The man gave a shrug. "I have no idea. You'd better ask the foreman."

"Which is he?"

The man looked round, then pointed at another worker, who was talking to one of the German engineers.

"That's one of them," he said.

Michel waited till they separated, then followed the foreman, who was heading for a canvas screen at the far end of the site. Michel pulled out a packet of American cigarettes and offered one to him. After a slight hesitation the foreman accepted.

After they had puffed away in silence for a time Michel repeated his question. Instead of answering the foreman glanced at him and said: "You're new here, aren't you?"

"Yes," replied Michel, "they sent me out from Rouen. Said you were short-handed."

"Well, then, my advice to you is not to ask questions. Our bosses don't like it."

"Really. It's so mysterious?"

"They don't tell us anything. We haven't even seen a plan. There's a *boche* in charge of each section and he simply tells us what he wants. It's a funny way of working."

"It must be something important then?"

"I don't know about that, but I can tell you they're in a hell of a hurry to finish. We're working in three shifts all round the clock."

"And this isn't the only one?"

"I should think not. They're all over the place."

"Do you know where exactly?"

"Well, there's one at Tôtes and another at Yerville, then at Le Bosc Melet, Brauquetuit, Abbémont, St. Vaast-du-Val . . ." The foreman broke off and looked at Michel curiously. "But why should that concern you," he asked, "since you've been sent here?"

"Well, I've got a pal who's looking for work. I told him I'd let him know if there was anything doing."

"Looking for work? That's funny. Most of them are trying to avoid it."

The foreman now moved away. Michel waited till he had gone before following. His barrow was standing nearby. He wheeled it once more past the cordon of sentries, reached the road, recovered his haversack and was soon on his way to Auffay.

There, after a short wait, he caught a train for Rouen, and late that evening arrived back in Paris.

He was sleeping at the small hotel near the Gare de Lyons where he rented a room permanently. It was on the first floor overlooking the *cour* and had a ledge outside the window which gave access to the roof and afforded a means of escape in an emergency.

Among other things he kept his maps there. They included one of the English Channel which showed Northern France and Southern England as far as London. Spreading it on the floor he drew a line from the approximate position of the site near Auffay along the bearing he had read off his compass. As he had guessed, it passed through London. In other words, whatever it was that the Germans were building, its axis pointed at the English capital.

It seemed that he was on to something good.

When he reported his find in Switzerland a few days later, "O.P." was not particularly impressed. Reports of "curious constructions" and "suspicious buildings" were common, and it often turned out that they were something quite innocuous, like a field laundry or recreation centre. The mission of which he was a member was expected to act as a filter; cluttering up the wires with useless information would not make it popular in London.

Had it been another informant, he might even have hesitated to pass the report on. The fact that a certain strip of concrete happened to be laid with its axis pointed at London—or so it appeared from a very approximate calculation—could be as easily accident as design; and to draw any conclusions therefrom was the sort of thing officially frowned on.

But coming from Michel it was rather different; the latter was now in the privileged category of agents whose information, however improbable, is treated with respect because in the past it has always proved reliable. He had only attained this position after a long period of trial and it had recently been confirmed by an outstanding exploit.

During the summer he had reported that work was proceeding at Marseilles on the construction of a new naval dock. This was dismissed by the British as pure fantasy. Since he had seen the thing himself, and at considerable risk, he was furious; and after promising to return with proof, left immediately for Marseilles.

The dock was being built under cover of an enormous shed, normally used as a warehouse, at the northern extremity of the Quai de la Joliette, and every approach was closely guarded. Michel arranged to arrive, disguised as a workman, just as the day shift was leaving and the night shift taking on. Mingling with the latter he entered the site, picked up the nearest tool and started excavating industriously under the watchful eye of the S.T.O.[1] foreman.

When the midnight break came he found a shadowy corner, and while the rest of the men crowded round the food trolley, proceeded calmly, under cover of a newspaper spread on his knees, to take photographs of the scene—brilliantly illuminated as it was by arc lights—with a "Brownie" Kodak which he had carried concealed under his jacket.

At the end of the break he resumed his labours and in the morning filed out with the rest of the workers when they returned to the barracks where they slept.

The next day he was back in Lausanne once again, and with a roll of film to support his statement. This was duly forwarded to London. A few days later the area was heavily bombed. After that no report of Michel's was ever questioned.

As a consequence, when he described his latest discovery, although his British contact knew no more than Michel of flying bombs, he took it seriously enough to forward the report to London.

If Michel knew nothing about the *Vergeltungswaffen*—the "revenge" weapons which were to turn the tables on the Allies—

[1] S.T.O.—initials of the Todt Organisation shown on the armlet worn by its employees.

the British Government at this stage were equally ignorant about the manner and direction of the coming attack.[1]

Since the end of 1942 there had been rumours of secret weapons and in April a report was received of an experimental station at Peenemunde, on the Baltic. But what the weapons were and how and against whom they were to be used, nobody outside Germany as yet knew. Some sort of rocket was thought most likely and this view prevailed for a considerable time.

The Government took the threat seriously and at the instigation of Mr. Churchill a committee was set up to study it under the chairmanship of Mr. Duncan Sandys.

In June there came the first report of an "air mine with wings." Two months later the report was confirmed by further information. By a curious coincidence it was through "O.P." that this came to the knowledge of the British Government and in the following circumstances.

Shortly after the visit of Michel mentioned above, "O.P." was in his office one Sunday afternoon when an unannounced visitor was shown in. Dressed in workman's clothes, dusty and unshaven, the visitor explained that he had walked from Luxembourg and carried a message which he had to deliver to the head of the British Intelligence Service.

"O.P." replied that this was not possible but offered, if his visitor cared to leave the message, to see that it reached its destination.

The Luxembourgeois shook his head and repeated that he must deliver the message personally to the head of the Intelligence. There followed a two hours' argument, during which "O.P." tried to overcome the man's suspicion, and the latter obstinately refused to be persuaded. Finally his confidence was won and he agreed to relinquish the message. This, as it transpired, was concealed in the heel of his boot and a screwdriver was required to disclose it. Having handed it over and refused

[1] For a full account of the "V" weapons, see *The Second World War*, by Winston Churchill, vols. V and VI, and *The Royal Air Force*, 1939-45, vol. III (H.M. Stationery Office).

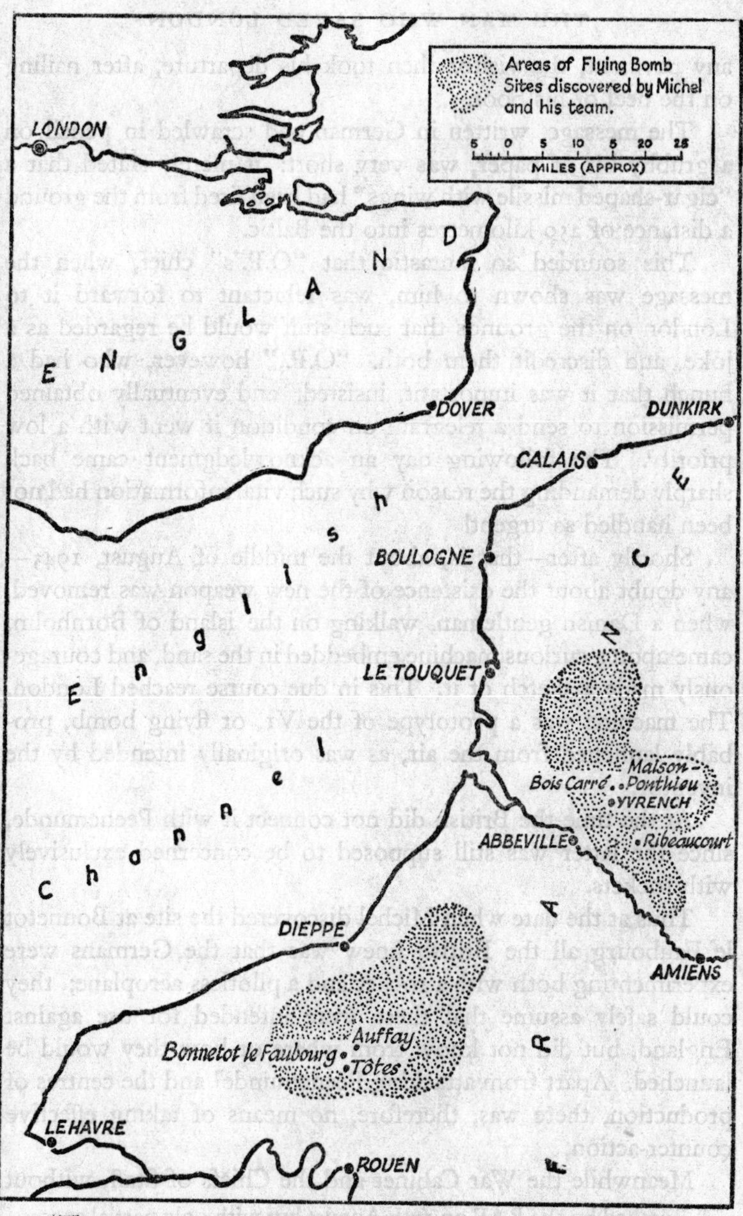

The groups of launching sites discovered by Michel's team

any payment, the visitor then took his departure, after nailing on the heel of his boot.

The message, written in German and scrawled in pencil on a grubby bit of paper, was very short: it merely stated that a "cigar-shaped missile with wings" had been fired from the ground a distance of 250 kilometres into the Baltic.

This sounded so fantastic that "O.P.'s" chief, when the message was shown to him, was reluctant to forward it to London on the grounds that such stuff would be regarded as a joke, and discredit them both. "O.P.," however, who had a hunch that it was important, insisted; and eventually obtained permission to send a telegram on condition it went with a low priority. The following day an acknowledgment came back sharply demanding the reason why such vital information had not been handled as urgent!

Shortly after—that is, about the middle of August, 1943—any doubt about the existence of the new weapon was removed, when a Danish gentleman, walking on the island of Bornholm, came upon a curious machine embedded in the sand, and courageously made a sketch of it. This in due course reached London. The machine was a prototype of the V1, or flying bomb, probably launched from the air, as was originally intended by the inventor.

At the time the British did not connect it with Peenemunde, since the latter was still supposed to be concerned exclusively with rockets.

Thus at the date when Michel discovered the site at Bonnetot le Faubourg all the British knew was that the Germans were experimenting both with a rocket and a pilotless aeroplane; they could safely assume that these were intended for use against England, but did not know from where or how they would be launched. Apart from attacking Peenemunde[1] and the centres of production, there was, therefore, no means of taking effective counter-action.

Meanwhile the War Cabinet and the Chiefs of Staff, without

[1] Bombed by the RAF on 17th August but with only partial success.

giving way to alarm, were increasingly concerned by the prospect of a new "blitz" of unknown ferocity which might seriously disrupt plans for invading the Continent. Mr. Morrison, responsible for Civil Defence, was naturally the most agitated of the Ministers and was having plans prepared for the evacuation of a million women and children.

It can be imagined, therefore, with what interest Michel's report was read in London. It was the first definite indication that whatever was threatening would be arriving from bases in Northern France and would be aimed at London.

Instructions were sent immediately that he was to follow up his discovery and concentrate all his resources on finding out more; and this was the directive he received from "O.P." on his next visit to Switzerland.

In the meantime, with the assistance of one of his agents, Pierre Carteron, he had inspected several other sites, the location of which he had ascertained either from the Labour Office or from the foreman at Bonnetot le Faubourg. The constructions and the lay-out were always the same, and seemed in every case to converge on the concrete strip which Michel felt must hold the key to the mystery.

The only difference between one site and another was the direction of the axis of the strip, as observed by compass. But if the direction was different the aim was the same. When he had plotted the lines on his map, they all converged on one point—London.

His hunch that he was on to something good had been justified, but he was still far from realising just how good it was.

Back in Paris Michel gave all his energy to the new task. The directive given to him specified two objectives: to locate all sites similar to those he had discovered, and to obtain a complete plan of the installation. As regards the latter, he was given no clue; nobody had even mentioned a possible connection with new weapons, and he himself was still ignorant of their existence.

The first need was to organise a search of the Channel area.

The sites he had inspected were all within twenty miles of the coast and it was safe to assume that the others would be about the same distance from it. He also knew that there had been a special recruitment of labour in the *Seine Inférieure* and *Pas de Calais* Departments. Thus a fairly well defined area existed in which to conduct the search.

Collecting a team of reliable agents, he provided each of them with a bicycle and allocated him a zone covering a stretch of the coast to a depth of twenty miles. Experience soon proved that this was not enough and the depth was subsequently increased.

Each agent was also provided with a map, and a description of what to look for. All he had to do, when he discovered a site, was to mark the exact position.

The results surpassed Michel's wildest expectations. In three weeks his team had located sixty sites, distributed along a corridor nearly two hundred miles long and thirty miles wide, and running roughly parallel to the Channel coast.

Michel toured the whole area weekly in order to meet his agents and collect the information, which he then took with him to Switzerland. Later the search was extended as far as Valognes, near Cherbourg. By the end of October a hundred sites had been discovered.

"O.P." was delighted by such prompt and effective action, but Michel was far from satisfied. For he was still without a clue as to the purpose of the sites, and had no plan to obtain it.

All inquiries had come up against a blank wall. German security was making certain there should be no leakage of the secret and none of the thousands of Frenchmen working on the sites had the remotest idea for what they were intended.

The problem seemed insoluble, but unless he could solve it Michel knew that he would have no rest.

11. *Victory*

As so often happens in life, Michel's greatest opportunity came to him by chance. This does not mean that the result was a pure accident. On the contrary, he had done everything possible to ensure it. But, like the most successful generals, he needed luck as well to achieve a really resounding victory. His merit was to be in the position, and have the will, to exploit good fortune when it came his way.

He and his team had discovered a large number of sites, and confirmed that they were all designed for an attack on London; but he had not yet succeeded in penetrating their secret. It was a problem which obsessed him day and night, and with increasing urgency as his agents reported the rapid progress of the sites and he envisaged the danger if the British were found unprepared.

Then one day something occurred which was to set in motion a whole train of fruitful events. One of his informants, a railwayman, known as Jo-Jo, employed at the Gare du Nord, introduced him to a young man called Robert Rubenach, who was anxious to join the Resistance. Of independent means but with business experience, temperamentally gay and carefree, Robert took a small boy's delight in pulling the master's leg; his favourite pastimes were to scribble ribaldry on German posters and to let out the air from German tyres. Now he wanted to help with something more serious.

As it happened, Michel had recently seen an advertisement by a German contractor for personnel to be employed at Cormeilles-en-Vexin. It was here that the unfortunate Bart had been arrested while taking notes of the aerodrome, and Michel was still looking for someone to replace him. He therefore suggested that Robert should answer the advertisement and if successful act as his agent.

Robert, only too delighted, agreed. Duly enrolled as a member of the *réseau*, he took the *nom de guerre* of Robert de Vic, after his native town in Lorraine.

He then answered the advertisement and was engaged as an accountant, not at Cormeilles-en-Vexin, but at Bernes, twenty miles north of Paris. Since this was also an important enemy airfield which the Germans were in process of developing, Michel was quite content.

The work had only just started, and more technicians were needed. This gave Robert the idea of proposing to a friend of his, a young engineer called André Comps, that he should apply for one of the vacancies, so that they could be together.

André, who had just taken his degree, was not very keen to start his career under German auspices; but when Robert hinted that it could be a means of helping the Allies he agreed to apply, and was engaged as draughtsman.

A few days later Robert met Michel in Paris to report on progress at the aerodrome. He found his chief distrait: obviously his mind was elsewhere. After a while Michel interrupted to ask Robert if he had heard anything of special sites being constructed near the Channel coast; and drew a rough plan to show what he meant. This was news to Robert and he promised to keep his eyes open.

On his return to Bernes he stopped by the board where notices were posted of interest to the employees. Since his departure earlier in the day a new notice had been posted. It was an appeal for certain categories of technicians, who were asked to volunteer for urgent work at an unspecified place, where they would be boarded and lodged on the spot.

Although there was nothing to indicate it, his instinct told Robert that this was connected with the matter in which Michel had shown so much interest. Among the personnel required were draughtsmen. Why shouldn't André volunteer?

The two were living at the same billet and it was there that Robert found his young friend.

"Listen," he said, "have you seen the new notice—the one where they ask for volunteers?"

"Yes, I did read it," replied André without much interest. "Why?"

"I've a hunch it's something important I've been asked to investigate. If you took it on you could probably find out."

"Do you think so?"

"Well, you could try, at least."

André was dubious. It was the first time he had been asked to do something illegal and he had never met Michel. Although he had come to Bernes because Robert had appealed to his patriotism, there had as yet been no opportunity to show it. Quiet and studious, and excessively shy, he was more interested in winning his spurs as an engineer than in engaging in clandestine activities against the Germans.

However, Robert continued to press him, and in the end he agreed to put his name on the list.

A few days later he was given his orders. With the other volunteers he was to report next day at one of the Paris termini. Without yet knowing his destination, he said good-bye to Robert. It was agreed that as soon as he had anything to report he should ask for a day's leave and come to Paris.

Nothing happened for a week, and then Robert, who had meanwhile informed Michel what he had done, telephoned to say that André was on his way and to suggest that the three of them should meet for lunch at his flat.

It was Michel's first meeting with André and he was not very favourably impressed. The young man struck him as immature and timid, without any strong convictions or real heart in the Resistance, and more interested in his profession than in helping his country.

This impression was soon to be belied. The truth was that André had not yet adapted himself to the double life into which

Robert had inveigled him, and which he had accepted without an idea of what it might entail.

He had arrived, he explained, from Yvrench, a village about ten miles north-east of Abbeville, and was employed on the construction of a site at a place called Bois Carré which answered the description given him by Robert. It was, in fact, one of those already discovered by Michel's team.

He then produced a few rudimentary sketches, which were scarcely more informative than those Michel had made himself; and with the air of one who is relieved to have finished an uncongenial task and hopes not to be asked to do any more, announced that he must be going.

"Wait a minute," said Michel quietly. "I'd like to ask you some questions."

Looking rather unhappy André sat down again.

"First of all, what is your job at Bois Carré?"

"Well, I was engaged as architectural draughtsman."

"And what does that mean exactly?"

"It means that I have to draw up the plans for the constructions."

"And how do you do that?"

"Well, there's a master plan, showing the general lay-out. My job is to draw up detailed plans for our site. Naturally they vary with each one—according to its size, surroundings, means of access, etc. I can tell you it's quite a business, and I don't get any help. However, I'm managing all right—at any rate the *boche* seems quite pleased with me."

"The *boche*? Who is he?"

"The German officer in charge."

"There's only one?"

"Only one permanently. The others come and go."

"So really you've got quite a responsibility."

"Oh, yes," said André proudly. "In fact, you could say that I'm the man who is doing the work."

"Very interesting," commented Michel dryly.

In his enthusiasm for the new job—after all, it was his

first since graduating as an engineer—André had lost his timidity. But now the anxious look reappeared in his face.

"I hope that will help you," he remarked nervously, glancing at the sketches. "Because I really ought to be getting back now."

"Not much, I'm afraid," said Michel. "In fact, it really takes us little further forward. What I need—and you are probably the only Frenchman who can obtain it—is a complete and detailed set of plans; in fact, a copy of those you are preparing."

André looked aghast.

"I'm afraid that will be difficult," he stammered.

"Why—since you have legitimate access to them? I should have thought you were the one person for whom it would be easy."

"That's true," André admitted with increasing embarrassment, "but—well—you see—since Robert asked me to do this the Germans have made us all sign an undertaking . . . not to reveal what we are doing."

"That means nothing," Michel snapped. "We are at war. Your labour is conscripted. You are not a free agent. An undertaking given in such circumstances is not binding."

André gave a dispirited shrug. "I suppose you're right. I hadn't thought about it."

"Is it perhaps that you are afraid?"

André kept his eyes on the ground.

"I hadn't thought about that either," he answered after a while, "but since you mention it, I must confess it seems to me that you are asking me to do something very dangerous."

"Good," said Michel. "Now we know where we are. Besides, it's perfectly natural. We are *all* afraid, and I more than any."

He got up and started to walk about the room. Robert had gone out to talk to his wife and he and André were alone.

In principle he never tried to coerce an unwilling person. The exceptions were when there was no alternative, and this was one of them. By a combination of luck and initiative he had secured an agent who was in a position to obtain the most vital information. The chances were slight of finding anyone else as well placed as André for his purpose, since on the other sites he knew of no Frenchmen employed above the rank of foreman. And time was running out. It was André or no one.

"Listen," he said. " I must speak frankly. You have the opportunity—possibly unique—of rendering a great service to our country. It is your duty as a Frenchman to do it—and I'm sure if you reflect you will see that. But I must warn you that if you refuse you will be just as guilty as a soldier who runs away in battle. And you will be treated accordingly. You understand?"

André nodded.

"Well, then?"

"Put like that I see it leaves me no choice."

"So you'll do it."

There was a pause before André murmured, "Yes."

"Good. I'll give you a fortnight. At the end of that I want you to meet me again here bringing copies of all the plans. The more detailed the better. Agreed?"

André nodded, but he still looked doubtful.

"It's going to be difficult to get away," he said. "The Germans won't give us any leave. I came to-day without telling them and I shall have to make some excuse when I get back."

"Then this is what you must do. During the second week you will start complaining of pains in the stomach. These will become more and more severe until you are unable to continue your work. You will then ask permission to come to Paris to be treated by your own doctor. Once you are here I'll arrange the rest."

"All right. I'll do what I can."

"I'm sure of it," said Michel. "I have confidence in you. And now you'd better be getting back."

For two weeks there was no news. Michel was away from Paris doing his round of the *Midi*, and heard nothing from Robert, who was his link with André. He had taken the latter's sketches of the site to Switzerland, where once again his British contact had impressed on him the urgency of obtaining more precise information.

By this time knowledge of the V1 in Britain was advanced to the extent that it was known that a pilotless aeroplane similar to the machine found by the Dane on Bornholm was being experimented with at Peenemunde.

This established the connection of the new weapon with the experimental station, which hitherto had only been associated with rockets; but it did not link it up with the sites in France, so that from the point of view of defence against the threat the British Government were not much further forward.

Meanwhile, Michel speculated anxiously on the progress made by André. Had he been wrong to stake everything on such a young and, apparently, timid person? Or had he perhaps misjudged him? True, the first impression had been unfavourable: and yet when at the end he had professed confidence in André, it was not only for the purpose of *giving* it to him. There *was* something in André which inspired confidence, if it was only his sincerity in admitting that he was scared. A less honest person would have made some other excuse.

Michel had arranged to return to Paris on the morning of the day fixed for their next meeting. As soon as he arrived he contacted Robert to find out if the meeting was on. The answer was reassuring: yes, André had sent a message the night before to say that they could expect him for lunch at Robert's flat.

When Michel arrived at the flat, André was already there. Before they had exchanged a word, his face showed Michel that he had succeeded. Although his manner was still shy the anxious expression had gone. In place of the timid boy there was a man with confidence in himself.

While they ate their lunch André told his story. To copy the plans he had already seen presented no difficulty. They were those he had made himself, based on the German master plan but adapted to local requirements. Except when required on the site, they were kept in the hut which he used as office and where he was usually alone. He had merely to wait for a quiet moment when he was reasonably secure from interruption and then take a tracing. This he had done within forty-eight hours of returning from Paris.

Unfortunately they were not complete. There was one piece of the jig-saw missing and it was the most important of all, for it alone showed what was to be erected on top of the concrete strip.

That a separate plan for this existed and had not been shown to him, André was well aware. Except for the excavation of some square holes down either side of it, no work had begun on the concrete strip; but he had frequently seen the German engineer examining it with a blue-print in his hand. He had also noticed that, after completing his inspection, the German always returned the blue-print to the inside pocket of his overcoat.

As the days passed André was more and more convinced that here was the missing link. Somehow or other he had to obtain that blue-print.

Exactly how, he could not see. As far as he could observe, it never left the possession of the German, who wore his overcoat even in his office, which was next to André's.

There was, however, one exception to this rule. Every morning at nine o'clock precisely the German left his office *without* his overcoat, walked to the edge of the site and disappeared behind the canvas screen shielding the latrines. Some time later he reappeared and returned to his office.

André could watch this proceeding from his window and he took to timing its duration. It varied between three and five minutes; the longer period was when the German took a newspaper with him.

For two or three days after making this discovery, André was seized with a sort of mental paralysis. He could not bring himself to accept the inescapable conclusion: that if he was not to fail in his duty, there was no alternative but to steal the blue-print and that this could only be done during one of the brief daily interludes when the German was separated from his overcoat.

But as the dead-line given him by Michel drew closer, fear of facing the latter with an admission of failure became a stronger motive than fear of the consequences if he was caught by the German; and two days before he was due again in Paris he took a firm resolution to make the attempt.

As luck would have it, it was one of the days when the German refused to be parted from his newspaper. He even started reading it before he reached the screen. This emboldened André, as it were, to jump the gun. Without waiting till the German was out of sight, he nipped into the next office, saw the overcoat hanging from a hook, put his hand in the inside pocket, and grabbed the blue-print.

Back in his own office, he made a rapid tracing of the plan, jotted down the essential measurements and made some shorthand notes. He had allowed himself three minutes for the operation, and by the time he had finished there were thirty seconds still to run: just long enough to walk to the next room, replace the blue-print where he had found it, and return to his place. When the German reappeared, after another minute had passed, André was working calmly at his drawing-board.

The next day he had reported sick, with vomiting and pains in the abdomen. The German doctor was sceptical; but, when André started retching in his surgery, agreed to his request to be treated at home and authorised four days' leave.

"You have done well," said Michel, when André had finished his story, "and justified the confidence I expressed in you. But you haven't finished your work yet. We'll need several days to interpret these drawings and produce an intelligible plan. Then I'll have to take it to Switzerland and there will be a further delay sending it to London. It is essential that you remain in Paris until it is received over there. We'll have to get you an extension of leave."

Thanks to Raoul Monod, the surgeon of the clinic in the Rue du Sergent Bauchat, where Joseph Bart had been treated, this was arranged. A certificate was dispatched to the German doctor at Yvrench stating that the patient required ten days of complete rest and requesting extension of his leave for another week.

The next problem was to find a safe place where André and Michel could work on the plans undisturbed. This was solved by André, one of whose relations owned a house, for the time being unoccupied, at La Varenne St. Hilaire, just outside Paris.

Here for the next four days the pair of them went to work. For security reasons, André had kept his material to the minimum, so that if it was found on him, or at his billet, he could have explained it away as "home work." It consisted of an assortment of rough sketches, tracings and notes, the latter in a shorthand of his own. Out of this assisted by his memory and technical knowledge, as well as that of Michel, who was also an engineer, there had to be pieced together a coherent plan of the site as it would appear when all construction was completed.

It was a formidable task and they were frequently baffled. Several times André, easily discouraged, came near despair, but Michel kept him at it, going out to buy the food and cooking it himself; and gradually a plan emerged, accurately drawn to scale, which revealed the whole scheme. One of André's rough sketches gave an idea of its principal features.

Rectangular in shape, and representing an area measuring approximately three hundred and fifty yards by two hundred yards, it showed a number of small buildings and concrete platforms connected by a network of communicating roads. As Michel had already noticed, the roads converged on a larger emplacement at the northern corner of the site: that is, the corner nearest to England. This was prolonged by the concrete strip, which had first attracted his attention at Bonnetot le Faubourg, and which he had always felt must hold the key to the mystery.

But now at last one could see for what it was intended. The copy of the blue-print stolen by André showed that its function was to support an inclined runway, or ramp, about a hundred and fifty feet long, rising at an angle of fifteen degrees, and carrying two metal strips rather like a small-gauge railway. With its axis, as André had confirmed, pointed at London, a hundred and thirty miles away, there could no longer be any doubt that it was designed for the launching of some missile aimed at the British capital. A rectangular structure at the foot of the ramp was obviously the firing point. The other buildings, including one designed on the non-magnetic principle, were respectively for assembly, storing, fuelling, etc.

There was also a curious feature whose significance for the time being remained obscure. Some of the buildings were extended by a curved section which, seen from the air, made them resemble a ski on its side. It was this that gave their name to the "ski sites," as they were subsequently called by the RAF. The ski-shaped buildings were, in fact, intended for the storage of the flying bombs, although they were also used as shelters to which the personnel could retire when the bomb was launched.

Armed with the sketch and the plans which accompanied it, an expert could reconstruct the complete procedure for assembling and launching the flying bomb, even though some of its details were only disclosed much later, after the capture of the sites and of some bombs intact.

Briefly the procedure was as follows.

When a bomb was to be launched it was first assembled and checked, with its war-head in place, on the Checking-out Platform. It was then moved to the Waiting Platform, at the side of which stood the office of the chief technician. From here it was taken to the *Richthaus*, a non-magnetic building whose axis was exactly parallel to the direction of the ramp.

In the *Richthaus*, which the bomb entered on rails, there was a sort of turntable which enabled it to be rotated before being brought into alignment with the axis. Its gyroscopic compass was then set at zero. If during its subsequent flight there was any deflection from course, the compass would send out electronic signals which corrected the error.

With its controls set the bomb was next moved to the foot of the ramp, fuelled and placed in position. It was now ready for launching.

Welded to the ramp were two plates with guide rails, along which the bomb travelled, its tail being supported on a sledge. Immediately below the rails there was a long cylinder—the firing tube—in which a dumb-bell shaped piston fitted. This piston had a protruding lug which engaged with the fuselage of the flying bomb, so that when fired it travelled at great speed up the tube carrying the missile forward with it.

As soon as the bomb left the ramp and became airborne it continued under its own power—it was driven by a simple type of jet propulsion engine—while the piston and the sledge described a parabola through the air before falling to the earth some two or three hundred yards away, whence they were recovered to be used again.

Power to launch the bomb was provided by a "steam gun" embedded in a massive block of concrete to take the recoil. While the pressure behind the piston was building up, the missile was held in leash by means of a bolt secured to a bracket at the base of the ramp. When the pressure was sufficient to shear the bolt, piston and bomb were released and shot forward together.

During the firing operation the crew retired to a bomb-proof shelter and firing cabin, from which the mechanism was operated by remote control. A narrow slit with a thick layer of glass enabled them to observe the operation. (In spite of this precaution, during the early stages many casualties occurred and it was reckoned that as many Germans were killed by their own weapon as in all the Allied bombing of the sites.)

When the final picture emerged, Michel and André felt something of the wonder of the archæologist who, from some scattered remnants, by dint of patient measurement, reconstructs the magnificent building of which they once formed part. It was difficult, in fact, to believe that between them they had really pierced the mystery; and yet Michel was certain that, even if he did not understand it all himself, he had in his hands the essential data which the British Intelligence Service had been so desperately seeking.

However, there was no time for self-congratulation. The four days' leave granted to André had expired and there had been no acknowledgment of his request for an extension. If the Germans started to investigate they might easily become suspicious. It was essential for Michel to get to Switzerland first.

After instructing André to make himself scarce, but on no account to return to Yvrench until he sent him a message, Michel returned to Paris. The same evening he left for the Swiss frontier, carrying the plans in his brief-case.

12. *Exploitation of Victory*

Michel's rendezvous with his British contact was never fixed in advance. He simply telephoned that he was on his way as soon as he had crossed the frontier. These conversations were always conducted in a code agreed at the previous meeting.

On this occasion he announced that he had bought the tickets and that the performance began at two o'clock. Then he added: "I've got very good seats."

"O.P." was therefore prepared for something exceptional, but even so he was staggered by the richness of Michel's haul. Consisting of a dozen architect's drawings and a master plan, it was a complete blue-print of a "ski" site, such as a constructional engineer would have required to build one.[1] Rapidly Michel told the story of its acquisition.

"O.P." was triumphant. "This is terrific. It's the biggest thing we've brought off. We'll send the whole shoot in the bag." He looked at his watch. "My God, they close it at four."

He dashed out of the room and a few minutes later returned

[1] Models were, in fact, made from it and used, among other purposes, for target identification by the RAF.

to say that all was arranged. The diplomatic bag, in which papers were sent to England and which was obligingly carried across enemy country by a neutral courier, would be delayed for two hours to give time for the precious parcel to reach the Embassy in Berne. This, as "O.P." explained, was unheard of.

"Now I must draft a cable," said "O.P." "You'll have to help me with that."

For an hour or so they worked together on the draft, trying to put into plain English the mass of technical detail which Michel had brought with him in notes and sketches. When finally "O.P." was satisfied and the cable had been sent for enciphering, he asked Michel what his plans were.

"How long will the bag take to reach London?" Michel asked.

"We must allow four days."

"And they'll acknowledge immediately?"

"Presumably."

"Then I'll return here in four days. Until I hear it's been received untampered I cannot allow André to return to Bois Carré. It would be sending him to his death—in fact worse. I told him to wait in Paris till he heard from me."

"Okay. I'll expect you."

Four days later Michel was back in Lausanne. He had used the interval to make a short tour of the *Midi* for routine contacts and collection of reports from his agents.

He was met by a beaming "O.P.," who, without saying a word, thrust a telegram under his nose.

"Booty received safely. Congratulations," Michel read.

"If we'd never done anything else," said "O.P.," "and never do anything again, this has justified our existence."

It was no exaggeration. The exposure of the V1 threat in all its details, long before the first flying bomb was fired, was a gigantic combined operation for which the British Government used all their resources and in which thousands of people were involved, from the Prime Minister feeding his energy into every branch of the public service, down to the humblest secret agent pedalling his bicycle through the dusty French lanes.

When all due credit has been given to others, however, there is no doubt that the plan of the site at Bois Carré had a decisive influence on the operation. When it reached London at the end of October the British Government already knew of the existence of the flying bomb—although it was still referred to as the "pilotless aeroplane"—and they also knew that it was being tested at Peenemunde. But they did not yet connect this knowledge with the sites discovered in France.

Some weeks after the receipt of the plan a photograph of Peenemunde taken by the RAF revealed an installation similar to that at Bois Carré in all respects, including the curious ski-shaped construction. Thus the connection between Peenemunde and the sites in France was for the first time definitely established and the suspicion that they were to be used as launching platforms for the new weapon—to which André's drawing of the inclined runway had given colour—deepened into near conviction.

This became certainty a few days later—to be exact, on 28th November—when another aerial photograph of Peenemunde showed a pilotless aeroplane actually sitting on its runway.[1] The final link in the chain of evidence had been forged.

Leading from Bornholm to Peenemunde, from Peenemunde to Bonnetot le Faubourg, from Bonnetot le Faubourg to Bois Carré, and from Bois Carré back to Peenemunde, it had been produced by the joint effort of ground and air intelligence, and in the former, as the Prime Minister acknowledged at the time,[2] the rôle played by the *réseau* "*Agir*" was of capital importance. It had found the first site, located most of the others, and produced the first complete plan of a site.[3]

[1] See *Royal Air Force*, 1939–45, vol. III, p. 147. (H.M. Stationery Office, 1954).

[2] In a letter to President Roosevelt dated 25th October, Churchill wrote: "We have an excellent system of intelligence in this part of N. France and it is from these sources as well as from photographs and prisoners that the story is built up."

[3] One other patriotic organisation also handled by "O.P." made a

Later Churchill was to pay a personal tribute to the agents—and they included, of course, not only Frenchmen but also Poles and other nationals—who risked their lives to save England from its peril. Summing up his account of the defeat of the V1, this is what he wrote:

> "Our Intelligence had played a vital part. The size and performance of the weapon, and the intended scale of attack, were known to us in excellent time. This enabled our fighters to be made ready. The launching sites and the storage caverns were found, enabling our bombers to delay the attack and mitigate its violence. Every known means of getting information was employed, and it was pieced together with great skill. To all our sources, many of whom worked amid deadly danger, and some of whom will be for ever unknown to us, I pay my tribute."[1]

Of all this, of course, Michel knew nothing. Like everyone else he had heard rumours—they had appeared in the Press—of new weapons; but he was quite ignorant of what had been discovered at Peenemunde and elsewhere, and how it fitted in with his own discoveries.

His British contact was probably not much wiser—it was not the policy of headquarters to share secrets with their subordinates—but, even if his superiors had seen fit to put "O.P." "in the picture," he would have been barred by the rules from passing it on to Michel.

There was a good reason for this. If an agent in the field is given a hint of what to look for, there will be a strong temptation to colour his reports accordingly. Moreover, to put him in

[1] *The Second World War*, vol. VI, p. 43.

---

smaller but valuable contribution by locating some of the sites. Its gallant eighteen-year-old leader was afterwards captured and shot by the Germans.

possession of other information is to risk the enemy finding out that you have it.

In consequence, apart from the congratulatory telegram, which was at least an indication of its value, Michel had no idea of the crucial importance which was attached in London to the plans of Bois Carré. It was just another job done. He had completed one more mission and it was time to return for the next.

It was too late for him to reach the frontier before dark, so he decided to spend the night at Neuchâtel. Having just brought off one of the biggest coups achieved by any intelligence service in the war, he might well have thought it an occasion to celebrate. The idea never entered his head. He drank very little anyhow, and the knowledge that he had succeeded and could sleep without danger was sufficient reward for his labours.

The next day he crossed the frontier and returned to Paris. He had telephoned earlier and found Robert and André waiting for him in Robert's flat. On Robert's insistence a bottle of champagne was now opened. Then André, whose extension of leave expired that day, had to depart to return to Bois Carré.

"The congratulations sent by the British are primarily for you," Michel said. "But that's not a reason for slacking. I shall expect you to keep me fully informed of all new developments at Bois Carré."

André smiled. He and Michel understood each other now.

"What are the English going to do with what we've given them?" he asked.

"We must wait and see," said Michel diplomatically.

It was a question often asked by his agents. Having risked their lives to obtain some information, they naturally liked to see results; and if it took the form of a heavy raid by the RAF, so much the better.

More often nothing happened at all; and then, to maintain

morale—perhaps the hardest of all his tasks—Michel could only assure them of the great value attached to their work by the British Ally.

On this occasion he had asked "O.P." the same question.

"I suppose they'll bomb the sites," was the reply, "but goodness knows when. They wouldn't tell us, anyhow."

For the time being he and André and the other members of the team had to be content with this.

Soon afterwards, Michel received another message from Rouen. It came from the station-master, Pierre Bouguet, who was a friend of Daudemard, the informant who had put Michel on the track of the sites. The message was to the effect that some unusually shaped crates had recently arrived at Rouen in a goods wagon and had been sent on to the station of Auffay.

Michel was always interested in Auffay, which had been the starting point of his most rewarding enterprise up-to-date. He therefore decided to investigate, and instructed one of his agents, Pierre Carteron, who had been highly successful in locating other sites, to meet him on the spot.

The station-master at Auffay, a M. Bourdon, to whom they first addressed their inquiries, was not known to either of them, but he was quite willing to talk. He informed them that the wagon, with its mysterious contents, had been shunted into a shed belonging to the local sugar factory, which was almost next door to the station but on the other side of the railway. The shed had been requisitioned and was closely guarded by German sentries.

A preliminary reconnaissance confirmed this news. The shed stood in a corner of the factory premises and was connected by a loop line to the railway, from which it was separated only by a footpath running parallel to the track. A sentry was walking his beat in front of the entrance.

After observing for a while from the platform of the station, where they pretended to be waiting for a train, they noticed that the sentry sometimes prolonged his beat. Instead of stopping when he reached the corner of the shed, he turned ninety degrees and continued about half-way down its side. From there he could see anyone approaching on the path.

It was therefore arranged that Pierre should walk along it and distract the sentry's attention at the moment when he was at the maximum distance from the entrance of the shed and no longer in sight of it. Michel would then cross the railway and slip inside the shed before the sentry returned to the front. All went according to the plan. Michel entered the shed without being detected, and set to work to examine the crates.

Their contents, whatever they were, were in three sections, and as far as he could make out, for he was working almost in darkness, consisted of a cigar-shaped body and two flatter parts. With a tape measure, which he had concealed under his shirt, he measured such portions as were accessible and made a mental note of their form. This took him nearly an hour, at the end of which he had a pretty shrewd idea of what the crates contained.

When he had learnt all he could he waited for the propitious moment, and then made his retreat by the way he had come.

A week later one of the first sketches of the flying bomb to reach England, with its dimensions accurately given, was on its way to London.

Meanwhile the team waited with increasing impatience for the retribution to come. André was reporting regularly on the progress at Bois Carré, which by now was practically ready to go into operation, and agents in other localities confirmed this impression. The first bombs had arrived and were being assembled under cover, and some of the sites were already being camouflaged. At any moment, it seemed, they would be ready. Were the British never going to take action?

At last the great moment came. On the 15th December, 1943—five days after Michel's return from Auffay—the RAF struck. The effect was devastating. At least a dozen sites, accurately pinpointed by agents' reports and aerial photography, were destroyed in the first raid. A few nights later Bois Carré was attacked; and to his enormous satisfaction, on arriving for work the next morning, André was able to see with his own eyes the result which he had done so much to bring about.

He could see at once that the site was beyond repair. The news had got around and only a few French workmen turned up. They were employed cleaning up the mess. The offices, though badly damaged, were still standing, and André was given the job of repairing them.

At La Loge (Somme) Pierre Carteron was actually present when the bombers dropped their load. He himself was lifted by the blast and lucky to escape with a broken arm. Casualties of both French and Germans were heavy. More serious from the German point of view, the workmen panicked and refused to return to the site. This reaction was general and was one of the reasons why the Germans abandoned the idea of repairing the sites, and concentrated on building new and smaller ones which could be hidden in woods or otherwise concealed from the air.

By the end of December fifty-two sites had been hit, and during the first half of January seventy-nine were attacked, including Bonnetot le Faubourg and Le Bosc Melet.[1]

On 7th January, Colonel Wachtel, commander of Flak Regiment 155W, which had been specially formed to operate the V1 weapon, wrote in his war diary: "If Allied bombing continues at its present rate for two more weeks, the hope of ever using the original site system operationally will have to be abandoned."

He was not being over-pessimistic. According to the enemy's own admission, between 15th December, 1943, and 31st March, 1944, nine sites were totally destroyed, thirty-five severely damaged, twenty-nine partly damaged, and twenty lightly damaged, out of a total of one hundred and four.[2]

The effect was to put the majority of sites out of action before they could be used. Long before the end of March, however—in fact, at the end of February—the Germans realised that their original scheme was in ruins, and turned their attention to improvising another, which in the event proved quite inadequate.

[1] See *Royal Air Force*, 1939–1945, vol. III, p. 150.

[2] *War Diary of Flak Regiment* 155.

About forty new sites were constructed on the same principle but much smaller and more easily hidden, and it was from these that the attack on London was eventually launched without any real success. What could have been a serious, and possibly decisive, threat to the Allies, was reduced strategically to not much more than a nuisance.

For the effect of the bombing of the sites was two-fold: it both delayed and mitigated the flying bomb attack.

Hitler had given orders for the attack to start on 15th December, with an onslaught of five thousand bombs a month. Had this plan been carried out—even assuming it made no difference to the Allied invasion of France—something like fifty thousand flying bombs would have been launched in the nine months before the capture of the sites by Montgomery's army in September, 1944. Of these, on the basis of actual experience, over fifteen thousand would have got through, as compared with the two thousand four hundred which actually arrived between June and September.[1] In other words, the attack would have been six times as severe and lasted six months longer. This might well have sufficed to alter the course of the war.

Here it may be appropriate to quote the opinion of a man who was in as good a position as any to estimate the effect had Hitler's original plan succeeded. Writing in his *Crusade in Europe*, this is what Eisenhower had to say of the V1:

"It seems likely that if the Germans had succeeded in perfecting and using these new weapons six months earlier than they did our invasion of Europe would have proved exceedingly difficult, perhaps impossible. I feel sure that if they had succeeded in using these weapons over a six months period, and particularly if they had made the Portsmouth-Southampton area one of their principle targets, 'Overlord' might have been written off."

The Germans had, in fact, sustained a major defeat; they had

[1] The total launched against London according to German official sources, was 8,564. Of those which failed to reach the target approximately 4,000 were destroyed by defences and another 1,000 crashed soon after launching.

played their last trump card and lost. They were, moreover, in no doubt of the reason: through his spies the enemy had got wind of their plans and countered before they were ready. Wachtel himself attributed his failure to the British Intelligence Service, asserting that their agents were swarming everywhere, especially in the launching area.

"Swarming" was an exaggeration. During the whole period of his investigation Michel never had more than six men working in the area, including himself, and his rival organisation probably not so many. The fact that the Germans came to see spies behind every hedgerow is a tribute to what was achieved by so few.

They reacted by redoubling their security measures. Wachtel, convinced that he was marked down for assassination, changed his name, wore a false beard, and dressed in a different uniform. Although most of them were now useless, the sites were more closely guarded than ever and most of the French workers, if they had not already taken flight from the bombing, were discharged.

At the same time the counter-espionage services, which had doubtless come under heavy criticism, intensified their efforts to track down the spies.

Although there was nothing for André to do at Bois Carré after he had repaired the offices, he had not been released from his engagement and had not asked for release for fear of arousing suspicion. Later he was employed patching up other sites, including one or two of the modified type which eventually came into action.

The fact that the Bois Carré site had been one of the first to be bombed, and that most accurately, was likely, he realised, to attract inquiries; these would inevitably lead to himself as the only Frenchman employed in a position of responsibility. Thus he waited with the sword of Damocles suspended over him. When another young Frenchman was put to work with him, whom he instantly guessed to be a *mouton*—i.e., stool pigeon—it was clear that the net was closing in.

At the time he was staying in a billet about half a mile from his work, to which he walked across fields every morning. One day as he was approaching he saw two large cars drawn up outside the offices. They were black limousines of the type used by the Gestapo, and he had no doubt what they were there for.

Turning round, he hurried off and avoiding his billet took refuge with another family about two miles away. Shortly after, the Gestapo arrived at his late habitation and searched it without result. After remaining in hiding for a month he returned to Paris and eventually found a safe retreat at Epinay-Sur-Orge, where he remained till the Liberation.

Soon afterwards, Robert was also in trouble, but this had nothing to do with the V1 sites. A Frenchman called Forly, a "collabo," also employed at Bernes, had been killed by a grenade thrown by a *résistant* while he was drinking in front of a café with two Germans. On his body was found a notebook containing a list of people known to be hostile to the Occupying Authority. It included the name of Robert, who never concealed his feelings and who was described by the informer as a "dangerous terrorist."

Robert, with two others, was arrested and taken to Maisons-Laffitte for interrogation. He defended himself by discrediting Forly; there had been a theft from the safe in his office and he was able to convince the police that Forly was the thief. He was not maltreated, and in consideration of the fact that he had volunteered to work for the Germans was released with a caution at the end of the day.

The other two were tortured savagely, and one of them subsequently died as a result.

13. Arrest of Michel

Anyone who leads the sort of life that Michel had been living knows that sooner or later it must end in disaster. It was more than a risk—almost a certainty—which he had accepted from the beginning, and of which he was constantly reminded, not only by the daily toll of arrests, but by the very circumstances of his existence.

Constantly moving, never sleeping two nights running in the same place, travelling under a false name with forged papers, alternately hunting and being hunted, he had something in common with a fox, who one day is breaking into a chicken run and the next flying for its life before the pack.

But after two and a half years, during which almost all the links with his former life had been broken, he had come to accept the present almost as normal. That he should never see his family, except for rare and fleeting visits, or go to an office, or meet his friends, or spend an evening listening to music or reading a book, no longer struck him as extraordinary.

In the same way he had become accustomed to living with danger. He had taken so many risks, had so many close escapes, that risk and escape seemed to belong to the natural order. He had got away with it every time, why not again?

Yet in his inner consciousness he knew it could not last. One by one some of his best men had already gone: Olivier Giran, Roman, the Maiffrets, Léopold Turcan—tortured beyond belief in a Blois cellar—and a dozen others who had endured a similar ordeal before being shot or deported. The surprising thing was that he, the most exposed of all, should have avoided the same fate for so long.

By the end of 1943, and especially after the flight of André, he could not believe it would be postponed much longer. Like a man condemned to death by his doctor, he began to look at people and things as though he was seeing them for the last time.

For some time he had had the feeling of being followed in Paris. To get rid of his "shadow" he found it best to use the *métro*. On arriving at the station he would loiter about the subway till a subterranean rumble announced the approach of the train. Judging the moment to a nicety he would then run down the steps and reach the platform just as the automatic gate was closing. While Michel squeezed through and flung himself on the train, anyone following was left immobilised on the wrong side of the barrier.

Unfortunately the enemy possessed a weapon against which no amount of courage or cunning could prevail. Like so many others, Michel was to be betrayed by treachery.

Towards the end of the year 1943, Mme. Simone Boirel, the proprietress of the Hôtellerie de Pierrelatte and one of Michel's most effective agents, received a visit from her old friend, Laure Lescane. A woman of thirty-five, pretty, elegant and well educated, Laure had known Simone since their schooldays, and the latter was delighted to see her.

In an exchange of news and confidences, Mme. Boirel revealed the work she was doing for the Resistance, mentioned the name of Michel, and suggested that her friend should join the *réseau*.

Laure Lescane was thrilled. As it happened, she informed her friend, she was engaged to a certain Comte de Kergoat, who was anxious to get in touch with the Allies in connection with an invention of his. Could M. Hollard help him?

Mme. Boirel replied that she was sure he could and promised to do her best to arrange a meeting.

Michel was not keen on the idea, but allowed himself to be introduced to Laure Lescane. As a precaution he would not commit himself to a meeting with her fiancé, and instead called on Kergoat unexpectedly.

He found the self-styled count installed in a luxurious flat close to the Bois de Boulogne. Kergoat[1] was a man of forty, of middle height, with abnormally broad shoulders and an enormous square, fleshy face. He received Michel seated behind a large desk, in an expensively furnished drawing-room which he also used as an office. His coarse appearance and vulgar manners made a bad impression on Michel.

He explained his invention: a new kind of air brake which enabled aircraft to land with a much shorter run. After years of experiment he had now perfected the device and was anxious, he said, to offer it to the Allies. As he understood that Michel was in touch with them, would he act as an intermediary?

Michel, who had taken an instant dislike to the man, saw that he was only interested in money. He was therefore extremely "cagey," made no promises, but suggested that Kergoat put his proposal in writing.

"If I do that," Kergoat objected, "they may take my idea and not pay me anything."

"You'll have to take that risk," said Michel. "Anyhow you don't have to go into details."

After some more discussion Kergoat agreed and asked when they could meet again. Michel was evasive, said that he was seldom in Paris, but that his secretary would receive any communication. The interview then ended.

During the next weeks Kergoat and an unknown woman made repeated attempts to contact Michel and several times called at his office. Michel's secretary, Madeleine Boulanger, herself a member of the *réseau*, invariably told them he was away.

This was usually true, for in addition to his usual round of visits, there was the special team observing the V1 sites to look after. Although they had accomplished their main task, they

[1] His real name was Henri Marette. An informer working for the Gestapo, he was convicted of treachery after the war and sentenced to a long term of imprisonment.

still had plenty to do, reporting on bomb damage and looking out for new sites.

In the last week of January he paid his routine visit to Lausanne, bringing the usual bulky dossier of reports from every part of France, including the V1 area. By this time it was known that the Allied bombing of the sites had been highly successful and reports of German despondency were already coming in. Hitler's high hopes lay in ruins.

It was the climax of Michel's achievement. He had covered himself with glory, and was being recommended, "O.P." told him, for the highest decoration they could get him.

Now he needed a rest—and deserved it. Would he spend a fortnight in Switzerland as a guest of the British Government?

Michel was sorely tempted. He was sick with accumulated fatigue and anxiety. But his men were still at their posts, and he could not abandon them. Deeply touched by "O.P.'s" offer, he thanked him warmly . . . and refused.

It was 8.0 p.m. when he reached Lausanne station. His intention was to take the train to Geneva, spend the night in a hotel and cross the frontier between Jussy and Machilly at dawn. Thereafter it would be the familiar round: Lyons, Avignon, Toulon, Nice, and then on to Nîmes, Sète, Béziers, Narbonne, Carcassonne and Toulouse.

As he followed the subway which led to platform three, he was overcome by an immense tiredness of body and spirit. His feet were like lead, and there was a burning pain in the soles (which had been revived by the heat of "O.P.'s" office,) while his back ached with rheumatism. He thought wistfully of the invitation to take a holiday and wondered if he had been wise to refuse it.

Never had the prospect of returning to France looked so bleak: the interminable journeys on overcrowded trains with perhaps two nights a week when he slept in a bed; the inadequate meals; absence of heating; and general atmosphere of depression produced by a shabbily dressed, under-nourished and cowed people.

By contrast, everything around him spoke of happiness and prosperity: healthy-looking men and women dressed in good clothes, gay young things and children with a glow on their cheeks, and all with that air of comfort and security, and unconcern for the morrow, which was so notably lacking in his own life.

While he waited on the platform for his train, a woman in a neatly starched apron came pushing a trolley and ringing a bell to attract attention. The trolley was loaded with every good thing: cigars, cigarettes of every variety, chocolates, caramels, nougats, thickly buttered sandwiches with generous portions of ham, and, best of all, *uncensored* newspapers which printed the Allied communiqués.

Contemplating all these treasures, Michel was seized once again with an overwhelming desire to put off his journey, and to enjoy for a short space, in the safety of a neutral country, the pleasures of a normal life.

To resist it he closed his eyes and thought of his family, and all the hardships they were suffering; of his team of cyclists, eating badly and going without sleep to do the jobs he had given them; of Gendron, one of his three deputies, tramping the roads in all weathers; of Jean-Henri dodging the sentries at Bosc-le-Hart. He thought of Pierre Carteron with his broken arm—blasted by a British bomb—wheeling his bicycle with the other; of Louis Villette roaming the aerodrome of Abbeville, and Louis Margot freezing in the winter dusk as he watched the mounting of a German balloon barrage.

That was enough: the temptation was mastered. Michel worked his team hard, as hard as he worked himself, and the more he demanded of them the more they responded. One could not desert such people, even for a day.

However, the devil had not finished with him yet.

The train for Geneva came in. Michel was about to board it, when he felt both his arms seized, and the next moment he was being impelled away from the train and towards the exit.

His captors were two Frenchmen living in Lausanne, whom he

had met on previous visits. They had happened to see him arrive earlier in the day and had remained at the station to intercept him with a view to inviting him to dinner.

The elder, Georges, had come to Switzerland to recruit French refugees for the maquis. He was a jovial individual, as well as a genuine patriot, who enjoyed the good things of life; and knowing the work that Michel was doing, and the kind of existence he led, was determined to give him an evening out.

The other, younger and less talkative, but equally devoted to the Resistance, was a friend of Georges and engaged on the same mission.

It was useless for Michel to protest. In any case, as he told himself, since he was crossing the frontier at daybreak, it made no difference whether he spent the night in Lausanne or Geneva. It seemed that for once he could allow himself a diversion; it would be the first since the day he had offered his services to the Allies.

They dined at the Auberge de la Sallaz, a first class restaurant overlooking the town. It was the first time since the war that Michel had been in such a place. The pleasant warmth of the room, the aroma of succulent dishes and expensive wines, the enormous chimney where fat chickens were being roasted on the spit, the gaily chequered curtains and tablecloths, and the soft hum of carefree conversation, filled his starved soul with a glow of well-being.

Later in the evening a talented pair entertained the diners. The man, famous in Switzerland for his anti-Nazi skits, was a brilliant comedian of the boulevardier type; his partner—red-haired with porcelain complexion and enormous eyes—a gifted *diseuse*, by turns witty and sad, with that mixture of tenderness and gaiety which is so uniquely French. Together they sang the songs which evoked the France that had been, and which Michel had not heard for four years; *La Closerie des Lilas*, *Le Mot de Cambronne*, *Quatorze Juillet*. Michel was entranced. It was as if a long nightmare were suddenly dissolved and one awoke to a world of sanity and laughter.

When they left the place in the early hours of the morning, he was still under the spell of the evening. Since the invasion of France nothing had brought home to him so poignantly the difference between the free and the oppressed. Like a man who has lived in darkness, he was dazed by the sun . . . and now he must return to the darkness, which would seem only blacker after his glimpse of the light.

It was snowing when he reached the customs post after a two-hour walk from Geneva. The guard, a genial giant who knew him well, proffered a steaming cup of coffee.

As he was taking his leave of this friendly person, Michel was unable to hide the anguish in his soul.

"Oh," he exclaimed, "if only I didn't have to cross this accursed frontier to-day!"

The guard had never heard him express such sentiments. He looked concerned and said: "Perhaps that's an omen. Who knows but you wouldn't do better to postpone your journey!"

"Oh, it's only a passing weakness. I don't suppose I'll think of it again."

They shook hands and then Michel took the path into the woods.

A little later he met another customs guard, standing in a clearing close to the stream which marked the frontier. This was a taciturn individual not usually very friendly, but for once he greeted Michel almost cordially and wished him good luck.

Again Michel felt the need of unburdening himself, as if by communicating it to another human being he could rid himself of the sense of doom which weighed him down.

"This time," he said, "I'd give ten thousand Swiss francs not to have to cross that stream."

"It's a lot of money," was the guard's only comment.

As Michel reached the French side of the boundary he recalled that it was his ninety-fourth crossing.

Something told him that it was also his last.

A few days after his return to Paris, Michel had a rendezvous with two of his agents and his secretary at a little café near the office in the Rue Beaubourg. The rendezvous was for 9.0 a.m., the date being the 5th February, 1944.

As it happened—a rare occurrence—he had spent the night with his family in the little house at St. Rémy Les Chevreuses to which he had moved them a year previously. Since he saw his wife so seldom and there was much to discuss, he was delayed in starting; and realising he could not keep the appointment he rang up his secretary to cancel it. Instead, he fixed a meeting for the evening at a different place, where he already had an appointment with two other agents.

During the morning, while Madeleine Boulanger was alone in the office, she received another visit from the Comte de Kergoat and the same unknown woman. She said that Michel was not available and invited them to leave a message.

But this time they were taking no excuses. It was absolutely essential, the woman pleaded, that she should see M. Hollard that very day. Somebody very dear to her was in danger and only M. Hollard could save him. It was a matter of life or death.

Remembering Michel's injunction never to betray his whereabouts, especially to this pair, whom he did not trust, for a long time the secretary resisted their entreaties. But finally she was persuaded that the request was genuine.

She could not get hold of M. Hollard during the day, she told them, but she knew where he would be that evening. She then gave the time and the place: 6.15 p.m. at the Café aux Chasseurs, 176 Faubourg St. Denis, opposite the Gare du Nord.

Michel had chosen the time and place for the evening rendezvous because it was convenient to the two agents who were to meet him. One was Robert Rubenach—known in the *réseau* as Robert de Vic—and the other a man called Mailly. Robert was coming from Beaumont, to which he had recently been transferred from

Bernes, and Mailly from Le Bourget, where he was employed as a railway clerk.

Both of them were due at the Gare du Nord by trains which arrived at about six o'clock, and they only had to cross the road to reach the meeting place.

The other two, whom he was to have met in the morning but had put off till the evening were Joseph Legendre, alias Gendron, and Henri Dujarier.

As Michel entered the café he had a sudden presentiment of danger. The place was full, as usual at that hour, but something about the scene struck him as abnormal. There was a man leaning against the bar at the corner nearest the street, and another standing in front of the door to the *lavabo,* who did not look like the ordinary customers.

It was not a definite impression but something he sniffed in the air, like an animal scenting an enemy.

Three of the people he was meeting—Legendre, Dujarier and Mailly—were already seated at a table. At the sight of Michel, Mailly stood up and handed him a small parcel containing his notes.

Before Michel had time to sit down, he heard his name called, and, looking round, saw a strange woman standing at the end of the room. This was something he did not like the look of. He had no idea that his secretary had given her the rendezvous and a stranger was the last person he wished to meet at that moment.

As he joined her in the little vestibule, she started to pour out some story about a friend who was in danger of arrest, and whom she was trying to get out of the country. Michel cut her short. "Listen, madame, it's impossible to discuss such things here. You must give the details to my secretary and I will do what I can."

Then, out of politeness and in the hope of getting rid of her, he invited the woman to join him for a drink and led the way to another table.

They had just sat down when one of the two men, whose

presence had already aroused Michel's suspicion, suddenly produced a revolver and shouted: "Hands up, everyone! German police."

In a moment the whole café seemed filled with armed men. Michel was still carrying in his hand the packet given him by Mailly, and as he raised his arms he dropped it behind the bench.

He was set on by several police in plain clothes and his hands handcuffed behind him. The other three, as lesser fry, were handcuffed in front. All four were then bundled outside, where several cars were waiting. Michel was put in the back seat of the first, with a guard on either side; the other three with their escort followed in another car.

As the cortège moved off Michel caught a glimpse through the window of the stranger struggling and screaming with two policemen. This was the usual pantomime which the Gestapo played when they pretended to arrest the decoy. It was intended to protect the traitor from reprisals, but seldom took anybody in.

The three other people who should have been at the rendezvous—Robert Rubenach, Lucien François and Madeleine Boulanger—fortunately arrived late. Seeing three cars stationed outside the café, they smelt danger and retired to the post office opposite, from the windows of which they watched the drama.

14. Rue Mallet Stevens

The car sped along the boulevards, crossed the Place de la Concorde and turned right to follow the river. From time to time it was stopped by traffic lights. Michel looked at the door and wondered if he could open it with his shoulder and make a dash. He quickly abandoned the idea. The two plain-clothes men, with revolvers in their hands, kept him pressed against the seat; with his hands locked behind him any move would have been hopeless.

On reaching Auteuil, the car turned and started to climb steeply. Michel could see the other one following. They were now in one of the richest quarters of Paris. Large blocks of modern flats, with spacious balconies and magnificent views over the Seine, were interspersed with private houses standing in their own grounds.

The road wound as it mounted, then straightened out. A little farther on the car turned sharply to enter a narrower road, which was also a cul-de-sac. As it turned, Michel read the name of the street: Rue Mallet Stevens XVIIIe. Two wooden-faced Paris policemen were stationed at either corner. A few yards down they stopped outside a large square building. Its severe grey façade, only broken by iron-shuttered windows, looked more like a fort than a private house[1] A short flight of steps led to massive double doors enclosed by a heavy iron grille. Over the entrance was engraved the number "5."

A moment later a large iron shutter in the wall was raised, revealing a garage big enough for several cars. Michel's car drove inside followed by the other. Then the shutter closed behind them with a crash, which to Michel was like the crack of doom.

The four men were hustled out, pushed up a short staircase, and locked together in a room without light. Michel had the impression that it was on the ground floor, as this was raised some distance above street level.

For a moment or so nobody spoke. It is always a depressing experience, to say the least of it, to be taken prisoner, and when the enemy is the Gestapo—for that's what it really meant, though they were technically in custody of the *Abwehr*[2]—the situation is still less enviable.

Even Michel, for once, was aghast, not so much for himself as for his three companions. He felt responsible for their arrest

[1] It was, in fact, a private house, the property of a French millionaire, requisitioned by the *Abwehr*.

[2] Counter-espionage branch of German military intelligence.

and was deeply disturbed by the thought that other members of the *réseau* might by now have suffered the same fate. How had it happened, he kept on asking himself.

It was Legendre who broke the silence, with his irrepressible cheerfulness.

"Well, here we are, chaps, and I'd give a lot to be somewhere else."

Michel's mind was already working again. By leaving them together the enemy had given him a chance which he must seize.

Before he could act, however, the door was flung open and the names of Gendron (Legendre's pseudonym) and Mailly were called out. They stumbled out, another person was pushed inside, and the door locked again. For all Michel knew their new companion could be a *poulet* (police spy) and he therefore decided it was safer to keep silent. He had often rehearsed with Legendre and Dujarier what they should say if questioned: they were employees of the *Gazogène* company and knew him only as manager of the business. As long as they stuck to this story they still had a chance. Mailly was different, as a railwayman employed at Le Bourget it was difficult to explain why he should be meeting Michel in Paris.

For himself Michel had no illusions. He could not hope to deceive the Germans, they knew too much about him. It was the logical end of his adventure and he had only one more duty: to shield his accomplices.

Five minutes passed, which he spent collecting his thoughts for the coming ordeal; then it was his turn.

As he emerged from the *cachot* he found himself in a hall, from which a flight of stairs led to the floor above. Propelled by his guard he mounted the stairs, until he could see through an open door the back view of Legendre standing in front of a table. At the same instant, Legendre, hearing Michel approach, raised his voice and almost shouted: "I repeat I am only an agent for the *Gazogène* company."

Realising that this was intended for him, Michel took new

heart. He knew now that Legendre had adhered to the plan agreed on.

As he entered the room, Legendre was brought out, and they had a chance to exchange glances of mutual encouragement.

It was a long high room with a cinema screen at one end and a gallery with a cabin for the projector at the other. The curtains of the two windows were drawn.

Seated at a long table were the four interrogators. Michel's impression was that they were all fairly young and well dressed in their civilian clothes. One of them, a man of forty, who did not look German, was not unsympathetic in appearance. The other three struck him as cold-blooded and cruel.

One in particular, who appeared to be the chief, was horribly repulsive. In his thirties, with a long oval face, a prominent cranium going bald, and bad teeth, he had the rat-like expression of a small-time criminal. The others called him Rudi. It later transpired that he was a Belgian.

In the background, standing, were the two plain-clothes policemen who had provided his escort in the car. One of them, the more brutal of the two, appeared to be French.

Now that at last he was faced by the actual apparatus which for four years had kept half Europe in submission, Michel felt his courage waning. It was the deadly coldness of these men—a coldness as of reptiles—that for a moment chilled him in spite of himself.

To resist it he concentrated on preparing his "line"—which was to take everything on himself and admit all facts that would not compromise anyone else. In this way he hoped not only to cover the other three, but to divert attention to his own misdeeds. He found that thinking what to say gave him back his courage and he awaited the first question calmly.

It was Rudi who conducted the interrogation.

"What were you doing at the Café aux Chasseurs this evening?"

"I was having a business meeting."

"Why should you hold it at such a place?"

"Because it was convenient to the other three, who live out of Paris."

"You're lying. You were meeting them in connection with your secret activities as an enemy agent."

"On the contrary, they know nothing whatsoever about that. Legendre is my senior salesman and I wanted him to meet Dujarier, whom we have just appointed as our representative at provincial fairs. Mailly was bringing me information about the cost of sending our goods by train. Until now we have always delivered by road—but, you understand, with the difficulty of obtaining fuel . . ."

"I'm not interested. So you don't deny that you are a British agent."

"I am a French patriot and I work with our Ally."

"Why?"

"As the most effective means of continuing the war against you. I regret that it's not possible to fight you openly."

"Well, you see that we're the stronger and that you've lost."

"*I've* lost, yes, but *you'll* lose the war."

"Are you disposed to tell us what your secret action consisted of?"

Michel made no reply.

"You might just as well. You see, we know all about you. That you travelled all over the *Midi* as a spy and took your information to the British in Switzerland."

The mention of the *Midi* was a useful clue. If the informer, as he thought, was the woman in the café, she must have revealed what she had been told by someone in contact with the part of his organisation in the south, which was limited to a few agents and from which reports were collected on behalf of Michel. Simone Boirel had been arrested in November, and although he did not suspect it at the time he now realised that it must have been due to the activity of the informer.

"I don't deny it. I collected all the information I could that I thought would be useful to our Ally, and made regular visits to the British Embassy in Berne. My reports were handed to

Colonel Cartwright, the Military Attaché. If you doubt my word, you can look up his name in the telephone book. It is no secret that he acts as the receiver of intelligence. That is the function of a military attaché, as you must know."

"And are you disposed to give us the names of your collaborators?"

"I had no collaborators. I worked on my own."

"We know that's a lie. You had many people helping you. We want their names."

"It would be of no interest to you. Most of them were simple people who did not even suspect my rôle."

"Nevertheless, we would like their names."

"I'm afraid I can't help you."

"You are really not disposed to tell us?"

"Absolutely not."

"You realise that may cost you dear?"

"It would not surprise me."

"And that is your last word?"

"I'm afraid so."

"All right. You won't sing. Well, to-night you shall sing like a little bird."

Rudi turned to one of the Germans and still speaking in French said: "You'd better prepare one electrode—no, both."

Then he turned again to Michel.

"Is that really your final decision?" he asked.

Michel nodded. Rudi fixed him with eyes as cold as a cat's, and said very slowly and softly:

"I tell you that to-night you'll talk. Yes, you'll talk so that there will be no stopping you."

When Michel returned to the *cachot* the other three had been removed and he was shut in alone in the darkness. Groping around he found an iron bar and for a time tried rubbing his handcuffs against it. Soon he abandoned the attempt. There was nothing to do but wait.

Everything had been taken from Michel, including his watch

and the diary in which he noted his appointments. So he had no means of telling the time, but he reckoned it was about midnight when they came for him again.

He was taken through passages to another hall, where the *mise-en-scéne* seemed deliberately designed to inspire terror. Leather whips and rubber hose, a length of rope and several pairs of handcuffs were strewn on chairs and tables in careless profusion.

Michel assumed this was the place where he was to be made, in Rudi's words, to "sing like a little bird"; but the sinister procession continued until it arrived at a ground-floor bathroom. Besides Rudi, the party consisted of the French *policier* and three other powerfully built individuals.

While the bath was being filled with ice-cold water his handcuffs were removed and he was ordered to strip. Then his ankles were attached and his hands tied behind him.

A punch in the face, delivered by the Frenchman, caused him to stagger backwards against the bath. In doing so he overturned and fell on his back in the water. For a moment he was completely immersed but managed to get his head out and came up spluttering.

Rudi was standing over him with Michel's diary in his hand.

"I see," he said, "that you have an appointment for to-morrow, 6th February, at 9.0 a.m., at the Gare d'Austerlitz, with a person whose initials are 'C.G.' You will now tell me the name of this person."

"C.G." was a certain Charles Guillard, an ex-officer of the Swiss Army who kept a wine shop at Etampes. He was employed by Michel to make plans of the new aerodrome of Mon Désir and to report on German air movements. He came regularly to Paris and was always met by Michel, either at the station, or just outside, or at the entrance of the Jardin des Plantes nearby.

"You won't tell me?" said Rudi as Michel made no reply.

Michel shook his head, and was immediately hit on it from above, causing him to immerse again.

Having been caught by surprise, he had not taken in much air and was soon forced to surface.

The question was repeated.

"Who is 'C.G.'?"

This time he was hardly given time to shake his head before an avalanche of blows forced him under again.

For the third time he came up gasping, only to receive the same treatment.

This went on for about half an hour, but with progressive effect as the beating became more severe and he was given less and less time to breathe before plunging.

He lost count of the rounds, but at the end of a certain time he was dragged out and given a ten minutes' rest. Then the process recommenced.

It was repeated four more times, each session lasting roughly half an hour, but at increased intervals as it was judged that his failing strength required longer to recover.

Michel himself has expressed the opinion that one more session would have succeeded. If he could have killed himself by drowning he would, but he was not allowed to. As it was he endured five, which, with intervals, lasted for at least three hours.

While he was resting after the fifth, literally more dead than alive, with his head supported on the side of the bath, he heard, through the mist of pain and dizziness and vomit, the exasperated voice of Rudi: "We're wasting our time with this pig-headed fool. We've better things to do."

Then he heard the gang troop out and the door slammed.

After a while he managed to summon enough strength to roll out of the bath and on to the floor. There he was lying, shivering with cold and weakness, when some time later the door opened and an elderly woman appeared. She was carrying a hunk of bread, which she proceeded to break into small pieces and offer him a piece at a time.

Gratefully, Michel allowed himself to be fed. When the last piece was swallowed he smiled his thanks—he was still incapable of speech—and the unknown angel withdrew. He afterwards discovered that she was one of an Italian couple employed as concierges in the building.

Nothing was better calculated to revive Michel's spirits. It was not only the nourishment, welcome as it was, that cheered him, but the gesture of humanity in a place from which all humanity seemed to have been driven.

Later, the guards returned, released him, and allowed him to dress. He was then handcuffed again and shut in a different *cachot*. He was in pretty bad shape, but comforted himself with the thought that he had won the first round and the match was not yet lost.

The well-known Resistance leader and author, who writes under the name of "Rémy," although he himself was never tortured, has made some pertinent remarks on those who were.

"A *résistant*," he says, "who fell into the hands of the enemy and who lacked the force to remain silent under torture was far from being a traitor. On the contrary, between him and his compatriots who remained passive there was all the difference between a combatant and a shirker.

"As for those who had the courage to resist to the end . . . who in other words remained indomitable, they belong to a small and exclusive élite. The memory of their struggle should be sacred and it should fill us with both astonishment and reverence."

This perhaps comes nearest to expressing what we all must feel about the very few who, like Michel, resisted *jusqu'au bout*.

His own comment on the performance was characteristically much more modest.

"*En effet le bon Dieu m'a donné une délivrance formidable en les fatiguant plutôt que moi.*"[1]

At eight o'clock he was brought a cup of coffee, and soon afterwards the French *policier* and one of the Germans came to fetch him. Michel was quite expecting to return to the bathroom, but instead he was led to the garage and placed in the back of a car, with his two escorts on either side.

1 "Indeed God Almighty gave me a wonderful deliverance in tiring them out before me."

As they were driven off the Frenchman said: "We are taking you to the Gare d'Austerlitz. We shall stop opposite the exit and you will identify 'C.G.' as he comes out. If you fail to do so before the last passenger emerges our orders are to shoot you on the spot. It will be to stop you escaping, you understand, and no questions will be asked."

Five minutes before the train from Etampes was due, the car drew up in the station yard slightly to the side of the exit. The engine remained running and the two escorts had their revolvers ready.

Michel had no fears as long as Guillard adhered to the rule: never stop or look to round if he wasn't there to meet him, but to proceed along the street towards the Jardin des Plantes.

It was nine o'clock by the station clock. Michel looked straight ahead and, as far as he could with his hands handcuffed behind him, tried to settle back in the car in an attitude of relaxation, knowing that it only needed the slightest reflex to betray him.

One minute past nine. A man came out of the exit carrying a brief-case. It was Guillard. The fact of his being the first passenger to emerge was so unexpected that in spite of his preparedness Michel visibly started. Had the two *policiers* been watching him instead of the exit he would have undoubtedly given himself away.

Fortunately they too had not counted on their quarry appearing so soon and Michel's slip passed unobserved. He saw Guillard cross the yard without looking to right or left and disappear into the street which led to the gardens. Meanwhile the other passengers were coming out, first in ones or twos, and then in a crowd.

When the last had emerged the French *policier* turned on Michel and struck him a blow in the face with the barrel of his gun.

"You filthy swine," he shouted. "We'll teach you to make a fool of us."

The other joined in and together they hammered him about

the head and face, until both eyes were closed, his lips cut, and blood was streaming down his face.

After that, the party returned to the Rue Mallet Stevens and Michel was locked in again.

Later that morning he was taken up to the cinema room again and interrogated by another Gestapo officer. This time the interview was quite short.

"If you will reveal your organisation we will release you at once."

Michel merely shrugged.

That night he could hear through the walls of his *cachot* three other prisoners being submitted to the torture of the *baignoire*. Two of them surrendered after one ducking, but the third held out as valiantly as Michel himself, and for three hours the latter had to share vicariously in a repetition of his own experience.

The victim, as he learnt later, was a young Frenchman, a naval officer called De Pimodan, of aristocratic family: as Michel described him "a *noble* by his birth and *un homme noble* by his conduct." He was later deported, survived the war, but with health undermined, and died in France a few years ago.

These nocturnal goings-on were naturally not calculated to raise Michel's morale. Hungry and shivering—it was snowing hard in Paris—he awaited his own turn, which he was convinced must soon come. One thought only sustained him: he had beaten the enemy once and was the stronger for it.

But the night passed and he was left alone.

In the morning he decided he must try to escape before another night came round. He requested to go to the lavatory and was allowed his hands free while the guard waited outside with the door ajar. By standing on the seat he could just reach a small window overlooking a court on the side of the house. He had got his head and shoulders through and was stuck when discovered.

The only result was another beating up.

That night again he waited interminable hours for the footsteps which would announce a further session with Rudi. But for once the building was quiet and in the small hours of the morning, when he was finally convinced it was not for that night either, he got some sleep for the first time since his arrest.

The next day, the third, he was taken for interrogation to a different room. The man behind the table was one he had not seen before, and from the respectful attitude of the others Michel gathered that he was a senior officer just arrived from Berlin.

His manner was courteous, almost friendly. Michel's handcuffs were removed and a chair was provided for him.

The interrogation proceeded on much the same lines as before, except that the German did not press him to reveal the names of any accomplices. Michel had made a clean breast of his relations with the British, although he had not given away any of his contacts except Cartwright—which, in any case, was no secret to the Germans—or the place of his meetings other than Berne.

His tactic, in fact, was to expatiate on this aspect of his activities, which involved no one but himself: but the German seemed anxious if anything to mitigate it.

When for example, Michel declared that his visits to Switzerland had been bi-monthly, the German replied, "That is every two months," and appeared to make a note accordingly, and when he stated that the British paid him 68,000 francs a month, the German repeated the "eight" but not the "sixty," as though he had not heard the first figure.

As the interview was concluding, Michel said: "I suppose this will cost me my head."

"Unfortunately, yes, Monsieur," replied the German gravely, almost as though he regretted it.

That was Michel's last experience of the Rue Mallet Stevens. The same evening, with his three companions in misfortune, he was removed to the Rue des Saussaies, the Gestapo headquarters, to be officially charged and registered as an enemy agent before being imprisoned at Fresnes. He and Legendre travelled in the same car, while Mailly and Dujarier arrived shortly afterwards, chained together.

Except for Mailly, whom he had glimpsed once at a distance, looking haggard and totally demoralised as he was dragged along by two guards, Michel had seen nothing of the others since his first interrogation.

Now, while they were waiting for the formalities to start, there was a brief opportunity to exchange news. Mailly was still too shaken to tell his story, but the other two were in relatively good spirits.

Apart from a routine beating-up, Legendre had not suffered. Dujarier had been suspended for several hours, head down, from the projector cabin in the cinema room, and in this position beaten intermittently. He had continued to protest his innocence and after this was not maltreated any further.

Their conversation was cut short by the arrival of an elderly officer and several soldiers, who took over charge of the prisoners from their plain-clothes escort.

As the officer was entering their names in the register, Michel said: "You've no right to detain these three men. They were arrested unjustly and are completely innocent."

"Then they have nothing to fear," replied the German politely and in good French. "Those who have done no harm will be released."

Legendre and Dujarier were, in fact, to be released three months later, no evidence being found against them. Mailly, on whom incriminating documents were discovered, was shortly afterwards deported to Mauthausen, where he died from his treatment a few months later.

15. Fresnes

A "Black Maria" was waiting in the courtyard. Michel and his three companions climbed inside and were locked in separate compartments. There was just room to sit down and it was pitch dark. The van started and Michel could feel it descending a slope, turning right and then accelerating as it set out for Fresnes through the silent Paris streets.

Half an hour went by, then the van slowed down, turned right and stopped. There was the sound of heavy iron gates being opened. The vehicle started again, jolted over some *pavé*, swung round, reversed and finally came to rest. The doors of the compartments were unlocked and the four men descended, surrounded by German soldiers. As they moved away Michel noticed that the driver of the "Black Maria" was wearing the blue cap of the *Préfecture de Police*, and that the small open car which escorted it was occupied by two French policemen. It always saddened him to see his countrymen doing the enemy's dirty work.

They were taken down a staircase into a basement passage, dimly lit and immensely long. From there another staircase led to a vast central hall. Rising to the full height of the building, it was surrounded on all sides by galleries. These were at four different levels and at each level a narrow bridge spanned the width of the hall. Beyond could be seen the serried rows of cell doors, each pierced by a circular peephole.

The handcuffs and chains of the new arrivals were now removed and they were conducted to different cells. Michel's was on the ground floor. Before locking him in, an elderly German N.C.O. asked him whether he was a "terrorist."

"No," replied Michel. "A patriot."

"Then you go in here, Mr. Patriot," said the German.

Producing an enormous key he opened a heavy door. Michel stepped inside and the door closed behind him.

It was quite dark but he could hear somebody moving on the ground. He introduced himself and received from his unseen cell-mate a cool but polite acknowledgment. Judging by the voice, he imagined a man in his fifties.

"You'll find some straw in the corner," said the stranger, "and here's something to cover yourself with."

Groping around, Michel found the straw, and the apology for a blanket which his companion had ceded him. He wrapped his feet in the blanket, pulled his light overcoat around him, and settled down to his first night in prison.

Long before dawn the cold awakened him, and for what seemed an interminable time he waited for the coming of day. When it was light enough to see, he perceived that his cell-mate was a much younger man than he had thought. Tall and dark, with a three-days' beard, he appeared to be an educated person.

Before they had exchanged many words, the door of the cell was opened and Michel was called out to join a column of other prisoners. Among them were Mailly, Legendre, and Dujarier. The column was conducted through underground passages until it arrived at a room fitted with showers and an enormous steam steriliser. Here they were ordered to strip and make a parcel of their clothes before washing under the shower. The parcels were then removed for sterilisation.

As the latter process took longer than their ablutions, there was an interval while the prisoners waited naked for their clothes. The door was open and through it Michel could see a small courtyard and, beyond, the outer wall of the prison. In between there was a building with a sloping roof, whose lower end was not much higher than a man, while the upper end rose nearly to the top of the wall. It occurred to him that two men, acting as ladders for each other, might scale the roof, reach the wall and drop the other side. The escort had withdrawn and the only Germans present were the two N.C.O.s in charge of the sterilising arrangements.

While they were dressing he managed to whisper a word to Legendre. The Breton, always game, gave a nod of assent; but at that moment the escort returned to conduct the prisoners to the cells. Any attempt to get away was then out of the question. All the same, the discovery of a possible escape route gave Michel something to think about and raised his spirits considerably.

They were next taken to a row of box-like cells, each about the size of a telephone kiosk, and locked in again, one man to a box. From time to time a prisoner's name would be called and he was then released to be conducted to his permanent abode in the prison.

Michel's turn came after a wait of several hours, during which he was brought some nameless but hot liquid and a small piece of bread. A long walk through passages and stairways brought him and his escort to the third floor of the third division. A door bearing the number 394 was unlocked and he entered his new home. It was Wednesday, 9th February, 1944.

The cell was very light and scrupulously clean. Daylight entered through a large window of frosted glass, the top section of which only could be opened to admit air. In the lower corner, however, a tiny portion of the glass had been cut out and could be removed or replaced at will. This enabled the occupants of the cell, by closing one eye, to obtain a restricted view of the outside world. As the third division was in the block nearest the prison wall, and cell 394 was on its outer side, there was a glimpse of fields and trees, of a road and houses, where people were still living in freedom. Anyone who has been in prison will know how much this meant to Michel.

In the corner nearest the door there was a water closet with a tap above it. Otherwise the furnishing consisted of two shelves attached to the wall and a single iron bed with four mattresses, artistically arranged to make it look like a divan. It was here that the four occupants of the cell, which was intended to house one prisoner, spent the greater part of the day.

When Michel arrived to join them only two were there. The third, they explained, was doing duty as *Kalfactor*: that was the prisoner who assisted in the distribution of meals and performed other small jobs for the guards. He was allowed out of the cell every morning and only returned to it later in the day.

The younger of the two was a boy of eighteen, by name Jacques Dognin. One of a large family, four of whom had escaped from prison camps to join the Resistance, he had been arrested at Rouen on the information of a Frenchman called Dordain. The same traitor had also betrayed one of Michel's agents, J. H. Daudemard, the informant at Rouen, whose tip had led to the discovery of the V1 site near Auffay.[1]

The older man, in his fifties, was a rather flabby-looking individual called Bougras. Proprietor of a small provincial café, he had no idea why he had been arrested, and looked forward confidently to being released. It seemed probable that his wife, who was also imprisoned at Fresnes, had been implicated somehow with the Resistance, and that the Germans, as usually happened, had assumed the guilt of the other partner.

The fourth prisoner, whom Michel did not meet till the evening, was a young career officer called Gardiol. Member of a Resistance group organised by the army, he was small, dynamic, and imbued with a burning patriotism.

Michel was still showing, on his face and head, and also on his wrists, where the handcuffs had scored them, signs of the treatment he had received from the Gestapo; and this was the best introduction he could have, at least to two of his new companions.

They welcomed him as a fellow fighter, and as a mark of solidarity insisted on his sharing the precious remains of a parcel of food delivered at the prison by Dognin's family.

[1] Dognin and Daudemard both survived deportation and it was through their efforts that in 1947 Dordain was finally convicted of treachery.

To find himself in such company was a great comfort to Michel. The good order in the cell, the friendliness of his cell-mates, and the high morale which they evinced, made him feel more like a member of an exclusive club than a prisoner; and almost allowed him to forget that in all probability he would only leave it to go to his place of execution.

During the next six weeks, Michel was twice taken out of his cell, handcuffed with his hands behind his back, and driven in the "Black Maria" to the Rue des Saussaies for further interrogation.

The second time he was simply informed that he had been condemned to death and that his defence had been conducted by a German advocate. He was then pressed to make a "complete confession."

"I have nothing to confess," replied Michel.

It was now that, for the first time, he gave way to despair. Through the hole in the window of his cell he could see the first signs of spring. The little field which rose beyond the prison wall looked green and lush in the sunshine, and the hedge beyond was already in blossom. He could hear the song of birds and sniff the sweet breath of the reawakening earth.

At the thought that he was to die and see none of this again, something like panic seized him. He had thought himself resigned to his fate and had accustomed himself to contemplate it coolly. But now that it faced him his calm for once deserted him; he felt his self-control breaking down.

Looking round desperately for something to distract his thoughts, his eye lighted on a bar of chocolate which had come in the last parcel brought by his daughter. He was saving it up to use as currency: either to bribe a guard to accord him some small favour, or to exchange with another prisoner for something he needed more.

He started to nibble at a corner; the taste was exquisite but it vanished too quickly. He nibbled another corner, then another . . . Soon the mutilated bar was past offering to anyone, and there was no longer any point in saving it. With deliberate greed he ate the rest, extracting from each bite the maximum of pleasure. By the time he had swallowed the last delicious morsel his moral crisis had passed. Satisfied physically, his mind recovered its strength. Once again he was master of himself.

Ever since his arrest he had not ceased to worry about the *réseau.* Left without a head, what would become of its members? They would know, from his non-appearance at the rendezvous, that something had happened to him. He hoped the deputies he had appointed would be in touch with them; but one of the three, Legendre, was in prison, and there was nobody designated, or qualified, to maintain liaison with the British.

His obvious successor was Legendre, the most enterprising of his agents and also the closest in his confidence. From the way the Breton's case had been handled—he had not been questioned again since leaving the Rue Mallet Stevens—there seemed some hope of his release. In this event he would need instructions from Michel, particularly in regard to contacting the British.

But how to communicate with him? No writing materials were allowed the prisoners. Paper could be obtained from the wrappings of food parcels, but there was absolutely nothing to write with. One day, as he was scouring the floor for something sharp, Michel discovered a minute length of lead, formerly part of a pencil. This was riches beyond the dreams of avarice. Armed with it, he spent a day writing in microscopic letters, on scraps of newspaper, the essential orders for Legendre.

The next problem was to get the message to him. He had discovered that Legendre occupied a cell on the same floor and not very far away. One way would be to give his letter to the *Kalfactor* and ask the latter to deliver it as he was doling out the soup but he decided this was too dangerous: the German soldier who was always present would be sure to spot it.

One day, as the German N.C.O. in charge of the division was inspecting the cell, Michel, addressing him in German, asked if there was any job he wanted doing. The German, who was not unfriendly and was pleased at hearing his own language, received the request favourably; and the next morning Michel was called out, handed a broom and told to sweep the gallery outside the cells.

He applied himself to the task energetically, taking particular care to sweep under the doors, where most of the dust accumulated, and even using his hands to assist the broom when necessary. He thus had no difficulty, when he reached the cell of Legendre, in slipping his note under the door without arousing the suspicions of the German guard who was supervising the work from a distance.

A few days later, on the pretext of lending his friend some underclothes, Michel obtained permission, under escort, to visit Legendre's cell. There he learnt to his intense joy that the Breton had been released that very morning.

This was the best news since the day of their arrest. It meant not only that the beloved "Gendron" was free, but that the line to Switzerland would reopen, and the *réseau* resume its function of supplying information to the Allies.[1]

It would be difficult to exaggerate the comforting effect this knowledge had on Michel. It set the seal on the victory he had won over his opponents in the bathroom of the Rue Mallet Stevens. Had he lost that fight—and talked—his whole organisation would have been destroyed. As it was, he knew now that it would survive; whatever happened to him, his work would go on.

Moriturus vinco, he could have proudly claimed at this moment.

[1] Shortly after his release Legendre arrived in Switzerland with the full story of Michel's arrest. Thereafter he assumed the leadership of the *réseau*, which continued its useful work until the Liberation of France. This was largely made possible by the initiative of Bart, who, after nine months in hospital, recovered sufficiently to assume the liaison between the *réseau* and the Swiss, which enabled agents to cross the frontier.

16. Deportation

One morning, towards the end of May, Michel was taken out of his cell alone. Except for his two visits to the Rue des Saussaies, this was the first time he had been separated from his cell-mates. Had the fatal day at last arrived, he wondered?

He was conducted to the prison doctor, treated to a summary auscultation, and then returned to his cell. Later in the day he learned from the *Kalfactor* that this was the usual prelude to deportation. His sentence had, in fact, been commuted.

The reprieve did not affect him so much as it would have done in the early days of his imprisonment. The passing of time without news of his impending execution had made the prospect of death recede. On the other hand, between death and deportation there was not very much to choose, so often the one was but a stepping-stone to the other. But at least it provided a respite; he could still make plans to escape.

A few days later the N.C.O. in charge of the division brought his brief-case and other possessions, and told him to get ready to leave. This was the friendly sergeant who had done him several small favours—for example, by turning a blind eye to such breaches of the rules as the receiving of cigarettes, playing cards, etc. A reservist in his fifties, formerly a cashier at Cologne Town Hall, he had always treated the prisoners with humanity. After giving Michel his instructions he added with a sad smile, "I'm sorry. They are taking the best of my charges."

Michel had little to pack—a few articles of clothing, a New Testament, and some photographs. When all was ready he grasped the hands of his two companions and together the three sang a farewell chant to the tune of "Auld Lang Syne." Only one of them was he to meet again. Jacques Dognin, though crippled in health, survived deportation and returned to France after the war. The unfortunate Bougras, still protesting his innocence, was swallowed up in Germany and seen no more.

At two o'clock he joined a group of twenty other prisoners. As their names were called out, Michel thought he heard that of Daudemard, his former agent at Rouen, but before he could check up the party were marched outside and loaded on board a motor bus. Four Italian soldiers armed with tommy-guns provided the guard.

The bus started off, passed the great iron gates—which immediately closed behind it—and swung on to the road to Paris. Michel gazed hungrily on the passing scene. The untidy straggling suburb, with its scattered houses, open fields and waste land, was not particularly beautiful, but to him it had all the freshness of an undiscovered world.

The bus soon arrived at the Porte d'Orléans and headed for the centre of the city. At the Place Denfert-Rochereau there was a little bistro where Michel had often stopped for a coffee and a cigarette after arriving by train from St. Rémy-les-Chevreuses. As they passed the place he glanced nostalgically towards it and recognised the patron in his usual place behind the bar.

On the Boulevard Raspail the bus stopped to pick up some passengers from the prison of the Cherche Midi. A crowd soon collected but were kept at bay by German soldiers. This, however, did not prevent two of the prisoners dropping messages, which were immediately picked up by passers-by.

With all its seats now filled, the bus set off again, travelling in a northward direction. Leaving the Gare du Nord on the left, it passed through the suburbs of Aubervilliers and Le Bourget before striking the main road for Senlis. There was little traffic. Private motoring had practically ceased and the only vehicles to be seen belonged either to public transport or to the occupying forces. For taxis people used bicycles towing tiny trailers.

Beyond Senlis the road entered the forest of Compiègne.

After a long lonely stretch with woods on either side, they passed through another village, and almost immediately came in sight of their destination: a vast enclosure, partly covered by low buildings and surrounded by a double line of barbed wire fencing with observation posts at each corner. The bus slowed down, turned off the road, and entered through a strongly guarded gateway. They had arrived at the stalag of Royal-Lieu-Compiègne.

The camp consisted of rows of wooden huts, with a large open space in the centre. Hundreds of prisoners were strolling about dressed in ordinary clothes, and as long as they kept away from the limits of the camp there seemed to be no constraint on their movements.

On descending from the bus the new arrivals were handed cards which they were told to hang from their necks. Each card bore a number. They were then conducted to their sleeping quarters: a long low shed standing on bare earth with a thin layer of straw for floor. A single window, permanently closed and covered with heavy wire netting, let in the only light.

After taking stock of his surroundings, Michel turned his attention to his room-mates; it was then to his joy that he recognised the man whose name he had heard pronounced during a roll call.

Jean Henri Daudemard was the informant who had put him on the track of the V1 sites. A brilliant engineer employed by the French State Railways, he had only been working for the *réseau* a short time when, thanks to a conversation overheard in a Rouen café, he had sent the report which led to the discovery of the first site. Shortly after, with Pierre Bouguet, the station-master at Rouen, he had been betrayed to the Gestapo, arrested and imprisoned.

He and Michel had not met for five months, and their reunion, even in such circumstances, was a happy occurrence for both of them. Daudemard knew nothing of the sequel to his action, and he was deeply interested to hear how much had followed from it.

For Michel, who had last met him in an imposing office surrounded by all the trappings of a responsible position, it was inspiring to meet a man who, in spite of degradation, remained calm, dignified and courageous.

In the morning the door was opened and the inmates of the shed were let out and distributed among the other huts. Here they were provided with bunks and blankets and settled down not too uncomfortably to their new life.

Apart from keeping their quarters clean and tidying up the camp, the prisoners had nothing to do, and most of the day passed in idleness only interrupted by periodical roll calls and meals. The food was plain but sufficient, and could be supplemented by parcels sent by the prisoners' families. To his surprise, one came for Michel on the day after his arrival, brought by his sister, who had cycled the fifty miles from Paris.

The discovery of his whereabouts so quickly was the result of detective work by his family. On the previous day his daughter had called at Fresnes with the usual parcel, only to be told that the prisoner was no longer there. It was at first assumed he had been removed for execution, but inquiries at the cemetery of Ivry, where death sentences were carried out, showed a blank entry in the register of shootings for that day. The family then concluded correctly that he had been taken to the transit camp Royal-Lieu-Compiègne, prior to deportation.

To help pass the time the prisoners organised lectures and boxing matches. There were also religious services, held in a hut which was divided into a Catholic and a Protestant section. The latter was in charge of a Swiss pastor called Bornand, who had got into trouble with the Germans for being too friendly to the condemned men to whom he had been appointed as chaplain.

After Michel had volunteered to assist him, they shared the duty of hearing confessions. Some of the prisoners were tortured by problems of conscience. One man, at the moment of his arrest, had prayed that his daughter be spared, accompanying the prayer with a solemn promise that, if she was, he would never see her again. The girl had *not* been arrested and the question for the anguished father was whether God expected him to keep his promise until death.

Michel did his best to reassure him.

"We cannot judge," was his answer. "To assist your prayer you were ready to accept a heavy sacrifice. That is the important thing. But how do you know that God demands that particular sacrifice? Rather show Him your gratitude by the firmness and serenity of your faith. That will enable you to surmount any trial."

Whether the advice was acted on he never knew, but of one thing he was certain, that the recipient left him with courage and hope renewed.

Thus a week passed, not unpleasantly. The weather was magnificent and to those who had been living in a prison cell the effect of it, in the relative freedom of the camp, was almost dazzling. Michel, however, was in no mood to appreciate the weather. He continued to be haunted by the need to escape, and realised that with every day that passed the moment was drawing nearer when it would no longer be possible. The intense activity of the Allied Air Force, flying high above the camp, he read as a sign that great events were impending, heralding perhaps the end of the war. This only made him more desperate to regain his liberty.

By volunteering for some work in a neighbouring factory, he had succeeded in making and secreting two small saws, one for wood and the other for metal. He had no plan for using them, but felt sure they would be needed.

On the 1st June—a week before D Day—the prisoners were assembled and the names called of those designated for the next transportation to Germany. They numbered two thousand eight hundred. These were ordered to surrender all personal possessions and, after being warned that any concealment would be severely punished, were searched, wearing only their trousers. Michel had stuck the two saws to the inside of his thighs with adhesive tape, and though he was "frisked" by two soldiers, who ran their hands down his legs, one in front and one behind, neither of them discovered the thin strips of metal.

After being provided with a piece of sausage and a slice of bread for the journey, the deportees were herded for their last night into a different lot of huts without windows. Here Michel found himself among a party of youths, whom he had often noticed in the camp, usually accompanied by a priest. This was an abbé called Le Meur, who had been arrested with them and acted as shepherd of the flock. Michel decided to attach himself to it.

Later in the evening he was approached by another prisoner, and recognised him as a man he knew: a De Gaullist, Captain P——, whom he had met at Montélimar some months previously. P—— had pressed him to work for the Free French instead of the English and had offered dazzling inducements in the form of money, cigarettes and food, which he said he could obtain by parachute. Michel, on his guard against a trap, had replied that he would only change his arrangements if ordered to do so by the High Command, and there the matter had rested. His suspicions of P—— were now set at rest, and he was glad to renew their acquaintance.

In the hut with their leader were two members of his former band: Jim, an immense negro, the camp's champion boxer, and Jo, an ex-combatant with a wooden leg, in which were concealed, P—— told Michel, all the tools needed to break out of a sealed wagon.

"We mean to escape during the journey. It's all laid on."

"I had the same idea," said Michel.

"Then why not join us," P—— suggested, "and we'll make our get-away together?"

Feeling that this was a better bet than the abbé and his group of youths, Michel gladly accepted the invitation; and when early next morning the deportees left the camp he marched in the same rank with P—— and his two companions.

Day was just breaking when the long column, five men to a rank, wound its way to the station through the streets of

Compiègne. On either side the route was lined with soldiers and behind them little groups of early risers watched the procession in silence. At certain points larger numbers of people, possibly relations of the exiles, had gathered to witness the scene. It struck Michel that they looked glummer than the prisoners themselves, perhaps because they knew what was in store for them, whereas the marchers only knew that they were going to Germany. After their relatively supportable sojourn at the transit camp, they did not envisage what lay ahead, and apart from home-sickness none of them as yet felt any real anguish.

This mood soon changed when they reached the station. Here the atmosphere was very different from that of the transit camp. Uniformed members of the Security Police, carrying short leather whips and pistols in their belts, took charge of the column and halted it beside a long line of cattle wagons. Then one of them counted the leading twenty ranks, totalling one hundred men, and ordered these to enter the first wagon. By the time half the number had squeezed in, it was full. As the remainder stopped, seeing there was no room for them the German started lashing those standing in the opening. In a few seconds room was made and the rest crowded in. When the last had forced an entrance, encouraged by blows, the door of the wagon was bolted and secured with a padlock.

Michel was near the rear of the column and by the time his turn arrived everybody knew the drill. Under the menace of the whip, men who had been friends a moment before fought with each other so as not to be the last, and all sense of obligation to one's neighbour vanished.

The process of human degradation, deliberately planned and scientifically carried out, had already started to work.

When the door had closed the only light inside the wagon came from a small ventilation hole covered over with iron bars. At first Michel could see nothing, but as his eyes became accustomed to the darkness he dimly perceived the forms of his fellow travellers. The hundred men stood upright, pressed against each other, with just room for their feet without treading on a neighbour. In the centre, but inaccessible except to those nearest to it, was a metal barrel open at the top: their sole sanitary amenity.

Michel kept close to P——, whose bodyguard, the negro Jim, had obtained places for them both against the side of the wagon. After a time, however, Michel gave up his to an older man. In his immediate neighbourhood were prisoners of every class and profession: a civil servant, a mechanic, a railwayman, a bargee, a farmer, a tailor, an abbé in his cassock, and a young man wearing the uniform of an air force officer.

Few words were exchanged. The brutalising experience of being herded like cattle, the physical discomfort already felt, and the knowledge that it was only just beginning, had a dulling effect which deprived the prisoners of speech.

The abbé[1] was the first to break the silence. Raising his voice so that it could be heard by everybody in the wagon, he proposed that, as the journey was likely to last for several days, some attempt should be made at organisation. If, for example, each prisoner had a number, it would help in the fair distribution of food—always supposing that food was distributed.

There was a murmur of assent and the men at the end of the wagon started calling a number in turn. All went well for a time, then two people called the same number: after that there was confusion and the rest became discouraged.

The abbé next suggested that as numbering was too difficult they should divide themselves into two sections: his own half of the wagon and Jim's. This too was agreed to, but before it could be acted on a series of violent shocks announced that the journey had begun.

With his thoughts still running on escape, Michel had carefully noted, while waiting his turn to entrain, the constitution of the convoy. It consisted of about twenty cattle wagons, with

[1] The Abbé Carlotti. He survived deportation and is now a Canon of the Church and President of the *Fédération des Réseaux de la France Combattante*.

passenger coaches in between which were occupied by soldiers. From these a constant watch was kept on the wagons by guards armed with rifles. A luggage van at the tail, with a machine-gun on its roof, served as an additional observation post. There was a rumour that it also carried a contraption underneath, designed to kill any prisoner who dropped on the line. Nevertheless, it was known that men had escaped on their way to Germany and Michel did not despair of doing the same.

All day the journey continued with very few stops, and those only at larger stations. As the sun mounted and beat down on the roof the heat inside the wagon became insufferable. Soon the inmates were gasping for water. A few who were rash enough to eat their bit of sausage were driven almost mad by thirst.

Night brought a slight fall in temperature, but there was no relief for cramped limbs, immobilised by the congestion. One of Michel's legs was causing him acute pain, but he did not dare to ease it by lifting his foot, knowing that if he did so part of his standing space would be taken.

All his hopes were now centred in P—— and his team, and as the night wore on he waited, keyed up, for some sign that the plan of escape was maturing. After hours had passed with no news of it, he managed to get close enough to his companion to ask him what was happening. In the darkness he could not see the other two and had no idea what they were trying to do.

"We need a saw," P—— replied listlessly.

"For metal or wood?" Michel asked.

"Wood."

"Why didn't you tell me before? Here you are."

From inside his trousers he produced his hand-made saw and handed it over to P——.

"Will you be ready to-night?"

"I shouldn't think so. We'll probably have to wait till to-morrow."

Michel's heart sank. The farther they travelled and the nearer they approached to Germany, the less were the chances of success. In any case, the attempt was only possible at night, so the delay meant postponement for another twenty-four hours. In that time the train might have crossed the frontier.

The second day passed like the first, except that the prisoners were weaker. Tortured by thirst, panting for air, some collapsed, while others became feverish. Michel was carrying in his pocket two lemons which had come with his last parcel of food. By means of his saw he divided them into thin slices, which he distributed among those he judged to be suffering most. The choice was not easy as nearly all were in desperate need.

Once or twice in the day, during a stop at some station, a bottle of water was passed in surreptitiously by some Good Samaritan in defiance of the guards.

On one such occasion the bottle was being passed towards a man who had fainted. As it reached him another prisoner, a young Marseillais, seized it and started to drink. At this Michel snatched the bottle and put it to the lips of the unconscious man. While he was still holding it, the bottle was snatched from him in turn. The next moment he saw the Marseillais, his face distorted with rage, raise it with the evident intention of smashing his skull. Just in time the madman was seized by some others and disarmed.

Such incidents were common, and few of the wagons arrived without their quota of corpses.

This treatment was quite deliberate and, from a German point of view, entirely logical. Deportation had a double objective: to remove enemies of the Reich and to obtain slave labour. Hitler's Germany had no use for weaklings and one of the purposes of the journey was to kill them off. Those strong enough to survive it would also be good, it was calculated, for at least several months in a labour camp.

17. *Journey's End*

The second night arrived and again Michel waited for some sign that the plan of escape was maturing. After three hours he forced his way to the side of P——, only to be told that the preparations were held up for want of a saw to cut metal. Exasperated, Michel handed over his own.

Shortly after, the train slowed down and stopped. By pulling himself up with his arms, Michel was just able to look out through the ventilator. He read the name of the station: Avricourt. This was just inside Lorraine, therefore on German soil.[1] Avricourt was, in fact, the new frontier station.

During the long wait that ensued, the doors of the wagons were opened and a minute inspection carried out for any signs of an attempt to escape. Then, to the astonishment of the prisoners there appeared on the platform an enormous container filled with steaming coffee. Mugs were produced and every man received a ladleful.

This was against all the rules and why it was allowed was a mystery. Many months later Michel learned that it was due to the charity of the French station-master, who had obtained permission by bribing the guards with a case of champagne. Undoubtedly his action saved many lives.

It was still pitch dark when the train started again. Although theoretically in Germany, they were still among a friendly population, who could be counted on to help a French prisoner; but once the eastern boundary of Lorraine was passed the last,

[1] Alsace and Lorraine, lost to France in the war of 1870 and reconquered in 1918, were re-annexed by Germany in 1940.

chance of escape would have gone. It was, therefore, now or never.

For the third time Michel sought out P——. He found him lying on the floor, supported by his bodyguard and taking up space at the expense of his immedate neighbours, who were deterred from protesting by fear of the negro.

On seeing him approach P—— muttered some lame excuse and in a flash Michel realised what a dupe he had been: the famous escape plan was an illusion and no preparations whatsoever had been made. He had put himself, and his precious saws, in the hands of a man of straw and in doing so had thrown away his last hope of freedom.

Too bitter even to utter a reproach, he turned his back in disgust, not only at his own deception, but at the selfish disregard for their fellows shown by P—— and his bully.

His disappointment would have been even greater had he known what he only learnt later: that during the same night, while the convoy was climbing a gradient near Bar-le-Duc, a group of forty-five prisoners escaped from another wagon and got clear away, and that this was none other than the party of youths, headed by the Abbé Le Meur, to whom Michel had originally attached himself. Had he remained with them instead of linking his fortunes with P——, he too would have escaped.

It was the abbé who organised and led the break-out. During their stay at Compiègne the party had procured four small saws and with the help of these they cut a hole in the side of the wagon. As the train slowed down they jumped in turn, using blankets—also brought from the transit camp—to lessen the shock of their fall. The escape was only discovered on arrival of the train at Avricourt.

With no further stop the convoy entered Germany. At the first light of day Michel hoisted himself up and took another look through the ventilator. All he could see was a forest of fir trees, but already he had the feeling of being in a foreign country, unfamiliar and hostile.

As the sun rose the atmosphere in the wagon again became suffocating. Two days and two nights its inmates had passed, standing bolt upright, their feet touching, with nothing to eat or drink, except one cup of coffee and a few drops of water. The need for fresh air, for space to move, and above all for liquid to quench their thirst, was ever more excruciating.

The train arrived at Cologne. Through the sides of the wagon they could hear the bustle of a large station. A loud-speaker announced: *Schnellzug nach Paris.* The thought that only a few feet away there were people occupying comfortable carriages, in a train bound for Paris, filled Michel with despair. A few minutes later a whistle blew, followed by a rumble of wheels. As the express gathered speed, the sound increased, then diminished, finally dying away like a last hope.

Soon the convoy moved off in the opposite direction. All the morning it pursued its interminable course through the pitiless heat of the summer day.

At one point Michel's neighbour, a young French policeman called Max, who shared with him a place near the ventilator, announced that he had seen the sea. Michel took a look but there was nothing in sight but a vast empty plain. The sea was an illusion, like the mirage of water seen by parched men in the desert.

Later there was a heavy shower of rain. The prisoners could hear it falling on the roof—and that was all the benefit they had from it. Max managed to catch a few drops, spattered through the bars of the ventilator, and sprinkled them on Michel's face. The effect was inconceivably refreshing, he felt revived as though by a cold shower.

At the next stop there was an unusual commotion outside. They could hear the soldiers shouting in German and the noise of people running.

Hoisting himself again, Michel looked out. The spectacle which met him was fantastic. The train had stopped in open country, and some thirty or forty prisoners, completely naked, were running up and down the track in front of a group of soldiers. Each time they passed the soldiers they turned their heads and saluted. Some of the men were elderly, others emaciated, all were weak and moved with a shambling gait, stumbling on their bare feet and sometimes falling.

This was as much as Michel could see before his strength failed and he had to drop to the floor.

After a while there was more shouting, and the sounds of wagon doors being opened and closed. Finally the din died down and the train resumed its progress.

What Michel had witnessed, without realising it at the time, was the reprisal taken by the guards for the escape of the forty-five. They had waited for a convenient moment on German territory and then forced the remaining inmates of the wagon to strip and carry out the grotesque performance seen by Michel. After that, the prisoners, still naked, were distributed among the other wagons.

Hours later the train stopped again. Through the ventilator Michel read the name of the place: Bergedorf, a small junction east of Hamburg. A railway official with a gold-braided cap, presumably the station-master, was walking along the platform. Speaking in German, Michel inquired if their destination was Hamburg. Without stopping, the official shook his head, raising his eyes at the same time in a way that to Michel was only too significant.

The train started to move in the reverse direction, and after another ten minutes jolted to a stop. There were sounds of footsteps and the unlocking of doors. The infernal journey had come to an end.

A skylight in the roof was opened from above. As daylight poured in—for the first time in sixty hours—the shocking scene inside the wagon, which had been felt rather than seen, was at last fully revealed.

About half the prisoners were still standing, the rest had either deliberately stretched themselves on the floor, selfishly taking up more than their share of space, or, after sticking it out as long as possible, had collapsed from weakness, and were lying inertly, in some cases on top of another body.

Their death's head expression, haggard eyes and foam-flecked lips, told of the ordeal which those who had withstood it had undergone. They looked more like living skeletons than men—but they were still standing!

One of them was the priest, the Abbé Carlotti, whose patience and fortitude had been outstanding. As the prisoners waited in a sort of daze for something to happen, he began to say a prayer of thanksgiving for their survival. Soon the words were being repeated by other voices.

There was the sound of padlocks being opened, and then a grinding noise as the door of the wagon slid sideways. Without waiting for orders the prisoners piled out. Dazzled by the daylight and crippled with stiffness, some of them missed the step and fell the three feet to the ground. Men of the S.S. in immaculate black uniforms were waiting to receive them with whips, and a lash across the shoulders was the reward for a tumble. From now on, the deportees were to learn, this was the only language they would hear from their guards.

For three days they had been treated as no animals would be in any civilised country. Henceforth they would be treated as slaves. It was something new in their situation, to which they were already adjusting themselves.

In their innocence of what they were going to, some of them had agreed during the journey that at the end of it they would lodge a protest, either with the officer in charge of the escort, or with the commandant of the camp. They could not imagine that any person in authority would have countenanced such conditions. So little had they understood the people they were dealing with. One look at the S.S. men was enough to open their eyes.

At Fresnes and other German prisons in France, and even at the transit camp of Royal-Lieu-Compiègne, the guards had been soldiers of the *Wehrmacht*. Consisting mostly of older men called up for the war, they were civilians in uniform with normal human feelings.

But the S.S. were a different race, almost a different species, educated and conditioned for one purpose: to assure the supremacy of the Nazi State. In the process they had been de-humanised and were no longer men but monsters: brutish, violent and pitiless. Michel noticed, for example, that even among themselves they never laughed or even smiled; their faces were masks set permanently in an expression which combined stubborn stupidity with callous indifference.

The prisoners were re-formed in a column of fives. Their liberation from the wagons had a reviving effect on most, while those who found difficulty in getting up and walking were assisted by kicks and cracks of the whip, which acted like an electric shock. Even so, some of them had to be supported by their neighbours. A number were beyond any treatment and their unconscious forms or corpses were left where they lay.

The sky was grey but the rain had stopped. From the time which had passed since daybreak, Michel estimated that it was late afternoon. The place where they had arrived was in the middle of a sort of desert, with neither trees nor plants nor cultivation. Two hundred yards away he could see rows of low buildings, and, nearer, a high fence of barbed wire stretched between concrete posts. Porcelain insulators indicated that the fence was electrified. No other habitations were in sight.

The column moved off along a concrete road. In a few minutes the head of it turned right and penetrated the fence through double gates guarded by armed men. Other guards were stationed every hundred yards all along the enclosure.

The column continued past the buildings until it arrived at a vast open space, where it was halted. From here the prisoners had a good view of their new surroundings.

Two groups of buildings, each consisting of forty units, were ranged on either side of the open ground. The buildings were long low sheds made of brick and painted a sickly green. At the end of the rows two new buildings, one story higher than the others, were in process of construction. The men working on them were dressed in a variety of ill-fitting garments, their faces were emaciated and their eyes deep-sunk. Their heads had been partly shaved, leaving a bald strip, about two inches wide, which ran from the forehead to the nape of the neck. On the back of their jackets a large St. Andrew's cross was painted in bright yellow. They looked at the new arrivals with the indifference of people who have lost hope and interest.

Another prisoner, wearing a sailor's cap and rather better dressed, but whose coat was also marked with the cross, came running across the ground shouting orders. This was the *Lagerältester*, or camp leader, one of the privileged class who were given authority over the other prisoners. They were usually Germans serving a criminal sentence, but included Russians and Poles. The *Lagerältester* was their chief and responsible for the internal discipline of the camp.

Soon a small handcart appeared, drawn by two men. These were dressed like convicts in canvas suits covered with broad blue stripes. On the cart was a barrel containing a steaming liquid. Some shallow tin mugs were filled and handed to the men in the leading ranks. There were holes in the mugs where the handles had been removed which had to be blocked with the fingers to prevent the contents escaping. After the leading men had drunk, the mugs were refilled and passed to the next rank.

When Michel's turn came, he thought he could distinguish a faint flavour of lentils in the otherwise tasteless liquid. Others diagnosed chicory or acorns. But whatever it had been, the liquid would have tasted like champagne to a man who had drunk practically nothing for three days, and Michel lapped it up greedily.

While this was going on an announcement was made in German that none of the water in the camp was drinkable. Michel acted as interpreter and took the opportunity of asking the *Lagerältester* where they were.

"For your great misfortune," was the reply, "you are, like us, in the concentration camp of Neuengamme."

An order was shouted and the column started to move. After advancing a short distance the head of it reached a building, where a steep staircase led to cellars. Here the narrowness of the passage caused a block and brought the column to a standstill.

Suddenly there was a violent movement from the back. The Russian and Polish *Kapos* placed in charge of the new arrivals were beating the rear ranks with sticks. To escape the blows the men surged forward, pushing those in front, who in turn propelled the ranks ahead of them. The effect was like the succession of shocks which occur when a long goods train is being shunted. Under its stimulus the column was set in motion again and in no time disappeared down the staircase.

There followed a wait of several hours while the several thousand men stood crushed together in semi-darkness. At intervals a hundred were taken out, marched to the bath-house and ordered to strip and wash. After this their heads and bodies were shaved by *Kapos*, their own clothes were removed and they were given their new apparel: a jacket and a pair of trousers handed out at random. Of every sort and shape, from a bus conductor's reefer to the full-dress tunic of a dragoon, these ill-assorted garments were distributed with no regard to size. Though clean, they were old and usually in need of repair, with most of the buttons missing. For shoes each received a pair of oval-shaped boards with a strip of canvas nailed across. When they arrayed themselves, the prisoners looked like clowns in a circus.

Their first reaction was to laugh at their comic appearance. But the laughter sounded false; it was only the instinctive rejection of their own degradation. They were soon to discover how quickly a man who is made to look despicable loses first his pride, then his last illusions about himself, and finally his desire to live.

While they dressed in their ignoble attire, two men stood by with brushes and paint pot to implant the brand of slavery: two strokes on the back in the form of a cross, two vertical stripes on the front of the jacket, and two more on the legs of the trousers.

Finally, each was marked with a number. This was printed

with a wooden type on pieces of canvas sewn to the jacket and the trousers. Michel's was F (for French) 33948.

When this last rite had been completed they were conducted to their quarters: four blocks of barracks set apart, where they were to spend the first ten days in quarantine.

The interior of the buildings was as bare as the outside: three tiers of wooden bunks and a long table were the only furniture. The bunks were two feet six inches wide and most of them were occupied by two, and sometimes by three men sleeping head to foot. A thin mattress and two horse blankets were provided for each.

At nine p.m. the lights were extinguished and all had to be in their bunks with their trousers removed. Anyone found wearing them after that was treated as an escaping prisoner and savagely punished.

Here at last, after three days and three nights on his feet, Michel was able to lie down. In his exhausted state neither discomfort nor hunger could keep him awake, and for a few hours at least he found forgetfulness in sleep.

18. Neuengamme

With the termination of their period of quarantine the new arrivals were absorbed in the population of the camp and lost something more of their own identity.

A number of them had already been sent to other camps, and the remainder were now distributed among the eighty blocks. Each block contained between seven and eight hundred prisoners, of whom the vast majority were Germans, Russians and Poles, and the French formed a tiny minority.

The day started at four a.m., when the lights were switched on and the prisoners were aroused by the shouts of the *Blockäl-*

tester[1] and his two assistants. Each man leapt out, carrying his shoes and trousers (which he had used during the night as a pillow), and joined in the stampede to secure a place in the wash-house. Since the number of taps provided was quite inadequate, they were usually monopolised by the camp aristocracy—that is the Germans, Russians and Poles. The same people also occupied all the seats at the four dining tables, while the rest ate standing, thinking themselves lucky if they found each a place to lean against.

Breakfast over and their bunks "made" in the regulation fashion, the prisoners converged on the parade ground, where they were allowed to stroll about and mix with one another until it was time to "fall in" for work. This was the hour of the day when they could meet their friends from other blocks, exchange news and enjoy some conversation. Because of the cold, everyone kept walking, either alone or with a companion, and for a short while the vast space with its human swarm, free from any constraint, was a scene of intense animation.

Then a bell rang and the *Kommandos* formed up behind their *Kapos*. The band started to play and in turn the columns marched off. In a few minutes the last had disappeared. The music stopped and the immense grey square was silent and deserted once again.

Michel's first day in a labour gang was spent shifting heavy plates of sheet iron. These, he gathered, were used in the construction of motor torpedo boats. After two hours of exhausting work there was a break of ten minutes, during which the Polish *vorarbeiter* in charge of the gang took Michel aside and inquired about his civilian occupation.

Michel replied that he had a business supplying gas engines. The Pole then disappeared, to return shortly afterwards with a *Meister*—one of the German foremen under whose direction the labour gangs worked. After questioning Michel to test his knowledge and receiving a satisfactory answer, the *Meister* made a note of his number and walked away.

[1] Block-leader.

Later Michel was informed by the Pole that he had been chosen as a technical assistant. This was considered a great privilege as he would work apart and directly under the orders of the *Meister*. The gas engines, burning wood, were being fitted to the new torpedo boats.

To the astonishment of the Pole, Michel showed no pleasure. He regretted that he had ever mentioned his qualifications. He had not risked imprisonment for refusing to supply gas engines to the Germans, only to assist them now with the benefit of his technical experience. Somehow or other he had to get out of it.

That afternoon, while the *Kommandos* paraded after lunch, a request was made for prisoners skilled in metallurgy. Seeing his opportunity, Michel stepped forward. With a number of others he was then enrolled in a special *Kommando* designated by the name of *Metallwerke*.

The next morning, when the prisoners marched off for the day's work, Michel's new *Kommando* left the camp by a different gate. It was the first time he had been outside the wire enclosure. After passing the inner and outer fences and crossing a seven-foot moat, the column emerged into open country. To right and left a flat expanse of marshy land extended to the horizon without interruption. Not a tree nor a house was in sight, and the sky-line was only broken by the M.T.B. workshops. Beyond could be seen the canal which connected the River Elbe with the camp.

Having penetrated another electrified barrier, the column arrived at the *Metallwerke* factory, a single-story brick building in two long wings.

Here the prisoners dispersed to their various jobs, while the new recruits were interviewed by the civilian manager, before being handed over to the foremen and allocated work. Michel was put in charge of four machines which were turning out breech parts for machine-guns.

From his point of view, this was better than using his expert knowledge for the production of gas engines. All the same, and though he had no choice, it was still a form of collaboration which he was resolved to reduce to a minimum.

His quota was two hundred breech parts a day, and as a beginning he made sure that for various plausible reasons his actual production never exceeded one hundred. That, however, did not satisfy him and he therefore conceived the plan of removing from the total four parts every day. These he concealed in the pockets of his trousers with a view to disposing of them on his return to the camp.

No action could have been fraught with more danger. Sabotage by prisoners of the German war production was punished with the utmost severity. During Michel's first week at the factory a Belgian working near him was hanged before his eyes for having deliberately weakened a welding.

On its march back to the camp at the end of the day's work the column was halted by S.S. men, while a number of prisoners, chosen at random, were searched. Anything found on them which they could not have obtained in the camp was assumed to be stolen, even if it was only a tooth-brush or a razor blade. It was confiscated and the possessor punished with a savage flogging.

Time and again men from the ranks just ahead or behind Michel were singled out for searching, but as luck would have it the guards always passed him by. Every evening when he took his place in the column he had to steel himself against a possible detection which could only lead to the gallows. On two hundred and sixty-one occasions he thus deliberately risked his head.

Of all Michel's exploits this was probably the bravest, as it was the most gratuitous, and, considering its negligible effect on the war, it might well be asked why he did it. After all that he had achieved and suffered in the cause, he was surely entitled now to look to his own safety. The answer is that, being as he was, he conceived it his duty to go on fighting to the end, and this was the last weapon left to him. Had he flinched once from the risk—and he never did, not one single day—he would have considered himself almost as a deserter.

Running the gauntlet of the S.S. was not the only danger.

When he had returned safely to the camp there was still the problem of getting rid of the four breech parts. Each of them measured twelve inches by one and a half inches by one and a quarter inches, and he had to conceal the bulge they made in his trouser pockets by pulling down the front of his cotton jacket and wrapping it across his thighs.

For a time he found it a fairly simple matter to drop the incriminating objects into one of the pits dug beneath the latrines at the end of each block. But as the pits filled up with discarded breech parts, the latter were no longer sufficiently covered, and the unloading of a new lot was liable to produce a dull clang as they fell on top of their predecessors. This would be heard by occupants of the neighbouring seats, for which there was usually a queue waiting, and since many of the prisoners, especially if they were Russians or Poles, were always ready to report another prisoner, the proceeding became highly dangerous.

In search of safer dumping grounds, he was forced to range farther and farther afield—which itself was risky—and often had to wait for an opportunity, while he hung about some block with his pockets bulging, trying to appear unconcerned. He nevertheless succeeded, without ever being detected, in diverting from their proper use over a thousand breech cases, and burying them in the bowels of the camp.

For the former chief of the *réseau* "*Agir*," controlling over a hundred agents and considered by the Germans as a dangerous enemy, this petty sabotage was a sad come-down, but it was the best he could do. More important, it kept alive his spirit of resistance, helped to preserve his self-respect and with it the will to survive.

19. *De Profundis*

By the spring of 1945 the population of the camp was much reduced. In the last months many had died, while large numbers had been evacuated to other extermination camps. The Danes and Norwegians, thanks to Count Bernadotte, had been repatriated.

The prison hospital was almost empty. The most seriously ill had been transferred to Belsen. Those who could walk were put on board a goods train, which left for an unknown destination. It was learnt later that after travelling for several days they arrived at Gardelegen, where they were shut inside a large barn. This was then set fire to by the S.S., when all the inmates perished, including the Swiss doctor, Morin, who had refused to leave his patients.

One day—it must have been about the 20th April—the sound of gunfire could be heard. It brought no joy to the prisoners. None of them expected to leave the camp alive, unless it was to be herded to their death elsewhere.

On the same day the twenty thousand still remaining were assembled on the parade ground and made to surrender their mattresses. The next morning the dispersal of the camp commenced, with the departure of the *Kommandos* to different destinations.

Michel, with a compatriot, Albert Cinotti, was to go with the kitchen *Kommando*, to which he had transferred on the closing down of the *Metallwerke* factory. At the last moment they tried to persuade a friend, Gacheny, to join them, but the latter was undecided; and since their group was already moving off they had to leave without him.

With the rest of the *Kommando* they were marched to the

railway, where cattle wagons were waiting to receive them. These were similar to those which had brought them from Compiègne a year previously. This time, however, instead of a hundred, there were forty men to a wagon, and the top of the door was left open. Two soldiers kept guard in each wagon. Army reservists, they behaved without brutality.

The train started, and after passing the little junction at Bergedorf was soon approaching Hamburg. For mile after mile the landscape was covered with ramshackle huts, where the inhabitants had taken refuge from the bombing. As they stared at the train from the doorways of their temporary dwellings, with their children standing beside them, they looked more like gipsies than citizens of a great city.

The train continued across country, skirting Hamburg to the east, until it arrived at a stone quay overlooking a canal. Later Michel discovered that this led into the estuary of the River Trave, outside the port of Lübeck.

Two cargo ships were moored to the quay side by side. The prisoners descended from the wagons, crossed the first ship, which was called the *Elmenorst*, and entered the second, the *Thilbeck*, through narrow doors in its side. They then had to climb down several iron ladders to reach the lowest hold in the ship immediately above the keel.

By the time Michel reached the bottom of the last ladder the hold was already nearly filled with prisoners. It was pitch dark and he had to grope his way to find a vacant space on the sloping side of the ship's bottom. With Cinotti crouched beside him he took up a position at the extremity, next to one of the two iron ladders.

From now on this narrow perch of slippery metal, on which he could neither stand nor lie down, was to be his only resting place.

Michel never knew how long he spent in the hold of the *Thilbeck* —he soon lost count of time—but working backwards afterwards he calculated that it must have been eight or nine days at least. As the place was in permanent darkness, there was no means of telling night from day except when the manhole was opened to allow food to reach the prisoners.

When the hatch was opened to admit food, or because some prisoner—always a Pole—was required for work, Michel would sneak up the ladder and spend a few seconds on deck. He was invariably driven below with curses and blows, but usually succeeded, before he was seen, in filling his lungs with fresh air, and sometimes even managed to find some water, in which to dip his hands and splash his face.

These moments of escape from the horror of the hold, which he achieved almost every day, albeit at the cost of several beatings-up, besides benefiting his physique helped to maintain his morale. The very fact that each time he defied authority, and took the risk of serious consequences, had a stimulating effect on his mind. Like his plans for escape at Fresnes, it was something to occupy his thoughts, kept him alert and prevented him from falling into the sort of fatalistic apathy which had overcome most of his companions in misery.

For none of them had any illusions as to their future. Obviously the Germans would not have hidden them in this living tomb if the intention was to release them on the arrival of the Allies. Otherwise they could simply have remained at the camp. Stories were already circulating among the Russians and Poles of shiploads of prisoners being taken to sea . . . and disappearing.

Michel's daily sorties on deck also gave him a chance of examining his surroundings. The ship remained moored in the same place, outside the other. Standing on the quayside were two or three goods wagons, one of which appeared to be used as a sick bay. A short distance away the canal was crossed by a revolving bridge. Once, while Michel was watching, a tram passed over, filled with men and women on their way to work. The tram disappeared into a tree-lined avenue going in the direction of Lübeck. The spectacle of people still free, or relatively, filled him with inexpressible yearnings.

When the hatch was opened for the issue of food, a fatigue

party descended carrying several containers of soup. The rush of starving men was such, however, that only those nearest had a chance, and even then, since no receptacle of any sort was provided, most of the liquid was spilt.

Fortunately there had been a distribution of food parcels, sent by the American Red Cross, shortly before the dispersal of the camp. The parcels had been shared by several hundred prisoners, some of whom, belonging to Michel's *Kommando*, had had the strength of mind to save a portion for their journey. They had existed on these for the first few days in the ship, and it was the empty tins which served as mugs for the soup.

One day there could be heard through the steel side of the ship the sound of winches turning, followed by the hum of turbines. When Michel next succeeded in reaching the deck he saw that their companion ship, the *Elmenorst*, had gone, and that the *Thilbeck* was now attached directly to the quay.

A few days later the sound of gunfire which had not been heard since the departure from Neuengamme, penetrated faintly to the hold.

Shortly after there was again the noise of preparations, of winches turning and chains grinding, but this time too close to come from another ship. Soon the vibration of the hull, as the engines of the *Thilbeck* started up, confirmed that she was about to leave the quay.

While the prisoners listened in the darkness, an ominous silence fell on the hold and its fetid atmosphere grew heavy with a suffocating sense of doom. All had read the signs correctly and each knew instinctively what they portended. It was the beginning of the end of their journey.

At that moment a voice was raised. Speaking in French, very calmly, Michel addressed the darkness.

"My friends, our turn has come to set out for the unknown. We are all afraid, and I must admit that the prospect is far from reassuring. Is not this the moment to show what sort of men we are? Some of us are believers, or claim to be. This is the time to show it. We learn in our catechism what Christ said:

'Where two or three are gathered together in my name there shall I be and they shall not call upon me in vain.' Should we not remember His promise now, since we shall never have a better opportunity of showing our faith in Him?"

He paused, but nobody spoke. Something in the quality of the silence, however, told him that his words had found an echo.

"We shall now make a chain with our hands and I will pray for God's help on behalf of us all."

There was a movement in the darkness as most of the French-speaking prisoners found their way towards the spot where Michel was standing. Hand groped for hand while a circle formed round him.

Michel lifted his voice again.

"O God, from the depth of our agony, we beseech you . . . to come to our aid and remove, if it please you, the danger that threatens the people in this ship. Remove it too from those it threatens in other ships . . . and whatever happens to us, protect, we implore you, our wives and our children and guard them against all evil. . . . This, O God, is the prayer we address to you, and we beseech you humbly to grant it."

For a moment or two longer the hands remained joined. Then the circle broke up as the men returned to their places.

But for many of them at least, as they told Michel later, the atmosphere was no longer so heavily charged with fear.

Michel had scarcely finished speaking when the noises on deck, which had formed an accompaniment for his prayer, suddenly ceased. At the same time the vibration of the ship's engines died away.

For a few moments complete silence reigned in the hold, while the prisoners listened tensely for what was to come next.

Then the manhole was opened and a voice shouted in German: "All French-speaking prisoners on deck!"

There was no move—for nobody had taken it in. A few moments later the order was repeated, but in a sharper tone.

Michel, who was standing at the foot of the ladder, was the first to understand.

"They want us out," he shouted in French. "All who can speak French. Up on deck. Quick."

He pushed his friend Cinotti towards the ladder. The rest followed, scrambling across the bodies of other prisoners. Some were almost too weak to climb and Michel had to assist them. When the last man had disappeared and he saw that the manhole was about to close, he followed quickly himself.

The ship was still at the quay. On the upper deck some two hundred prisoners—French, Belgian, Swiss and Dutch—were filing past a table, where a woman of the S.S. was entering their names and places of birth in a book.

None of them knew what this portended, but there could be read on every face a presentiment that it augured well. This was confirmed when a hose was turned on and they were allowed to wash the grime from their bodies.

It was a warm spring afternoon. Michel stripped off his filthy garments and let the cold water play on his body. He could not yet believe that they were really saved. So prompt an answer to his prayer bordered too close on the miraculous. But, whatever happened, a bath was at least something to be grateful for.

Shortly after, hopes were damped again when the two hundred were shut in another hold, nearer the bows of the ship, which was already occupied by Russians and Poles. Once more closed in total darkness, their future seemed as uncertain as ever.

There was, however, one encouraging sign. For a change the Russians and Poles showed no hostility to the other nationals, who seemed to have acquired a new prestige in their eyes. The French took this as a favourable omen: the instinctive mark of respect paid by the condemned to the reprieved.

The next morning the two hundred were called on deck again. This time there could be no doubt. They were leaving. A gangway was in position and the first prisoners were already filing across it.

On the quay there was now only one wagon left. Standing

in its doorway was a tall white-haired man whom Michel recognised as a former camp-mate: an American doctor.

He went up and wrung the American's hand warmly.

"You must come with us," he urged.

The doctor made no answer but, raising his arm wearily, pointed to the prostrate figures covering the floor of the wagon. They were the bodies of his dying patients.

Michel could not wait, the column of prisoners was already moving off and he had to run to catch up with it. As he joined the last rank he looked round and saw the doctor gazing after him.

It was his last view of this devoted American.

At the end of the quay a number of lorries were waiting. The men in charge of them were not members of the S.S. and did not even look like soldiers. They wore leather belts but carried no weapons.

The prisoners mounted the lorries, which then drove off. They did not go far, however, and in a very short time arrived at another quay, where two fine merchant ships were lying.

Each was flying a blue flag with a golden cross, and her name could be read on the counter. One was called the *Magdalena* and the other *Lily Mathessen.*

The prisoners filed on board the *Magdalena*, and after descending a couple of decks found themselves in a well-lit, clean, and relatively spacious compartment. When they had all arrived a tall young man with fair hair handed to each a large ship's biscuit. It was the first solid food any of them had eaten for a week.

The impression of favourable developments became stronger. There was, however, one disturbing factor: the gangway to the ship was guarded by a German N.C.O., while an officer of the S.S. supervised the embarkation.

Several hours passed during which the other ship also received a contingent of prisoners. These were all women.

At last the engines of the *Magdalena* started up. Through the portholes the prisoners could see the widening gap as she moved slowly away from the quay. But they could also see, following in the wake of the ship, a German naval vessel, and the S.S. officer was still on board.

Soon the *Magdalena* had passed the estuary and was heading for the open sea. Rapidly the land was left behind. When it was nearly out of sight the ship was stopped and a ladder lowered over the side. The S.S. officer climbed down it and stepped on to the escorting craft, which then turned and headed for the shore.

Only at that moment did the last doubt vanish. They were no longer prisoners but free men. Someone started to sing, and with one accord Frenchmen, Belgians and Swiss burst into the *Marseillaise*.

For Michel, however, a shadow hung over the jubilation. Mixed with immense relief and thankfulness for his own safety was the thought of those who had remained in the holds of the *Thilbeck*. What had happened to them? Haunted by a foreboding of the terrible evil which he could not know was being consummated almost at that moment, just over the horizon, he found he had no heart for celebrations.

Nor was he in a state to inquire into the cause of his deliverance, which was only revealed some weeks later. It then transpired that he and his companions owed their survival to the action of one of their number, a Frenchman. This man, during the performance of a fatigue duty which necessitated his landing from the *Thilbeck* and walking some distance along the quay, had passed some sailors wearing a uniform which did not appear to be German. Thinking they might be foreigners from some neutral ship, he contrived, when he was next allowed ashore, to scratch on a piece of stone an SOS message and leave it in the path where he had seen them. It seems probable that this was read by the Swedes and resulted in the release of a small part of the *Thilbeck's* prisoners.

If so, it must have been a purely local arrangement, made between the S.S. commander and the captain of the Swedish ship, possibly in exchange for food or medical necessities in which the Germans were lacking. Had it been the result of higher orders, presumably all the French-speaking prisoners would have been released, whereas in fact only one of the *Thilbeck's* holds was opened and that in which Gacheny and many others were held remained battened down and its inmates did not even know of their more fortunate compatriots' escape.[1]

It is true that for many weeks Count Bernadotte had been conducting active negotiations with Himmler and his chief of staff, Schellenberg, for the release of all political prisoners, but up to the moment of the German collapse, although he had succeeded—in perhaps the greatest single-handed rescue operation in history—in saving nearly all the Scandinavians and some twenty-five thousand others, mostly women prisoners, from Ravensbrück, the fate of the rest was still in the balance.

It is also true that Bernadotte's main effort, apart from Ravensbrück, was directed at Neuengamme, where he had persuaded Himmler to assemble all the Scandinavian prisoners as a first step towards their repatriation. He was still working to obtain the release of the remaining twenty thousand survivors of all nationalities—of which Michel was one—when the abrupt evacuation of the camp on 18th April, 1945, dashed his hopes. All he ever knew of their fate was that they had been removed in cattle wagons for an unknown destination and repeated inquiries addressed to Thurmann, the camp commandant, always met with the reply that there was "still no news" of them. Thus it can safely be assumed that Michel's escape was due to a lucky chance, and not to any deliberate decision by the high German authorities.

One question remains. If the intentions of the Germans towards the twenty thousand were that they should disappear—and of this there can be little doubt—what was their motive? The war was lost, the Third Reich collapsing hourly, what was to be gained by adding yet another to its crimes?

The answer can only be found in the German mentality and in the determination of the Nazi chiefs, if they were to fall, to drag

[1] Later Gacheny was transferred first to the *Cap Arcona* and then to the *Athen*.

the whole world down with them. To these maniacs, apart from the natural desire to remove evidence of their crimes, the twenty thousand, up to the last moment, represented an asset, something they still controlled, and except in exchange for some advantage, such as an amnesty for themselves from Allied retribution, they were not going to surrender it. When it became obvious that the prisoners could not be used as a bargaining counter, the logical course, from the Nazi point of view, was to destroy them—as the only form of scorched earth policy still practicable. They had lost the rubber but could still take a trick. And after all, it was so many fewer enemies of the Fourth Reich which must surely arise from the ruins of the Third.

Zigzagging to avoid minefields and anchoring at night, the *Magdalena* took three days to reach the Swedish coast. On the way she passed many German warships, coming from the east with their flags at half-mast. It was rumoured that Hitler had perished, but nobody really believed this.

Many of the prisoners stayed in their bunks, having collapsed as the result of their experiences. Most of the others remained on deck, unable, in spite of the cold, to tear themselves away from the sight of the sea. Michel employed his time removing several hundred lice from his body.

Late on the third day the ship entered a small port and secured alongside a jetty. The two hundred survivors, less two who had died on the voyage, disembarked. Many had to be supported, while those who could not walk were carried ashore on stretchers. Women of the Swedish Red Cross were waiting to receive them with cigarettes.

The fittest were taken to a public bath and, after their clothes had been removed for burning, were energetically scrubbed by hospital nurses wearing protective overalls, rubber gloves and masks. They were then provided with a new suit, linen and shaving gear. The fact that the suits actually fitted was almost unbelievable. Men who had long since ceased to think of themselves as such, on seeing in their reflection decently clothed people, suddenly recovered their self-respect. It was as though with their grotesque and hideous garments they had thrown off all the shame and degradation they had suffered.

Next, postcards were distributed by the French Embassy, and, after each had written a message to his family, were collected for official dispatch to France.

Michel duly filled in his card, but, having little faith in official channels, obtained another and dispatched it to his wife by the simple method of throwing it out of the window—for fear of infection the survivors were confined indoors—and signalling to a passer-by to post it.

This precaution was fully justified by the result. The unofficial card reached Paris in five days, the other, sent through the Embassy, arrived ten days later.

However, it was not by a postcard that Mme. Hollard heard the news of her husband's escape. The day after his arrival in Sweden she received a visit from a high British official who informed her of the fact that Michel was safe and would soon be joining her in Paris. He added that His Majesty the King had been informed, had expressed great pleasure in the news, and desired to mark the occasion by graciously conferring on her husband the highest military decoration for which a foreigner was eligible, namely the Distinguished Service Order. Moreover, the visitor stated, he was charged by His Majesty's Government to inquire in what further way they could show their gratitude for the great services rendered by Captain Hollard.

Mme. Hollard warmly thanked her visitor, said she was extremely touched by His Majesty's interest and the Government's offer, but could not, on behalf of herself or her husband, accept any material reward.

Although Michel had stood up better to the ordeal than most, it was six weeks before he was considered fit to travel.

On the 18th June, an RAF plane landed in Sweden with orders to fly him back to France via London, where a special reception was being arranged for him.

Unfortunately it arrived too late. Michel had already left—though only a few hours earlier—being one of a party of ten ex-prisoners, the first to be repatriated by the Swedish Red Cross. This privilege, which he had not sought, was accorded him by the unanimous vote of his own compatriots.

To conform with military requirements the D.C.4 flew over the sea, following the coast line of Denmark, Holland, Belgium and France. During the whole of the flight, which lasted five hours, Michel remained glued to a porthole, so as not to lose an instant of the marvellous journey.

"Marvellous" is perhaps not sufficiently expressive. That he should not only be returning from an exile, which until the eleventh hour of the last day there appeared no hope of surviving, but doing so as a free man to a free country, seemed more like a dream than reality.

Over Dieppe the plane crossed the coast and, turning south, followed the direction of the main road to Rouen. Leaving Auffay on the left, it passed close enough to the V1 site at Bonnetot le Faubourg for Michel to see the effect of the RAF bombing eighteen months earlier. The place was still a mass of rubble and twisted girders.

This was the climax of the dream. To be able to look down in perfect security on the ruins of the diabolical device, which he himself had helped to defeat and which was intended to destroy the freedom he had just recovered—that for Michel was the supreme experience, the miracle, and it was still as one dazed by a miracle that, half an hour later, he stepped out of the plane to be welcomed in the arms of his family.

Carve Her Name with Pride

The Story of Violette Szabo

by

R. J. MINNEY

T.G.W.S. N

FOR TANIA

who is old enough now to read this story of her brave and wonderful mother

"She was the bravest of them all"

ODETTE CHURCHILL

Contents

ACKNOWLEDGEMENTS

I AM indebted to a large number of people who helped me unstintingly by giving me their time, their memories of Violette Szabo, letters and photographs, and for going through those sections of the manuscript which dealt with incidents with which they were familiar. Of them all my greatest indebtedness is, of course, to Violette's parents, Mr and Mrs Charles Bushell, with whom I had many talks before they went to Australia, and who have supplemented in long letters every episode on which I sought information. Miss Violet Buckingham, her cousin, Mrs Florence Lucas, aunt, and her son Norman Lucas, Mrs Winifred Sharpe, who was her girlhood friend Winnie Wilson, and Mrs Elsie Grundry, who was with Violette in the ATS, as well as the Battery Commander, Lieut.-Colonel J. W. Naylor, all helped greatly with the earlier episodes; Colonel Maurice Buckmaster, Miss Vera Atkins, Mr Selwyn Jepson gave me details of her enlistment, her training and her work as a secret agent, with very valuable supplementations from Robert Maloubier (Robert Mortier), Miss Jacqueline Dufour (Anastasie's sister), Mr Harry Peulevé, and Mr F. F. E. Yeo-Thomas. I owe my thanks also to Monsieur and Madame Renaudie and many farmers and villagers at Salon-la-Tour, to her school teachers, Miss Beatrice Hardy, Miss Margaret Douglas and Miss Elsie Lowlett, to Miss Olive Bird, manageress of the perfumery department at the Bon Marché at Brixton, Sergeant Eric Ford and Miss Eileen R. Smith of the mixed ack-ack battery, Miss Winifred Mason, of the FANYs, Mrs Margaret Edwardes of Havant, Major Roger de Wesselow, Major Stephen Stewart, Mr Jerrard Tickell, Mr Paul Dehn, Mr C. M. Gosden, Mr Bernard Newman, Miss Cynthia Sadler, Miss Jean Overton Fuller, Miss Peggy Minchin (who was her conducting officer in Scotland), Mrs Nancy Roberts, Mr Louis Lee-Graham, also a secret agent, who was a prisoner at Torgau for two years, and for the Ravensbrück scenes in particular to Mrs Geoffrey Hallowes (Odette Churchill).

ACKNOWLEDGMENTS

I am indebted to a large number of people [illegible] fortunately [illegible] and [illegible] through the [illegible] of the [illegible] which they were [illegible]. Of them all [illegible] M. and [illegible] Charles [illegible] before they were [illegible] have supplemented a [illegible] Miss [illegible] and [illegible] Mr Walter [illegible] and Mrs [illegible] Maurice [illegible] and [illegible] and Mrs P. [illegible] Thomas. I am very [illegible] also [illegible] and Martin [illegible] and [illegible] to the school teachers: Miss [illegible] and Miss [illegible] department at the [illegible] and [illegible] of the [illegible] Mrs [illegible] Bernard [illegible] and Mrs [illegible]

INTRODUCTION

This is the story of a girl, born of humble parents, one English, one French, and brought up chiefly in the back streets of London. She did not appear to be different from others. She had no discernible talents. There were no early signs of her being a prodigy either as a pianist or a painter, a singer or a dancer. She had beauty, a haunting beauty, though she did not exploit it. But there were qualities, noticeable only to a few, which, in a moment of crisis and peril, made her resolute, fearless, unresponsive under agonising torture, so that in Britain's proud story she has her place as a heroine.

In the recent war, though millions were engaged in it, individuals had mobility and were able by their ingenuity and valour to win renown. Not many women served as secret agents; the toll was high, for nearly a third of them died. This is the story of one of those who did not come back.

As you read here of her heroic exploits you will no doubt ask yourself: "What were her feelings, what were her thoughts at such moments?" She was more intelligent than many, both boys and girls, who were at school with her. Were her actions then governed by the power of her thoughts, was she able to discipline and control herself by reason? She was imaginative but apparently knew no fear, she was sensitive but not it seems to pain, and her powers of endurance were extraordinary, for she seemed never to run out of strength. Her sense of fun and mischief was not a cover in a moment of tension, for she always had these traits; and her matey-ness was not a war-time development, a drawing together in the face of danger, as happened to so many during the stress of war, even at home, in the shelters.

She was not dominating, assertive, vain or egocentric—extraordinarily enough she was not, though so many whose deeds are marked by heroism were. She must have enjoyed, one feels, the notice her beauty attracted, but she did not seem, outwardly at any rate, to be flattered by the attention of men. She seemed to take it as normal and met them on terms of unself-conscious equality, without any coyness or posturing or finesse. But one feels she must have enjoyed the experience of being looked at and admired. By becoming a secret agent she had to reverse this natural instinct, for she had to avoid being conspicuous, nor could her ego be elated by the unusual role she had assumed, for she was unable to talk of it either to her family or her friends, or to proclaim it by any badge or uniform for others to recognise and admire. She had to merge herself into the life around her, especially while moving among the simple country people in enemy-occupied France.

She was indeed simple in herself, devoid of all affectations and completely without guile. But, with the gradual deepening of her purpose beneath her outward airiness and frivolity, she developed instincts of which she had been utterly unaware. Hating domesticity, she cheerfully undertook distasteful chores and eagerly volunteered for work that she knew would be exacting and perilous. She was aware that the price for what she hoped to accomplish might have to be paid with her life; in which event others would, she knew, as readily step in to complete what she had begun. Most of the time she battled alone, and against overwhelming odds, with the cunning and might of the Gestapo and the myriads they employed for their vile tasks. By her daring and astuteness, again and again she managed to outwit them; later the battle assumed even more alarming proportions when she had to turn and fight a powerful detachment of the Das Reich Panzer division, consisting of 400 men and two armoured cars—which roused the admiration even of the enemy. But, thereafter, all the cruel weight of the German nation was used to crush her, but she remained unyielding, although even mature and valiant men have confessed their inability to endure the agony of sustained torture.

Posthumously the George Cross was awarded her. It was presented by King George the Sixth to her daughter, Tania, then a child of four.

CHAPTER ONE

EARLY INFLUENCES

VIOLETTE BUSHELL was the daughter of an English father and a French mother. Her parents met during the First World War while her father, Charles Bushell, was fighting in France. He was billeted at Camiers, just outside Etaples. Mlle Reine Leroy, slight, petite and pretty, was staying in the village too with her cousins. They met, fell in love and after a courtship carried on amid the distractions and dangers of war for two interrupted years, were married just before the Armistice at Pont Rémy, near Abbeville.

Bushell regarded himself as a Cockney, though in fact he was born at Hampstead Norris in Berkshire, where his father was a farmer and a crack shot with a sporting gun. Young Bushell joined the regular army in 1908. He spent some years in the Royal Horse Artillery, transferred to the Royal Flying Corps when it was formed, but his plane crashed and he was invalided out. On the outbreak of war in 1914 he rejoined the army, became a motor driver in the Royal Army Service Corps and was engaged in driving army lorries when he met the girl he was to marry. She, though French by birth, had a partly English ancestry, for she was descended from a Lancashire family named Scott. The war over, the Bushells came to England and their first child, a boy named Roy, was born in London in 1920.

The wave of prosperity which followed the Armistice soon spent itself and daily hundreds of men and women found themselves trudging the streets looking for work. Slowly the great army of unemployed grew. Mr Bushell, having no wish to be one of their number, decided to take his small family to Paris where he felt his energy and enterprise might find an outlet. With his gratuity he bought a large and attractive second-hand car and, using this as a private taxi, he drove visitors not only round Paris, but took them, when required, on much longer journeys. He took, for instance, an American family all the way from Paris to Venice. He had many noteworthy fares, among them the ex-King George of Greece and the much-married American actress Peggy Hopkins Joyce. Mrs Bushell was by now expecting her second child and it was in the British Hospital in Paris that Violette Reine Elizabeth Bushell was born on June 26th, 1921. She was a small baby, scarcely as big as her name. She was dark, strong and very healthy.

Mrs Bushell, taking the child home to their small apartment, looked forward to a life of ease and happiness in Paris, which she knew well, for she had worked there as a midinette and later as a dressmaker for Lucille and Paul Poiret. But they did not stay as long as she would have liked. In less than three years they were back in England. Times were not so good in Paris, and anyway Mr Bushell was glad to be out of it, for he could not cope with the language despite all his years in France during and since the war.

But with nothing definite to come to in England it was to his parents' home at Hampstead Norris that he took his family, Violette aged three by now, and the boy just over four. Once again his resourcefulness supplied Mr Bushell with an income at a time when unemployment was soaring to terrifying heights. He started a private bus service. He drove the bus himself and picked up passengers whenever hailed as he plied to and fro between Hampstead Norris and Newbury.

So Violette's earliest memories were almost entirely of the English countryside. Of Paris she retained fleeting sounds and scenes which were to reverberate as echoes when she revisited it many years later at a time of tension, for, at such times more than at any other, nostalgic memories are apt to possess one and to offer a certain melancholy solace. At Hampstead Norris she played in the garden, roved the fields, fearless of cows, bulls or even mice, as children generally are, but she was to retain this fearlessness. Papa used to place an apple on her head to Mama's recurrent alarm while he tried his prowess with a gun in the familiar William Tell manner. Fortunately he never failed, but the child did not flinch once. Nor, when, after persistent effort, she climbed by herself a lofty wall and began to walk along the top of it, did she cry when she fell off. Her head was cut open, her nose broken, but there were no tears. It was Mama who cried and fussed and carried her, a mutilated and bleeding little mite, up to her bed, and even Papa was a little pale with fright. But Violette merely smiled at them from her bed and reassured them by saying: "It doesn't hurt much—not really"—and they were to learn with the passing years that nothing ever did. She shut her eyes, said she wanted to 'go dodo' and fell asleep at once.

She was a sturdy little child, strong and always active. Nothing her elder brother attempted seemed beyond her, and she would challenge him to fresh feats of prowess which, when he failed, she would undertake herself and accomplish successfully to the astonishment of all and to his intense annoyance. "She should have been a boy," both her father and mother declared, for she was not at all interested in dolls and other girlish diversions of the sedentary kind, which is perhaps not surprising seeing that her sole companion was a boy. But they noticed also a boyish impishness, an unflagging indulgence in mischief, which earned her inevitably the tag of 'little monkey'. This apparently she never outgrew, for even in maturity this faculty for fun was undimmed. But in childhood, as later, her pranks rarely got her into a scrape: occasionally the blame was visited on another, as, for example, when she induced her father to lift her by her ankles high above his head and waltz her round the room with her head imperilled by central ceiling lights and the hard, unyielding edges of wardrobe tops and brackets. Not that she feared or evaded punishment. Those who knew her as a child remember quite vividly the way she would look right into one's eyes and say: "Yes, I did it." Nothing seemed to daunt her. She shinned up trees, making her brother Roy follow her until she got him so high that he was too scared to attempt coming down without help. He called shrilly for Dad or anyone else who could hear and with assistance was brought down again. Violette could hardly be blamed, for she had gone a great deal higher and needed no assistance at all to descend. She turned cartwheels all over the house, in the sitting-room, the kitchen, in and out of bedrooms. She was like a fire-cracker. She jumped into the river, any river, and taught herself to swim and was soon a great deal better at it than her brother.

Life in the country did not last long. The family moved to London where Papa felt he could make a better living by buying and selling motor-cars. Mama was by now expecting her third child. It was a boy this time and was named John.

Living in the close, confined, often stifling back streets of Fulham, Violette missed the freedom and freshness of the countryside, as Mama missed them too, for much of her life had been spent in the countryside in France. So she took Vi, as the child was now inevitably called, on visits to an uncle and aunt and a host of cousins of Mr Bushell's, who lived in Twickenham. Violet Buckingham, the only girl in this family, though some years older than Violette (who was given her name in its French form), remembers these visits well and in particular the first time the child stayed with her for a period of three weeks. Violette was not quite five, "but she played me up quite a bit. Once, when we were out for a walk, she ran off all by herself, in and out of various roads, with me panting behind until she was right out of sight. I was terrified that she would rush into the traffic on the main road. I called after her but got no answer and eventually, after an agony of anxiety, I found the little monkey some distance away, standing with her two arms round a red pillar box, smiling impishly at me, vastly amused at the flurry and concern she had caused.

"She had an adventurous spirit," says Violet Buckingham, "and thought running away was great fun. She was constantly doing it. She used to run remarkably well—I found it impossible to keep up with her. If she was missing for a moment I never knew what mischief she was up to or what danger she was in, either on land or in the water, for she was constantly drifting off towards the river.

"She was really afraid of nothing. I remember one day she was upstairs helping me to make the beds—or rather trying hard to. We were busy for a while, then I missed her and to my horror saw her seated on the window-sill with her legs dangling out. She was talking cheerfully to my youngest brother, who had just got back from school. When I told her to get in she refused and was about to drop on to the scullery roof below, walk along its ledge and leap down to join my brother, but I stopped her just in time and brought her back in tears into the room. I had to console her by letting her make my brother's bed into an apple-pie disorder. All my five brothers were very fond of her. They used to throw her up into the air and toss her from one to another like a ball. She thought it great fun. She used to spar quite a lot with them and went at it hammer and tongs with the youngest one who, though some years older, was nearer her own size. At skipping she beat them all. She loved getting on to the back of the motor-bike. Speed, thrill, excitement—that's what she loved. She had a temper too and a very strong will. You could never make her do anything she didn't want to. She would purse her lips together and her little chin would harden as she said—I can hear her saying it now—'I won't. I *won't*.' She said it with emphasis and determination. She had great determination—even when she grew up."

She seems to have got her determination and her resourcefulness from her father—and also her gaiety, for Mama was a quiet little woman, very charming and quite placid, taking all the knocks of life without turning a hair.

Towards the end of 1926, when Violette was five-and-a-half, Mrs Bushell had her fourth child, a boy again whom she called Noel. It was the year of the General Strike. Unemployment rose by leaps and bounds and things weren't going too well again for Mr Bushell. So the entire family went to try their luck in France. They lived this time with Mrs Bushell's relatives at Pont Rémy. This had been the scene of their marriage. There was a stir of happier memories and their hopes ran high, for expenses were negligible in the house they shared with her father and his sister, Tante Maria. Her own sister, the children's Aunt Marguerite, kept house for them. Pont Rémy is a small town with four bridges across the River Somme. Open country lies all round and not far away is the main road from Boulogne to Paris. Mr Bushell found conditions not much better here. Yet they stayed for three years. Mrs Bushell made a bit of money by dressmaking, while her husband tried his hand at this and that. But the children were growing fast and it was felt that there should be an end to this nomadic life. They decided to return to England so that Violette and the three boys might have the benefit of an English education. Violette was nearly nine now. She had received some schooling at the local convent and spoke French fluently—they all did, except Papa who still found the language quite beyond him.

In England, they roved for a further three years, going first to West Kensington, then all the way to Leicester, then back again to London to live in Bayswater. The children moved from school to school. Violette had to face the ordeal of receiving instruction in a language with which she was only colloquially familiar. She seemed an alien to the other girls, for she spoke with a marked accent. But her voice was as pretty as her face and they found it fascinating to listen to her as, with her large violet eyes wide open, she told of the fun and diversity that life offered to a little girl in France.

Papa was out almost all the time looking for a job and with Mama away most of the day, for she provided much of the income now and had to go out fitting her customers, the care of the boys fell inevitably to Violette. She had to wash and dress them and prepare a snack of sorts when she and Roy and John came back from school for their midday dinner; little Noel, not quite three, needed of course additional attention. These were among the things she did not enjoy doing, but as the only girl in the family, it was a role she had to assume. She undertook it cheerfully, for she never grumbled or sulked—that formed no part of her temperament. It helped, of course, to develop in her a sense of responsibility, of keeping to a routine, since meals had to be served at well-defined times and they had to be back in school before the bell went. But they all looked extremely clean and neat in the clothes their mother made for them and they had remarkably fine manners.

In the summer of 1932 the family went to live in Brixton where they were to remain for the rest of Violette's life. She had already, at eleven, run through nearly half her allotted span. Hitler even now stood snarling in the wings, getting ready for the grim drama in which she was to play so heroic a role.

CHAPTER TWO

BRIXTON

WHEN Mr Bushell went looking for rooms in Brixton he said, aware that landladies may jib at a large family, that he had three sons, one of whom was going to stay with relatives in France.

Mrs Tripp, who let out rooms at No 12 Stockwell Park Walk, showed him the small top flat and the family moved in two weeks later. It was then discovered that there was also a little girl. The two boys who came were Roy and John. The youngest, Noel, had been parked with Aunt Marguerite at Pont Rémy.

Mrs Tripp, a quaint soul with a most generous heart, mothered the enormous household of assorted lodgers. She had with her her own two children, now almost grown up, and a nephew and niece, both orphans, whom she had taken under her care from childhood. Of these the one nearest in age to Violette was Winnie Wilson, five years her senior and at that stage not regarded as a contemporary, for there is little that a girl of sixteen can have in common with a girl of only eleven. Among the lodgers was a German named von Kettler: he was always referred to as 'Mr Hitler', casually at first with that name so much even then in the newspapers, but constantly after the remarkable rise to power a few months later of the Charlie Chaplin-like corporal who became the Führer. How Kettler got the 'von' nobody knows; it is possible that he did not assume it since his father was a friend of von Papen's, then actually the German Chancellor and at one time a German spy. But the link was without significance, for von Kettler has no part in this story other than by his presence in the household, where he remained until the time of Munich and showed a desperate anxiety amid the flurry and excitement to return to his own home so as not to be seized and interned here in the event of a war. He was regarded by the others as very charming and was always smartly dressed in a household that was far from affluent. But Violette saw little of him for she did not mix much with the grown-ups downstairs. Her father, on the other hand, was constantly with them, playing billiards with the boys, swopping yarns, going round for a drink at the pub, gay, genial and known to all as Charlie.

The first they saw of Violette was one evening when a timid knock was heard at the kitchen door and a dark attractive little girl came in holding out some coppers in her hand. She wanted a sixpence for the gas-meter.

Winnie, who was sitting at the kitchen table working at her shorthand, remembers the moment well. "The little girl was very beautiful. Both my aunt and I gasped when we saw her and Aunt said afterwards, 'What a lovely little girl—isn't she remarkably pretty?'

"She had large violet eyes with a dash of green in them. They were very expressive eyes and seemed to change in colour. She had very long black silken lashes and two tiny beauty spots, one by the side of her mouth, the other on her chin.

"She had a small but fascinating voice. There was a marked French accent, which she later lost, but at that time one might almost say she spoke broken English. At any rate that is the impression we had. She was quite unaffected—a very natural, unspoilt child. We all got to like her very much. Aunt was particularly fond of her."

Violette and the two boys went to the school in Stockwell Road, just round the corner. It is an enormous London County Council school and takes nearly 1000 children, boys as well as girls, about a third of them juniors. The building is unattractive and stands back from the busy Stockwell Road with its roar of traffic, its buses, its many cycle shops and second-hand car marts, all painted a hideous red, its ill-kempt housewives with their shopping bags and baskets, its boxes of fruit and vegetables spilling from the shops on to the pavement, its stalls of whelks and winkles and, at that time, the buzz, flash and clatter too of large bouncing trams. Violette and her brothers had to cross the road to school, with its apron of a playground in front, its large solitary tree and high walls topped by wire netting.

Quite a large number of the children here were the children of the costermongers who sold flowers and fruit from barrows in Brixton Market. A few were the children of theatrical parents, of whom there had once been many in this neighbourhood; but their numbers had been declining for some time and were swelled only at intervals by troupes of children who performed in the evenings in pantomimes or as a dance act on the music-hall stage and were of course required by law to attend a school. A small sprinkling of the children came from the homes of policemen, of whom quite a number lived in the district and there are now even more. Surprisingly they all mixed well, if a little noisily and boisterously.

But even in this varied setting Violette stood out, partly because of her French accent and exotic mannerisms and gestures, but chiefly because she was strong-limbed, lithe and exceedingly daring. There was no drain-pipe she could not climb, no wall she could not scale, feats that were often beyond the scope of even the boys; when faced with a challenge and pitted specifically against another, to the shouted delight of them all, Violette always triumphed. It was a skill she had acquired in her endless contests against her brothers in the countryside and in the water, in England and in France, and even inside the home, for Mrs Tripp and the others found the Bushell children involved in an unceasing clatter overhead and could never determine whether the girl was fighting both her brothers at once or was merely having a game that involved a great deal of rough-and-tumble.

It is denied, even by her schoolmistress, that there was any sense of superiority or boastfulness in Violette's behaviour. She did it all confidently and quite unself-consciously, and, far from rousing jealousies and antagonism, she managed to win the admiration as well as the affection of those with whom she talked and played. "Her manner was friendly, her disposition gay and vivacious, and with those large, lovely eyes, she looked like something not quite of this world," says one of her teachers. "Indeed with her ability to speak French and her life in the French countryside of which she often talked, she seemed to many of the children to possess the key to two worlds—and yet she remained quite modest and unassuming, as though it was natural for her to be different."

The teachers found she had a quick and lively mind. Although she had already been to a number of English schools, there was still a need for much adjustment, not only in arithmetical calculations, which in her early instruction had revolved wholly round the metric system, but in the use of phrases and idioms which differed so markedly from those current in her home where she still talked a great deal of French with her mother and brothers.

"Physically she was very strong," says the physical training instructress, "she had firm and sturdy limbs and was quite outstanding in everything I set the girls to do." But at history and geography she was not quite so good, however hard she strove in those overcrowded gas-lit classrooms. At needlework, as at all other domestic tasks, such as cooking and work in the laundry, which she really detested, her progress was equally lagging.

"She vibrated with personality. She seemed to have a lot of push and drive. She was a sort of immature leader," says the then headmistress; "where she led the others followed eagerly—and the interesting thing is that she did not lead them into any mischief or naughtiness. She was indeed very amenable to discipline. Mind you, she had a strong will, but it was well controlled."

She apparently never got into trouble. It is of course possible that she contrived to be careful enough never to be caught at her innocent mischief. If indeed she possessed such early astuteness it would certainly have been a great asset to her in the work she was called upon to undertake during the war; but this is doubtful. The one thing above all else that they recall in school as at home is that she would never tell a lie. She faced up to every situation unflinchingly and at times a little defiantly.

It was before the days of school meals. The really necessitous children were collected by bus and taken off to an LCC centre where special meals were served to them. The others either ate sandwiches their mothers had packed for them or went home for their midday dinner. Violette and her brothers went home. They would not want the stigma of poverty to be applied to them, for they were proud, and besides Papa was working now for a builder he had met through the Tripps and was indeed fortunate to get a job so soon after the 1931 crisis when unemployment spread even more rapidly than before. Through good times and bad Violette and her brothers always looked well cared for and well fed. In school she wore the navy tunic and red jersey which the children wear to this day.

Going home they sometimes encountered in the street some of the rougher boys who, having finished their meal of fish and chips out of a newspaper, lay in wait to rub the greasy wrapping into the face of any passing girl. They did not, however, try this on Violette, for they must have known that, although she was always ready to join in every sort of fun, one could only go so far with her and that, when roused, she would turn and fight them with her fists, whether her brothers helped her or not. So she was allowed always to pass unmolested. In contrast to this readiness to fight like a fiend if anyone tried to get the better of her, she was generosity itself at all other times and gave away her most prized possessions if her brothers and even casual school acquaintances coveted them. But if one tried to take anything from her by force or by stealth, it generally ended in a stand-up fight and she was almost always victorious. As a result she was able to cow them with just a glare of anger and defiance. They knew that nothing would make her give way by one iota. One would not have thought, looking at this pretty wide-eyed girl of eleven or so, that she had so much determination and inflexibility in her.

The school holidays led to the children being divided up. Some went to stay with Mr Bushell's sister, who had a pub in Hereford: in the summer, Violette and one or other of the boys generally went to France to spend a few weeks with Aunt Marguerite.

Stockwell Park Walk, the street in which they lived, was a turning off the main road, not many yards from the school. It was a small street which had known better days, but now had just a few unpretentious houses. It ran down to what was once The Green, but the Astoria Cinema stood there now and the queues, when the film was popular, wound round to the back and extended almost to their front door. At night, as she lay in bed in the curtained landing that was her bedroom, Violette could hear the whoops of cowboys and Indians, the firing of pistol shots, the whang of an arrow, and of course the gay syncopation of the music on the sound track of each picture.

They lived here for three years. Noel came back from France and the flat became more crowded than ever with six in it; but Roy, leaving school, got a job as a page boy at the Savoy Hotel, where his mother often went to attend to her customers, and things became a little easier financially. Soon Mrs Bushell was expecting her fifth child and it became obvious that they would have to find a much larger place for Mr Bushell's mother had also come by now to live with them. They did not need to go far. A hundred yards or so down Stockwell Road, another turning on the same side is Burnley Road. There at No 18 they found ampler accommodation in the basement and ground floor, with a room on the first floor and the use of a small garden at the back; and here the next month still another boy was born called Richard. He was of course largely under Violette's care while her mother was at work. She attended to him at the midday interval from school and again in the afternoon when she got home. For the rest of the time the child was left with Mrs Tripp in Stockwell Park Walk.

Theirs was one of the smaller houses in Burnley Road. Winter and summer children played in the street with a ball and tore along on skates, while the smaller girls sat on the kerb and nursed their shabby cloth dolls. Violette would have joined the boys undoubtedly in their sturdier games, and possibly did when her father wasn't about, for he sternly forbade any playing in the street.

In June 1935, Violette, having reached the age of fourteen, insisted on leaving school. Nothing would induce her to stay on, much though her parents wanted her to. It was her mother's hope that she too might be a dressmaker. There was a ready income from it as they all knew, for it had sustained them through many difficult years. But try how she would, Mrs Bushell could not get Violette sufficiently interested in using her needle, except for emergency repairs. Violette's own great ambition was to be a hairdresser, to work in a shop and one day perhaps to have a place of her own, where women would come and have their hair washed and curled in new styles of her devising. Her parents, recognising it as a humdrum occupation for one bubbling over with so much personality, at last, after much persistent persuasion, agreed to let her have her own way. But various sums ranging from £50 to £100 were demanded as a premium for her training and this they were quite unable to raise. So Violette had to adjust her aspirations and be content with a job in a shop. A place was found for her with a French corsetière in South Kensington. She had to get there very early in the morning, clean out the place, make coffee in the forenoon and tea in the afternoon for the other girls, and go out delivering parcels all day long. She found it boring in the extreme, but revelled in her new-found liberty.

At week-ends and during the long summer evenings she diverted herself, as always, out of doors. She joined a cycling club and soon became so skilled that the others were no longer a match for her. Wearing shorts, even in midwinter, with her bare knees flashing up and down, she used to tear away in front of the rest on their Sunday morning outings and often would turn off to visit her cousin Violet Buckingham, who had suffered so many fluttering anxieties when Violette was left in her charge as a child. Miss Buckingham now lived at Harmondsworth on the Great West Road. Having arrived there, Violette never stayed long. After performing many acrobatic twists and turns on her bicycle she would set off with the five Buckingham boys for Burnham Beeches or for Runnymede, where she would plunge into the river and indulge in all forms of aquatic tomfoolery. They generally finished up at a pub where she loved to play darts and in time became good at that too.

At times one or more of her brothers came with her and they made a party of eight or ten, with her as the only girl among so many cousins and brothers. If the weather was wet or cold, instead of going into the country, the boys would induce her to come into London and they would go to one of the shooting galleries which at that time abounded in the West End; and at the gallery at Marble Arch or in Coventry Street or the Strand each would try to match the other's skill at winning a prize, which was generally no more than a packet of cigarettes. The boys were good at this but she had no intention of being outclassed. With her great determination and the aid of a steady hand and eye, she was able to forge ahead of them and was eventually refused a gun because she unfailingly won all the prizes.

She liked being with men. She liked the terms of easy equality, the chaffing and chipping that went on. She liked the opportunity it offered for emulation and was spurred on to greater endeavours, to see if she could not meet them on their own ground and do even better—and generally she did. She was emerging from childhood, and these were the lines along which she developed.

She very rarely settled down with a book. She was not fond of reading, but occasionally she would be seen curled up in a chair at home, her head bent as she pored over a magazine or a book that happened to engross her, and, seeking what it was, again and again her parents were puzzled by her choice, for it was not girls' stories that she read, not romances or even books and articles on sport, but stories about spies. Generally they were women spies. She read two or three books on Mata Hari and used to go round to the public library to ask for more. They wondered at the flights of fancy of this child of fourteen. Was this the sort of role in which she fancied herself with her recurrent daring and her innocent devilry? Did she, while cleaning out the shop in South Kensington and going out on her varied errands, or when changing her little brother's nappies and giving him his bottle, dream of venturing into the midst of some imagined enemy, vamping some exalted statesman with her beautiful eyes and hiding important documents in her corsage? Of course it was all nonsense and they put it down to her childish love of excitement.

She certainly caused them a great deal of excitement and anxiety some months later when she failed to return home after a long day at work. Mrs Bushell couldn't imagine where she had got to. Had she gone on to see the Buckinghams? Was she swimming in the river at Runnymede or had she gone to one of the near-by baths at Clapham or Camberwell? Perhaps she was at a shooting gallery or had gone to the pictures with one of the other girls at the shop? Surely she would have told them she was going to be late, got a message through somehow even if no one was at home. Mrs Bushell phoned the shop, but there was of course no one there at that hour, so she could do nothing but wait. Mr

Bushell, however, intended to deal sternly with Violette when she got back.

The evening advanced and there was still no sign of her. Mrs Bushell, not unnaturally, got increasingly alarmed. Had the child met with an accident? Had she been drowned? Then, her normal calm asserting itself, she wondered if Violette had gone to bed with a headache. She hurried upstairs to the little room on the first floor, but the bed was empty. Her alarm grew as she saw that the dressing-gown, the nightdress, the slippers and all the toilet fittings on the dressing-table were missing. It was obvious now that Violette had packed her things and left. She knew that Violette disliked the drab monotony of the daily round at the corset shop and with certain chores at home on top of it things had no doubt completely got her down.

But where could she have gone? In a panic Mrs Bushell rushed round to see some of Violette's friends, girls who had been at school with her and lived not far away. But none of them knew of her whereabouts. It was now getting on for midnight and the alarm of the family may be imagined if one remembers that Violette was not much more than fourteen.

The Bushells decided that it might be best after all if they got in touch with the police. They went round to the station and reported that their daughter was missing, dreading all the time that the police might already have bad news to impart. But fortunately they had none. Taking down particulars of her dress and appearance, the police asked:

"Has she any relatives she may have gone to?"

"Most of her relatives are in France," said Mrs Bushell.

"She could have gone there, of course."

"Oh no," said Mrs Bushell, "she was there only a few weeks ago."

"Has she her own passport?" the police asked.

"Yes," said Mrs Bushell. "She has her own passport."

"Do you know," they inquired, "if her passport's at home?"

"I didn't look," said Mrs Bushell, "I'll go home and see." Hurrying back she discovered that the passport was not there. The police were instantly informed and she supplied at the same time the address of Aunt Marguerite at Pont Rémy.

The police took up this trail. Inquiries made in France showed that Violette had been seen in Pont Rémy. They tried to contact Mlle Marguerite Leroy, but learned that she was no longer there. She had left a few days before for Valenciennes.

Violette, faced on arrival with this dilemma, was neither bewildered nor baffled. A resourceful child for her years, she soon surmounted her difficulties.

"Nothing ever defeated Violette," Mrs Bushell says; but she was worried all the same when another day passed without Violette being found. The child had meanwhile, although by now almost penniless, managed to locate her aunt's whereabouts and had gone on to Valenciennes where she eventually traced the friends with whom Aunt Marguerite was staying. This, in due course, was reported by the French police to the police at Brixton, and the Bushell family sighed at last with relief. But Mr Bushell was very angry.

When Violette returned she had to find a new job and jobs weren't at all easy to find at that time. Eventually she got into Woolworth's in Oxford Street where she served at the counter as a sales girl. 'Nothing Over Sixpence' was the slogan at the time, and the alleys were thronged with shoppers, particularly at the lunch-hour. Her father too was fortunate enough to fall on his feet now with an excellent job at Rotax, the firm which made electrical equipment for aircraft.

Violette, who always had a great love for music and was often as a child found humming a little tune she had heard, sung possibly by a strolling player in the street, made an effort to improve her musical education. She took lessons on the violin, but made little progress. She thought the piano might be easier and turned to that, but it was a slow and painful process, so she contented herself by going to dances where she could express herself with her limbs. Her progress at this was rapid, for she gave a lot of time to it, going to dances with her brother Roy or with one of the Buckingham boys. In a little while there wasn't a dance she could not do. She evolved steps of her own and people drew back on the dance floor to watch as she whirled past gaily. As a variant to these outings she stayed at home and joined the small card-party Mama often had in the evenings. It was usually pontoon, but Violette never had any luck at it. "She was a good loser though," says Mama, "which was just as well because she always lost."

Her cousin Violet Buckingham, who saw much of her at this stage of adolescent development, mentions that, despite her athleticism and her love for dancing, which was often almost acrobatic, she somehow escaped being either noisy, raucous or crude. She had indeed a grace and a gentleness which were quite unexpected, and very marked feminine traits, such as her love for fine clothes. In that strange amalgam within her there was a great capacity for sympathy and a tenderness which constantly showed itself, and she was able to remain perfectly calm and self-possessed when others were flurried and distracted. For example, after saving for some months for it, Violette bought herself a new bicycle of which she was very proud. She rode it all the way to Harmondsworth to show it to her cousin and was eager that she should try it out. Violet Buckingham got on, swooped delightedly along the road and on her return, while trying to negotiate her way through the narrow gate, she fell and lay sprawled along the newly gravelled drive, her knees terribly bruised and bleeding. "I felt awfully ill," says Miss Buckingham, "and could hardly move. My mother rushed out, but—and this is what surprised us—it was Violette who took complete charge of the situation. She raised me up and took me into the house. There she bathed my knees and bandaged them, then made me a strong cup of tea. About three weeks later, while we were in the garden, Violette saw a stray cat go by, limping. Picking it up, she saw that one of its paws was hurt. She instantly bathed the injured paw, brought the cat some warm milk and generally made a fuss of it. The cat would not leave after that and remained with us for the rest of its life."

It was a happy girlhood, though in view of the conditions prevailing at the time often an uncertain one. She had to take the job that was going and when retrenchment imposed a reduction in the staff she had to try to find another of a somewhat similar kind. Many thousands of girls of her age went through the same uncertainties in those years of depression and had to do without diversions and often even without necessities. But Violette kept cheerful and had fun. Her sense of mischief, given an outlet from her earliest childhood, exercised itself harmlessly in making apple-pie beds for her brothers, sprinkling itching powder in the beds of the Buckingham boys and using quite divertingly some of the things one buys at small cost for the perpetration of practical jokes, such things as a rubber mat attached to a tube which tilted your plate when you sat down to eat. They were rather childish and were not always received with laughter. Often her brothers got furious, but her air of 'do your damnedest' made them realise that it was not the slightest use for them to be physically menacing. It was better indeed to accept the joke—and they did.

In the autumn of 1937, shortly after she was sixteen, Violette went to her first ball. Her brother Roy, who was still working at the Savoy Hotel, was invited to the staff dance and he took his sister as his partner. It was a great moment for her. The whole family shared in the excitement. Mrs Bushell made her a lovely evening frock, the first long dress Violette had ever worn. It was of white satin trimmed with gold lamé. There were little gold slippers to go with it and the landlady's daughter, who lived in the flat above, gave her a gold snake necklace to wear for the occasion. All agreed that Violette looked lovely as she set out, and at the dance too she attracted a great deal of attention.

She was blossoming now into lovely young womanhood and wherever she went boys inevitably turned to look at her. In the streets they whistled after her, but she walked on unheeding. At parties the men swarmed round her. She was told incessantly that she ought to be a film star. Finding herself without work for a time, she went along to a film studio and took a job as an extra. But no director singled her out from the crowd. No offer was made to train her as an actress and, being without the means to pursue it herself, she reverted to the humdrum role of a shop girl.

But of her pretty frock she made the utmost use. With Roy or one of her cousins, John or Charles Buckingham, or Norman Lucas, Aunt Florence's son, if he happened to be up in town, she went to dance after dance and many were the rows she had with Papa if she happened to stay out after eleven at night. He refused to recognise that at sixteen one was grown up. Mama declined to take sides, but says: "She was so proud of her lovely evening gown, I could not blame her for wanting to show it off."

Without fail every year she still went to France for a few weeks in the summer. She was in fact with her Aunt Marguerite at Pont Rémy, near Abbeville, when Hitler attacked Poland on September 1st, 1939. France by virtue of her treaty was immediately drawn into the war. The holiday had, of course, to be cut short. With Violette was her youngest brother Dickie, aged only four. They had the utmost difficulty in getting a boat back, but managed, with Aunt Marguerite raising her voice amid the chaos and confusion at Calais, to get on to one that was just leaving and they arrived in England only a few hours before England too was at war.

CHAPTER THREE

THE WAR BREAKS OUT

VIOLETTE was eighteen when the war broke out. Soon after her return from France, she got a job as a sales girl in the perfumery department of that popular store the Bon Marché at Brixton. It was right in the heart of the setting with which she had been familiar through childhood, girlhood and what she now regarded as being grown up.

It did not apparently occur to her at this stage to do any war work, though all three services were recruiting girls of her age—the ATS, the WAAF and the WRENS; nor did she think of going into a munitions factory or of work on the land. Not that the war had not been brought close to her. She was in France during the stir and uneasiness of the call-up, which affected all the men at Pont Rémy and at Abbeville. At home her brother Roy joined up at once. He went into the Royal Army Medical Corps. Her father, not young or fit enough for military service, was working in an aircraft factory at Morden in Surrey. John, the brother next below her in age, was only fifteen, but he too joined up before long and went into REME. The two youngest boys, Noel, aged thirteen, and Dickie, only four, were evacuated to live with relatives in the country. Mama, being French, was very worked up and could think of nothing but the war, which had involved France twice in her own lifetime.

But Violette stayed on at the Bon Marché during that first quiet winter of the war. Despite the black-out and the rationing, and the Buckingham boys and her cousin Norman Lucas as well as two of her brothers being involved in it, the war somehow seemed remote to her. One saw, of course, many uniforms in the streets and the sky was full of those amiable silver monsters the barrage balloons, but life still went on more or less normally. One could go to the flicks or go out dancing in the evening. She did. The idea that there was something she could and should do in the war germinated extremely slowly in her mind.

She was greeted by many on her short walk from her home in Burnley Road to the Bon Marché and exchanged passing jests with them. At the shop they found her self-assured and efficient. Her accurate and attractive pronunciation of the names of the French perfumes greatly impressed the customers. There was still, happily, quite a large range of choice, both of perfumes and cosmetics, and as Christmas approached the display was widened to include fancy goods and gifts. Customers poured in all day long and Violette and the dozen or so other girls were kept extremely busy.

"She certainly had a way with her," says Miss Olive Bird, who was, as she still is, the manageress of the department. "Her pleasant, half playful manner went down well with the customers. She was a very good worker. The other girls liked her enormously, as I did too. She was really a delightful person to be with—always happy, always laughing."

The simple dress she was required to wear suited her slight, slim figure. Her dark hair, her sallow complexion and her large sparkling eyes made everyone turn to look again and come up, eager to be served by her.

She stayed until April. Then the war really got going. Denmark and Norway had been invaded by the Germans and the stir of events made her aware that she should do much more than serve in a shop. She had been seeing something of Winnie Wilson, the girl who lived downstairs when the Bushells were in Stockwell Park Walk. Though older than Violette, the difference in their years no longer mattered now that Violette was grown up. With their homes so close together, they often stopped and talked in the street and spent an occasional evening at the pictures or in a dance hall.

Discussing the war with her, Violette announced that she had decided to leave the shop. She could not stay on now, she said.

Winnie Wilson, who is now Mrs Sharpe, says: "Violette kept saying to me she'd like to do some war work. As I had had a nervous breakdown not long before, I told her: 'Don't join one of the services. I'd like to come with you and I can't do anything strenuous. What about the Land Army?'

"Vi said 'All right'. So we went together to Tothill Street in Victoria and were sent to pick strawberries at Fareham in Hampshire."

Fareham, a small market town, stands on a creek known as The Lake, which dips down to Portsmouth Harbour. All round is fruit-growing country. The girls slept in tents, about ten or twelve to a tent. There were quite a number of girls, and a small band of gipsies who lived nearby in their caravans. On a cliff just above a small pebbled beach was a solitary searchlight battery manned by a group of marines in khaki.

Violette had here her first experience of an air raid, for London had not yet been bombed and the Battle of Britain was only just about to begin.

"When the raid began," says Winnie, "the woman warden insisted that we should all go to the shelters, but nothing would budge Vi. She refused point blank to come. Everybody else went, but Vi stayed in the tent.

"Bombs were dropped and one of them hit an oil storage depot not far away. Soon the air was filled with the acrid smell of burning oil. Our warden, thinking it might be a gas attack, made us put on our gas-masks. She got worried about Vi lying there in the tent with no protection of any kind, so she went along, with her gas-mask on, to fetch her.

"She found Vi fast asleep. She shook her and shook her and finally woke her up. Vi, seeing a gas-mask so close to her face, couldn't imagine what on earth was going on. She said afterwards that it gave her quite a fright, but I don't believe it did, for she turned over and went to sleep again. Vi used to say: 'You've got to take a chance in life. All life is a chance really.' That's the way she looked at things always. She was utterly fearless."

After their day's work in the fields, Violette and Winnie and at times one or two of the others, changing from their rough dungarees to something more comfortable, would go down to the pebbled beach and lie there, jesting and talking through the long rainless summer evenings of that remarkable June of 1940. At times they sang choruses and they were joined quite often by some of the boys from the searchlight battery on the cliff who brought down a portable gramophone to which they tried to dance, but it was not at all easy on pebbles. The boys had cigarettes and chocolates which they distributed most generously and the girls in return gave them jugs full of strawberries which formed their share of the day's pickings. Occasionally they were invited by the boys to the camp and danced there in more comfort; or they went along together, a group of ten or more of them, to the nearby pub, where they played darts and drank beer. Often at night they could hear the anti-aircraft guns at Portsmouth and at Hayling Island firing at intruding enemy aircraft.

One evening, while Winnie and Violette were out for a walk on their own, they came across some of the gipsies. Winnie says one of the men, who was a little tipsy, came up to her and slipped his arm round her waist. "Come along," he said, his grip tightening. "Come along and have a drink with us."

"I was terrified. I struggled, but he would not let go. Vi was some distance behind me, but, hearing me cry out and seeing me struggling, she rushed up and, with her hands on her hips, faced the gipsy defiantly. 'Leave her alone,' she said in a sharp voice, 'or I'll let you have it.'

"I thought the others who were looking on—there were about five or six of them—would laugh at a little chit of a girl challenging a group of gipsies. But they didn't. They didn't even intervene.

"Vi really looked wonderful—pretty, but stern and quite unafraid, despite the odds against us. The man glared at her for a moment, then released his hold of me and, rejoining the others in his party, walked on with them. I thought it was amazingly plucky of Vi to do that. I was too terrified to speak or even walk. But she comforted me and helped me back to our camp."

While they were at Fareham, France fell and the war took on a much grimmer aspect. The assault on Britain by air began and the Battle of Britain was fought out overhead at intervals all day long. This made Violette conscious that such contribution as she was making to the war effort by working on the land was relatively quite negligible. She wanted to do much more and talked to Winnie of going back and joining the ATS or one of the other services open to women, even though Winnie, as she realised, would not be able to accompany her.

They returned to town. She found her mother, normally so calm and placid, most gravely concerned about what was happening in France. There had been fighting at Abbeville and all round her own home. Dunkirk followed, with further evacuations from Le Havre and St Valéry: and then came the shaming surrender by Pétain who was now trying, with Laval, to run the country from Vichy at the dictate of the Germans.

Violette had been home only a day or so when her mother said: "Tomorrow is Bastille Day—our Quatorze Juillet. There are a lot of French soldiers in London, heartbroken at what has been happening to our country. It will be a sad anniversary for them so far away from home. They will be feeling lost and lonely. Why don't you, Vi darling, go out tomorrow and bring one of them back to spend the evening here with us. It will at least be of some comfort for him to be with French people. Don't you think so?"

Violette thought it a good idea. But she was diffident about going alone on so delicate a quest. So she slipped along to her friend Winnie Wilson and they arranged to go together the next morning in search of a French soldier.

To mark the day General de Gaulle, who had escaped from France only three weeks before, arranged a parade of his Free French Forces at the Cenotaph in Whitehall, and it was to this that Violette and Winnie went in the first instance. They saw representative detachments of many famous French regiments—sailors with red pompoms on their caps, young airmen in blue uniforms, soldiers carrying their rifles against their right shoulders, a corps of women in khaki tunics and smart forage caps, crews of French tanks in their distinctive padded helmets with a pistol in their belts, and smartest of all, they thought, the French Foreign Legion in steel helmets and white knitted scarves. In a motor-coach sat a group of wounded French soldiers in their hospital blue.

At ten o'clock precisely General de Gaulle arrived; tall, lean, impressive in his blue and gold képi. He was received with round upon round of cheers from the troops, and the vast crowd of spectators joined in the ovation. Two steel-helmeted trumpeters then sounded a call and General de Gaulle laid a large laurel wreath at the foot of the Cenotaph. It was bound with the tricolor ribbon and bore the inscription *Les Français Libres*. Calling in a stentorian voice "*Salut aux Morts!*" the General came sharply to the salute. The French troops sprang to the salute too, and cried "*Vive la France . . . Vive Général de Gaulle.*" They then marched to the statue of Marshal Foch in Grosvenor Gardens in Victoria where de Gaulle placed another wreath. So great was the excitement among the onlookers that France, as represented by these men and women, should still be in the fight with us, that they broke through the police cordons and mingled with the troops. Violette was too diffident to offer her invitation at such a moment, so she withdrew with Winnie for a snack at a nearby restaurant and then they went on to Hyde Park. There, seated on a bench at one of the intersecting paths, they glanced a little shyly at the passing soldiers and airmen, most of them British, a few Dutch, Polish or Norwegian. At last a French soldier came by. Neither girl was bold enough to take the lead in initiating a conversation. While they hesitated he was gone. But soon another came along, an officer of the French Foreign Legion. He glanced at them, particularly at Violette. Still neither girl spoke and he too was gone. But he did not go far. A few yards along he turned and came past them again. Then, taking the initiative himself, he addressed them. But he must have been a little shy too, for though he had been staring hard at Violette, it was to the other girl that he now spoke. What he said was in French, which Winnie did not understand at all. He said: " Pardon me, Mam'selle, but could you tell me what the time is?"

Violette, smiling as she drew his attention to the watch on his wrist, told him the time. He laughed, and with the ice thus broken, he asked if he might sit with them on the bench. The girls agreed. They talked together for a while, at least he talked to Violette, for he knew no English, and eventually it was he who issued an invitation. He asked the girls if they would care to have a cup of tea with him.

They accepted and over tea Violette, feeling she had by now got to know him, unfolded her mother's plan. The young French soldier was overjoyed, for it was becoming increasingly clear that he was deeply interested in Violette.

The girls took him back with them to Brixton. They entered the house in Burnley Road, but found it empty. Mr and Mrs Bushell were out. The three sat in the front lounge and talked till, hearing her parents return, Violette rushed to the front door and greeted her mother excitedly with the words: "Mummy, I have brought one home for you."

Her parents had no idea what she was talking about. "Come in and see," she urged them. As Mr and Mrs Bushell entered the lounge, the French soldier stood up, brought his heels together and bowed, announcing at the same time his name. It was Etienne Szabo.

He was of medium height, well-built and good-looking. His smile, they thought, was delightfully charming. One would have put his age at about thirty. He said he came from Marseilles, but Mrs Bushell was relieved to find that he did not have the Marseilles accent.

Mr and Mrs Bushell had been at a neighbour's where, remembering that Winston Churchill was broadcasting a Bastille Day message to France, they had tuned in to listen. They came home greatly impressed by what Churchill had said. He had raised their hopes and their spirits in what was a very dark hour.

"I proclaim my faith," he had said, "that some of us will live to see a Fourteenth of July when a liberated France will once again rejoice in her greatness and her glory, and once again stand forward as the champion of the freedom and the rights of man."

They talked of it all through dinner. They could talk of nothing else. Mrs Bushell tried to recall Churchill's words, and with Mr Bushell prompting, together they recaptured some of his phrases. "Britain," Churchill had said, "would so conduct itself in the war that every French heart would glow as every British victory brought them one step nearer to the liberation of the continent of Europe." With pride and with hope the small group round the Bushells' dining-table raised their glasses to the resurrection of France.

While they talked, both during dinner and after it, Mr and Mrs Bushell could not help noticing that Etienne Szabo kept glancing eagerly at Violette after every word, no matter who spoke it, in order to note her reaction. They noticed too, and this certainly surprised them, that Violette showed a responsive interest in him. It was as yet only an awakening of interest, but it was, for the first time to their knowledge, not the general lively interest which she normally showed, but a more concentrated interest, focused directly on one man.

CHAPTER FOUR

ETIENNE SZABO

ETIENNE MICHEL RENÉ SZABO was born on March 4th, 1910, at L'Estaque, which is practically a suburb of Marseilles. He was eleven years older than Violette, which made him thirty at their time of meeting. At five foot six he could not be considered tall, but he was more than three inches taller than her. His broad shoulders made him look a little stocky, but he had a fine oval face with well-chiselled features and could justly be considered good-looking. His smile was fascinating and the women thought him most attractive. Rather shy, yet lively and playful, he had a fund of anecdotes about his experiences and his travels.

His parents died when he was very young. His father had served in the gendarmerie in Marseilles and rose to the rank of captain. Etienne, seeking a career at the early age of sixteen, decided not to confine himself to wrestling with the vice and crime of his native city, but to venture further afield. He joined the French Foreign Legion and was sent out to North Africa. Dressed in the picturesque uniform of the Legionnaire, with leather straps crossed upon his chest, baggy trousers and a white képi with its flowing linen *perruque*, he fought under the blistering sun of the desert shoulder to shoulder with men from a dozen countries—Norway, Sweden, Belgium and even Germany, some of them fugitives from justice, others soured by life or jilted by a girl, a few merely adventurous in spirit. They were drilled and disciplined and welded into an astonishingly fine fighting force.

Etienne Szabo already had behind him a dozen years of fighting. He had been in action in Algiers, Tunis and Morocco against wild and merciless tribesmen and had even fought as far afield as Syria and Indo-China. He had been wounded and his breast was abundantly decorated. To Violette, as the exploits were unfolded with a pleasing diffidence, he must have seemed a sort of P. C. Wren hero such as she had seen in *Beau Geste* on the screen. He had endured hardships and faced perils that roused her own stout spirit. These were the things she would have liked to have done too. With him in the Foreign Legion as his captain was that great French soldier General Koenig, who, when France fell, rowed across the Channel in a fishing boat, was raised to the rank of General by de Gaulle and was in command, as it happened, of the section of the Free French forces with which Etienne was now serving in England.

The outbreak of war in 1939 did not immediately involve the French Foreign Legion. They waited through the tedious months of the phoney war, wondering where and when they might be used. It was not till November that they left Africa for France. Arriving at Marseilles they had a night or two in Etienne's old familiar haunts in that city, then they were moved to a camp at Larzac and trained on the slopes to fight surprisingly on skis, for they were to be sent to Finland to assist that little country in its grim struggle for survival against the armed hordes of Russia. But before they were ready, Finland capitulated. Early in April 1940, when Germany surged northwards through Denmark and Quisling's Fifth Column brought Norway under German domination, the Legionnaires got ready once more to fight amid the snows of the Arctic.

Etienne sailed from Brest for England on April 22nd and joined the Allied expedition about to cross the North Sea. The plan was to stop the advancing Germans at Trondheim, about halfway up the Norwegian coast. But, finding the Germans too strongly entrenched there, the expedition went on to Narvik, in the extreme north, where the position looked more hopeful. Here, together with a strong British contingent which included the Scots Guards, the Irish Guards and the Welsh Borderers, the French Foreign Legion, numbering close on a thousand officers and men, were landed and were joined by the Chasseurs Alpins. To these two famous French regiments a young Scots Greys Captain was attached as British liaison officer. His name was Geoffrey Keyes and he was to win undying fame the following year by his daring raid on Rommel's headquarters two hundred miles behind the enemy lines in North Africa. There incidentally Etienne Szabo was also to go fairly soon. Geoffrey Keyes was awarded the Victoria Cross posthumously. At Narvik, with Etienne, he shared the fortunes and perils of the French Foreign Legion.

The country was wild and mountainous. A fierce wind whipped the snow into their faces and howled hideously in their ears as the Allied troops and what remained of the Norwegian Army launched attack after attack on skis. They fought against overwhelming odds. They were short of ammunition and equipment. German planes bombed them by night and by day with hardly any aircraft of our own to prevent them. Rations were often inadequate and, through a lack of billets, many slept in the open and suffered severely from exposure. The Foreign Legion in particular sustained very heavy casualties. There were incredible escapes. But they acquitted themselves well, for French morale, here at any rate, was high.

While the fight for Narvik was still in progress, the Germans at dawn on May 10th launched their attack on Western Europe. Swarms of troops rained down by parachute on Holland, Belgium and on France, ahead of the advancing panzer divisions which were supported by tanks and by planes. Soon all was confusion. By a circling move to the coast the Germans trapped the bulk of the British Army. The evacuation from Dunkirk followed. The attempt to capture Narvik was thereupon abandoned and a similar and almost simultaneous evacuation was begun there. In destroyers and transports the various regiments were brought back from Norway to the Clyde. Here on June 13th Etienne and the remmants of the Foreign Legion were landed, suffering from frostbite and fatigue. The Germans entered Paris the next day and France fell little more than a week later. De Gaulle, however, refused to accept defeat. Defying the policy of Maréchal Pétain, who was shortly to establish his Government at Vichy, he jumped into a plane and came to England to carry on the fight.

Some of the French troops brought back from Narvik to England insisted on repatriation, but Etienne preferred to stay on and volunteered for service with the Free French Forces of de Gaulle. He was sent to Liverpool for his training, was given a new uniform, British made, with the proud Cross of Lorraine, the emblem of the Free French, on the lapel. With thousands more of his countrymen he marched and drilled under the changed mechanised requirements of modern warfare. On the eve of Bastille Day he was sent up to London for the parade with a small group of Legionnaires. They were housed in the vast Exhibition Hall at Olympia and granted a few days' leave before joining their new regiment at Aldershot. It was his good fortune, he considered, that on his very first day off he should have met Violette and, seated around the table with her family, was able to converse so freely in his native tongue. Orphaned in childhood and detached for many years from any such setting, it gave him a pleasant sense of belonging. From the start he seemed to merge into the warmth of their friendliness.

They talked for hours after dinner and it became increasingly clear that it was his intention to see Violette again both on the next day and on the day after that—until in fact the time came for him to go to Aldershot.

It was very late when he left that night. The Bushells were not at all sure that he hadn't missed his last bus back. But he regarded that as immaterial. Saying good night at the door he kissed Violette's hand a little too fervently perhaps, and asked, shyly, half apologetically, if she would show him something of London.

She smiled, flushed a little and agreed at once. Her parents exchanged understanding glances and the young pair were thus launched within a few hours of their meeting upon a whirlwind courtship.

To the Bushells, as they talked about him later in their back bedroom, he seemed quite a desirable young man. He had a pleasing personality, a gay manner, and was keenly intelligent. True, he had made the army his career, but so for that matter had Mr Bushell, and they did not see anything wrong in that. He was an officer with a blaze of ribbons on his breast and a fine fighting record. He would, they felt, undoubtedly go far: one never knew but he might even by the end of the war attain the exalted rank of colonel. Violette, they knew, was not disposed to marry yet: indeed she had said on her return from Fareham, only a day or two before, that she had no intention of marrying until she was twenty-five, and that was six years away. None the less they speculated on the possible developments and indulged in the luxury of visualising their daughter living in Algiers or Tunis, visiting Casablanca, Rabat and Marrakesh, and retiring with her colonel to a small villa either in Paris or just outside it, honoured, respected by her neighbours, and with a young family around her.

Etienne met her in town the following afternoon. They went for a bus ride to Richmond, had tea there and spent the evening at the Academy Cinema, seeing a French film—just opposite the branch of Woolworth's where she used to work before the war. The next night he came to Brixton for dinner. Not many of the family were at home now. Roy had joined the army and was at Aldershot where Etienne had every intention of seeing him. John, now in his sixteenth year, had recently joined the Engineers. The two younger boys had been evacuated to the country. Grandma Bushell went up early to bed. So when the parents tactfully left the front lounge, Violette and Etienne had it to themselves.

For the end of the week Violette arranged a little outing. Into it she drew her friend Winnie Wilson and asked Etienne if he could bring someone to form a foursome. He arrived at Brixton for lunch, with a young French soldier named Marcel, who also, alas, could speak no English. So on Violette all three had to rely for inter-communication.

After the meal they left for Hyde Park by bus. It was a beautiful July day, warm and sunny. They reclined in deck-chairs and talked for a while. Poor Winnie could see the others laughing and jesting without being able to participate in it. At intervals Violette supplied a synopsised translation, but in this form, unshared, it did not appear to be funny. So they abandoned their chatter, hired a boat and went rowing on the Serpentine. Violette was good at it and won approving glances from Etienne, and Marcel too was ungrudging in his commendation. They had tea afterwards at Lyons' Corner House at Marble Arch and, walking to the bus stop, Etienne bought her an enormous bunch of roses from a barrow. Marcel followed his example and Winnie accepted his offering entirely in dumb show. Through consideration for her, they went to see an English film at the New Victoria, and Violette now had to do the interpreting for the men. This was actually Etienne's last day in town. His leave had come to an end and the following morning he left for Aldershot. He had promised, however, to write, and within twenty-four hours his first letter arrived at Brixton. He also saw to it that the link was maintained by more than the exchange of letters, for one of the first things he did on arriving at Aldershot was to call and make himself known to Violette's brother Roy.

Violette wrote to Roy. Roy wrote to Violette. Every day Etienne and Violette wrote long letters to each other. She stayed in now in the evenings to write to him and to read his letters through again and again. After a few days, since Aldershot was only thirty-five miles away, quite suddenly Etienne came up to spend an hour or so with her. Then Violette declared a day or two later that it was high time the family went down to see Roy. But before she could arrange it, Etienne came up again with twenty-four hours' leave and Mrs Bushell gave him a shake-down for the night on the settee in the sitting-room. Breathlessly the young pair told each other again the many things they had said already in their letters.

Soon things began to move swiftly. His regiment was under orders to go abroad. Pressure was at once applied by Violette on the family, who realised suddenly that it was now most urgent for them to go down and see Roy. At the last minute Mrs Bushell was unable to come, but Violette insisted that her father should accompany her. They were met at the station by both Etienne and Roy. What puzzled Mr Bushell was Etienne's strange behaviour. Etienne had apparently learned a word or two of English and was intent on trying them out on him, since no conversation in French was possible with Mr Bushell. But words like 'very good' and 'yes' cannot get one very far and, having said them, Etienne, aware of Violette's watchful eye on him, took refuge in a sort of shy laughter. He remained, however, by Mr Bushell's side and on a sudden inspiration walked him on briskly ahead of the others. This was neither to Mr Bushell's taste nor understanding. He kept turning round to inquire in an ever louder voice, as Violette and Roy lagged further and further behind, what on earth Etienne was trying to say in a very carefully mouthed and precise French, interspersed with the few irrelevant and entirely out-of-place words of English he had acquired.

But Violette was not very helpful. She seemed suddenly unable to translate. One might have surmised from this what was in Etienne's mind, but Mr Bushell remained bewildered and was quite astonished when he was taken to a remote bench and asked if he would mind sitting down for a little talk. Mysteriously at that precise moment Violette and Roy disappeared from sight.

Mr Bushell sat down and gazed about him in wonder. Etienne remained standing. He cleared his throat, straightened his tie, and poured out a volley in fast French, which was of course completely beyond Mr Bushell's comprehension. Papa looked round again for Violette, and even called to her, but she seemed to be nowhere. About to rise, he was thrust back into his seat. Etienne, straightening his tie again, began again. This time he decided to rely almost entirely on gestures. He pointed to where Violette had last been seen, placed his hand on his heart, and rolled his eyes, from all of which Mr Bushell gathered that it must be a declaration of love and that Etienne was asking for Papa's consent to their marriage.

It took Mr Bushell completely by surprise. He had been aware that a romance was developing, but he did not expect a proposal quite so soon. They had only known each other for two weeks. Less than a month ago Violette was saying that she had no intention of getting married until she was twenty-five—then along comes this fellow and bowls her completely over. Come to think of it, they didn't really know very much about him. Mr Bushell frowned as he reflected on all this, then, his mind made up, he said, speaking of course in English: "I think she is far too young. She's only nineteen, you know."

It was Etienne's turn now to look for a translator. Surprisingly Violette was near enough to have heard, for at that moment she emerged from behind some trees barely a yard or two away.

Turning to her father she fixed him with a determined eye. "Daddy," she said, "you either give your consent or I shall marry Etienne without it."

It was clear that his consent was no more than a formality

with which, as a Frenchman, Etienne felt it was important to conform. Papa shrugged his shoulders. Before he could say anything the young couple were clasped in each other's arms.

Etienne insisted on going there and then to buy a large bunch of roses for her. The ring he already had in his pocket—it had a square emerald surrounded by diamonds. With a smile he slipped it on to the appropriate finger. Over lunch the talk was largely concerned with plans for the wedding. Etienne's regiment was to sail within three weeks and the wedding would obviously have to be within the next week or so.

The date selected was Wednesday, August 21st, and Aldershot was the obvious place for it. But before then Etienne came up to town for a day and was shown off to the Buckinghams and the girls at the Bon Marché. "She was so proud of him," says Miss Bird, manageress of the department Violette had been working in not many weeks before. "She hung on to his arm all the time she was in the shop."

Only Mr and Mrs Bushell were able to go down for the wedding and Roy was there too, of course. Violette looked extremely pretty in a dark high-necked dress, a pull-on trilby-style hat and a belted camel coat. Etienne, wearing a khaki béret slightly tipped over his right ear, looked handsome and debonair. They were honoured by the presence of General Koenig himself, who had known Etienne since his earliest years in the Foreign Legion. Tall, lean, with a high-bridged nose and a small moustache, he was magnificently impressive and played the role not only of commanding officer, but almost of a father. About twenty men from the regiment came to the ceremony. Lieutenant Etienne Kiss was best man.

But they had no sooner assembled at the registrar's than the air-raid sirens went and they all had to troop out again, as the regulations required, and take refuge in the nearest shelter. There the bridal party sat uncomfortably on long hard benches facing each other. Violette held Etienne's hand and wrinkled her nose as she smiled up at him. Roy made facetious jests and each of the French soldiers in turn had a jibe of some sort at the expense of bride and bridegroom. They sat there for nearly two hours. It was for the young couple an agonising wait. They could hear the guns.

Quite a heavy fire was being directed at enemy planes. But no bombs were dropped and no planes were brought down.

At last with a sigh of relief they heard the All Clear and returned to the registrar's. It was a war-time austerity wedding and, not being in France, there were no accordions and no singing and dancing. But there was champagne and a large meal to tuck into. General Koenig kissed the bride, then honoured the bridegroom by kissing him on both cheeks. He next approached Mr Bushell, who nervously expected to be kissed too, but got only a handshake. Mrs Bushell's fingers were raised to the General's lips. Toasts were drunk and amid a great deal of hilarity and laughter photographs were taken. When the bride is beautiful, cameramen never fail to appear, but this was also an international occasion. A Free French soldier had married an English girl after a very brief courtship. Since Etienne could not speak to the reporters except in French, Violette told them proudly of his heroism in many battles in Morocco, Syria and Indo-China, of his wounds, of his decorations. Etienne's wedding gift to her was a very beautiful gold bracelet.

The honeymoon had necessarily to be brief. It was spent at a small hotel just outside Aldershot. A few days later Etienne sailed with his regiment and Violette returned to the home of her parents in Brixton.

CHAPTER FIVE

BRIEF HOMECOMING

For Violette, after the lively developments of the past five weeks, everything—her thoughts, her outlook, life itself—had changed. But the cause of the change was no longer with her and there was an emptiness all around. No more the quick exchange of letters, of hearing the bell and finding him at the front door with an armful of roses; no hurrying to catch a train to join him. Every day in fact bore him further and further away to some vague and Heaven knew what destiny.

Etienne was travelling many thousands of miles round the Cape and up the east coast of Africa. No direct passage through the Mediterranean was any longer possible. Mussolini, having come into the war on June 10th, when the fate of France was clearly sealed, had embarked on his cherished dream of establishing a new Roman Empire around the Mediterranean. He had large armies already in position for the fulfilment of this purpose—in Abyssinia, in Eritrea, in Somaliland and on the frontier of Egypt, and had the satisfaction of knowing that no French army from Tunis could any longer attack him from the rear. His aircraft, and Nazi aircraft too, had for the time being almost the whole of the Mediterranean at their mercy.

Even before Etienne and the French contingent sailed Mussolini's forces had begun to move in each of these scattered fields of operation. To which of them Etienne was being sent even he did not know. He wrote long letters home to his wife and sent numerous postcards to Mr and Mrs Bushell, to Roy and even to aunts and cousins such as the Buckinghams at Harmondsworth and the Lucases at Hereford. The cards came from Durban and from Eritrea—a simple sepia landscape for Mama, a half-nude native girl reading a book for young John Buckingham with

'Mes meilleurs souvenirs et une bonne poignée de main. A bientôt.' To them, because of the difficulty over his Christian name, he was known as Stephen. All the place-names were struck out, and the scenes remained unidentified, but a hint of the setting was conveyed in his references to '*ce pays très chaud*' and his longings—'*Je rève d'un demi de bière bien glacé*'. It was at Asmara that his regiment was ultimately landed and they made their way southwards to deal with the Italians in Abyssinia.

For Violette the solace of occasional, overdue cards and letters that arrived in batches was scarcely enough. She had to fill the emptiness with work—and yet Etienne had specifically stated that he did not want her to do any work at all. He was doing the fighting. He wanted her to live quietly at home as befitted the wife of a French officer. The allowance the Free French Army made her of five pounds a week should be sufficient for this purpose, he felt. She tried to adhere to his wishes—indeed it was her intention when he left to observe them to the letter—but she found it impossible to sit idly at home fretting, brooding. So after some weeks she took a job as a telephonist at a new automatic exchange in the City located in one of the numerous alleyways that existed then around St Paul's Cathedral. The air assault on London opened at about the same time. The Battle of Britain, begun early in July and fought chiefly above the countryside around London, leaving white streaks across the sky like ski trails, had by now been lost by the Germans, and they sent their planes to vent their wrath upon London, which it was their resolve to paralyse and if possible destroy. Indiscriminate bombing of the metropolis began early in September. Punctually as darkness fell each night the bombers came, at times they came also by day. Through it all, like millions more, Violette carried on with her work. A shelter to her was anathema, nothing would induce her to use it. She went out quite unconcernedly at night through the heaviest raids, usually to the cinema, occasionally with Winnie to the Locarno at Streatham. In this richly decorated dance hall, with its soft lights and encircling balcony, they would sit over a drink or a coffee and listen to famous entertainers like Adelaide Hall and Jessie Matthews singing to the troops, and they would dance to such tunes as 'So Deep is the Night', 'Begin the Beguine',

'The White Cliffs of Dover', and inevitably at the time 'Run, Rabbit, Run'. The place had a lively, cheerful atmosphere which helped one to forget the grim times through which one was living. Winnie recalls occasions when they had to stay at the Locarno all night because no transport could be found while the raid was on. To the clatter of shrapnel falling on the Locarno roof Violette remained of course indifferent, smoking, chatting, having more coffee and, when the dawn came, going back with Winnie to have tea in her sitting-room in front of a roaring fire.

Almost every morning fresh bomb damage was revealed all round them: windows had been blown out, houses lay in heaps of rubble, ambulances waited and search-parties dug in the debris for people buried beneath it. One morning in December, walking along Stockwell Road, Violette saw a scene of great disorder round her old school. The road was cordoned off in front. A part of the old drab building had been burnt out, leaving charred ruins against the grey sky. Where her old classroom had been there was now a gaping void. A single oil incendiary bomb had done all this damage. Three weeks later it was the place where she worked that lay in ruins, for on the night of Sunday, December 29th, 1940, the German air force made a concentrated attack upon the City. Most of the water mains were burst open by the initial assault. There then followed a downpour of land mines which left a vast wreckage, destroying entire streets, skeletonising many lovely Wren churches and damaging even the Guildhall. By a miracle St Paul's Cathedral escaped, though all around it there was the greatest devastation.

Violette and the other girls working at the telephone exchange were given a few weeks off until new premises could be found. The exchange was eventually housed in such accommodation as was available—a cold, damp cellar in which the girls had often to sit on the floor. But they carried on. Violette was more than ever resolved now to join one of the Services. The one she had in mind was the ATS, but her mother insisted that Etienne should first be consulted. He had apparently accepted her being at the telephone exchange, though one could not say that he approved of it. But there was no doubt in either of their minds that he would be livid when he learned of her being exposed for many hours of the day, and often also the night, to the damp and the cold of this cellar. As for her going into one of the Services, well—Mama just shrugged and reminded her that in every letter of late he spoke of coming home in the summer and it was obvious that he would not want, while here on very short leave, to find her posted at the other end of Scotland. None the less Violette wrote as her mother had suggested. She wanted, she said, to take a much more active part in the war. There was, she felt, something worthwhile she could do. She hoped he would feel the same way about it.

While awaiting his reply, she took a hacking cough she had developed in the cellar on a brief spell of convalescence at her Aunt Florence's place in Hereford. She had a lively time there. Her cousin Norman was home on leave and they went careering together all over the countryside on his motor-bike, with her clinging on behind. She had barely got back from this brief respite when a telegram from Liverpool informed her that Etienne was home. She packed hurriedly and caught the first train out, impatient to be with him again.

It was a great thrill to be reunited. His sudden homecoming, without weeks of anticipatory waiting, made it all the pleasanter. After a year under the tropical sun, Etienne looked bronzed and exceedingly fit. He had, he revealed, been fighting in Abyssinia. It had been a long and victorious campaign and he had emerged from it unscathed. The Emperor had been restored to this throne in May, and the Allied units there had been moved to the north to partake in the Western Desert battles. Auchinleck had by now taken over from Wavell, who became Viceroy of India. On the other side stood Rommel, who had won his reputation by his swift sweep across the Somme and in the fighting all round Abbeville and Pont Rémy where Violette had played as a child. Most of the desert wrested from the Italians by Wavell had been recovered recently by Rommel. A great battle was obviously in the offing and in this Etienne was to be engaged when he returned from his leave of only seven days.

But neither of them wanted to think of the war now. Etienne knew Liverpool well, for he had been training there for some weeks on his return from Narvik. He engaged a luxurious room in one of the best hotels and they embarked on a second honeymoon. They dined in restaurants, went to the theatre and went dancing. It was an ecstatic week, but, dread it though they both did, inevitably the morning came for their good-bye. He returned by plane to Cairo and she had to try and settle down again to the humdrum round of life without him.

But she had extracted his consent to join the ATS and, on arriving in London, went straight on to the recruiting office in Victoria to join up.

The war had now become for her much more fierce and personal. A vital part of her was closely involved in it—had been returned for a moment and was then snatched away again. They had talked a great deal of what their life would be after it was all over. He had said: "I want to take you to Paris, which you can't remember really, as you were only a child. And we will go together to the Madeleine to give thanks for our survival—that is, if I survive." He had added this with a smile, and she had kissed him fervently to reassure herself and him: of course he would survive, she could not bear to contemplate the alternative. They had talked also of having a family and had argued playfully over the number of girls and boys there should be. And now he was gone, many thousands and thousands of miles away, to fight with who knew what outcome.

CHAPTER SIX

WITH THE ACK-ACK BATTERY

VIOLETTE joined the ATS on September 11th, 1941. She got her first uniform and, though only a private, was proud of the opportunity it gave her to serve. After being put through all the processes that recruits have to endure, but without a rifle, for girls were not allowed them, she was sent on to Leicester, where she had lived as a child of eight, not quite a dozen years before. Parts of the town were consequently familiar to her. She had been to a local council school, one of her very first in England, and she had been in and out of the shops with her mother. Now, with the other girls in the ATS, she enjoyed a number of evening diversions and dances, especially arranged for men and women in the forces.

The work she was called upon to do did not particularly appeal to her. It consisted of the usual chores that are assigned to women, such as cooking, waiting at table and attending to the laundry. She had heard, however, of a plan for using women in anti-aircraft batteries, not on the guns, but to aid and direct the guns by operating predictors, height-finders, and other instruments. An experiment along these lines had in fact been started not many weeks before in view of the increasing shortage of men. It was regarded as successful and women were accordingly invited to volunteer for such work. Violette was among the first to join. She felt in a way that she was following in the footsteps of her father, who had begun his military career as a gunner in the Royal Horse Artillery.

The battery to which Violette was posted was Battery No. 481(M). It was under the command of Major J. W. Naylor, who had himself served, like Mr Bushell, in the RHA. He went to France on the outbreak of the Second World War, returned shortly before Dunkirk and was given command of an anti-aircraft battery in western Scotland, where enemy attacks were constant and lively. His appointment now to take charge of a mixed battery was not at all to his taste. He did not welcome having under his control 'a bunch of giggling females', as he phrased it, and regarded it as hardly the way an old soldier could be expected to serve his King and country. To us now this attitude may seem old-fashioned and stuffy, but it should be remembered that girls had not, save in this recent experiment, been used yet in active warfare with artillery. Those who then knew Jim Naylor would stoutly deny that he had in him even a hint of the blimp mentality: for one thing he was only in his early forties, and they knew that behind his keen efficiency lay a light-hearted and jovial personality; and to them at any rate it was not surprising that, after he had worked with the girls and had begun to know them, he should develop a regard and even an admiration for their enthusiasm and skill. "There was no hardship the men faced that the girls weren't prepared to endure," he says. "Their devotion to duty was really remarkable and I found that, though slow starters at everything that was technical, they became in time just as efficient as the men."

The battery, composed entirely of recruits, was assembled at Oswestry in Shropshire, in the third week of October 1941. The girls outnumbered the men. Some, like Violette, were shop girls, others were secretaries or had worked in factories; there were also children's nurses and school teachers with university degrees. Others had come straight from their homes. A few were married —one was the mother of four children. Such was the raw material Naylor had to train and shape into an efficient fighting unit. He was aware that critical eyes were upon them, watchful for such embarrassments as might arise from the close association of large numbers of men and women, who, besides working together, were to share their hours of relaxation and diversion. The position was undoubtedly delicate. Wisely he laid down no stern and rigid restrictions, but decided to deal with eventualities as they arose. He was greatly assisted in this by Junior Commander Vida Torry and her two ATS subalterns Blanche Johnson and Diana Hewitt, who always ignored irregularities that seemed to be merely departures from normal army standards and accepted the laughter, the gaiety and the good humour as part of the more varied life of a mixed unit.

Adjustments also had to be made in the attitude of the men. The battery sergeant-major, for example, on being told that the ATS officers ought to be addressed as 'ma'am', decided to ignore the direction. He felt outraged at the very presence of women in the camp and declined to admit even to himself that they were there. So whenever one of the ATS officers addressed him, he sprang to attention, saluted and said: "Yes, sir." Naylor had a long talk with him about this, but it made no difference. Every woman officer remained 'sir' to him until the end of the war.

Violette attracted unwittingly a great deal of attention from the outset. The impression seemed to have got around that she was really a member of the Free French Forces, to which her slight French accent lent some colour. There were whispers that she had contrived to come out of enemy occupied France, had undergone many adventures and had some very narrow escapes. In their eyes she became in consequence something of a heroine, but she soon dispelled this by informing them that it was her husband who was serving with the Free French and that she herself was only half French and had been free anyway. She sought neither the glamour nor the glory of the heroine. They were drawn to her by her frankness and modesty and liked her because, as one of them says, she was gay, vivacious, intelligent and very pretty. She had a great sense of fun. Her eyes used to dance with mischief when the thought of playing a prank came into her head. They were innocent pranks, schoolgirlish in fact, as, for instance, when she put her foot on the fire hose and, just as the sergeant-major peered into the nozzle, threatened to lift her foot and let the water spurt right into his face.

They had Nissen huts to live in, the girls segregated in one group, the men in another. But in the general canteen there was no such separation. The good-natured chipping between the sexes soon developed into a warmth and friendliness, and after supper, if a mobile film unit or ENSA entertainers were not visiting them, they danced or put on an improvised show.

The exaggerated hip movements of the girls on parade, which made them rather like a musical comedy chorus, were corrected and they were sent out on long route marches. All wore trousers, always scrupulously well creased; lipstick was only allowed off duty; and the canteen now carried an extra line of hair nets, vanishing cream and other feminine requirements.

A series of early tests revealed what each girl was best fitted for. Some were made cooks, others were put on to clerical and administrative work. Violette was not only relieved but highly excited when she was selected to work a Vickers predictor. It would give her a chance to make a direct contribution. The bombing she had experienced in London she would now be able to answer. Working in a team of six girls, of whom she was quite the smallest, she could barely reach the telescope and appeared always to be standing on tiptoe while operating her predictor. None the less she proved to be extremely good at following the target and always got the men right on the mark. This and other indications of her efficiency finally dispelled the doubts at first entertained by Naylor as to whether a girl so small and light-hearted would make a good soldier. At his weekly inspections he always found her smart in appearance, her bed and her kit were well looked after and beautifully laid out. "She was more pains-taking, more eager to please, than the rest," he says, "and my pats on the back made her flush with gratification. She was unselfish in the extreme. The team spirit was strong in her. Girls in her unit who were in need of her guidance were shown by her just how their own things should be attended to, with the result that her hut was the best kept of all the huts in the battery—and I include in that all the men's huts as well.

"She was a gay little thing and her gaiety was most infectious. In whatever we were doing, in every new phase of the battery's life and its varied activities, Violette was always the leading light. Yet she never pushed herself forward or tried in any way to be regarded as better than the rest. Whatever had to be done she was eager that they should all do it together and that it should really be done well.

"She had, it will be seen from this, despite her gaiety, both an earnestness and a sense of purpose. She was aware that the times were grim, that tragedy had touched many millions of lives in Britain, in France and elsewhere on the continent of Europe. That same menace hung over her husband and so far over two of her brothers.

"She was particularly proud of her husband. She asked me whether, in view of the fact that he was fighting with the Free French Forces, she might be allowed to wear the Free French flash on the shoulders of her battle-dress blouse. Permission to do this was obtained and when the flashes were sewn on, one detected a sort of swagger as she swung her shoulders while moving about the camp.

"She made friends easily. Her comrades in the battery had come from all sorts of homes, many of them extremely humble, like her own. Violette was friendly with all of them, not only the other girls on operational jobs, but even with those who were cooks, drivers, telephonists and clerks."

She wrote and told Etienne of all this, her letters not quite so long now, but still full of amusing details. He was back in the Western Desert, getting ready to take part in the long-awaited offensive against Rommel. Inexplicably the attack kept on being deferred, although, with the Germans so heavily engaged on their Eastern front ever since they plunged into war with Russia, it seemed undoubtedly a good time to strike. But not until the middle of November was the attack at last launched. Our blow had immense weight and we made some headway. But within three days Rommel counter-attacked and drove us all the way back. Our tanks seemed to be no match for the Germans. We suffered a series of reverses and for a time even the safety of Egypt was at stake. Rommel was, however, halted eventually and the tide was turned suddenly in our favour. Tobruk, still held by us in the heart of enemy-occupied territory, was relieved. Rommel stopped to lick his wounds and there followed a gratifying pause. But one realised that soon, inevitably, it would all flare up again.

Early in December, by the Japanese attack on Pearl Harbour, the war was extended to many new fronts and a powerful ally, America, was brought in on our side.

All through the autumn the weather at Oswestry had steadily worsened. It became bitterly cold. Snow lay thick on the ground.

Often it rained heavily and the girls marched with their hair hanging in rats' tails.

After some weeks of this the battery was sent to a practice camp at Anglesey where their operational skill was put to the test. Using their predictors and radar location, the girls assisted the gunners to aim at aerial targets towed by planes. The weather there too was appalling, but nothing damped their ardour, least of all Violette's. The camp commandant, greatly pleased with their progress, granted them extended home leave before putting them on operations. Violette returned to the parental home in Brixton and had a month to go about and see her friends. She saw Winnie of course and went to the Bon Marché to show off her uniform to the girls. Eager questions were asked about Etienne and promises were extracted that he would be brought there again on his next home-coming.

The battery reassembled at Crewe station a week before Christmas and moved on to join the Mersey anti-aircraft defences in one of the most active bombing areas in the country. One half of the battery was stationed at Alvanley, the rest, Violette among them, at Sutton Weaver, seven miles away. They had an air raid to deal with on their very first night.

Coming for the first time into a fully operational area a new unit is apt, possibly through a nervous over-eagerness, to run into certain unforeseen difficulties, such as giving a false alarm of enemy raiders overhead. It brought most of the Mersey defences into action with nothing to hit at. There followed inevitably a good deal of bitter sarcasm, but Violette took it all with her customary cheerfulness. Her jesting at moments of stress, without a sign of fluster or concern, happily proved infectious and helped to allay the misgivings of the battery commander as to the girls' ability to face up to real danger. Violette's behaviour, he states, had an admirable effect. The exclamatory gasps and shrieks, the loud-voiced *ooh*-ing and *aah*-ing to which girls are so often addicted, slowly gave place to a more orderly, one might almost say a disciplined, good humour.

As an example of her comradeship and influence on the others, he cites the occasion when one of the girls, an ATS spotter, seeing an unfamiliar type of plane overhead, sounded the alarm. Both

Britain and the Germans, he states, had new types of aircraft which closely resembled each other. The alarm brought them all to action stations and just as they were about to fire, the error was detected. An inquiry was ordered and the distress of the ATS spotter was great. But Violette allayed her fears. "You cannot be blamed for doing what you considered was right," she reassured her. "It might easily have been an enemy plane, and it was your duty to report it."

The brigade commander, Brigadier V. R. Krohn, came down to the gun site. Violette, standing with the others, watched the frightened little spotter as, trembling a little, she came before him. She glanced quickly towards Violette. The other girls stole a glance at her too, as though half expecting her to intervene. But the brigade commander was understanding and just. After listening to the girl's halting explanation, he congratulated her on acting so promptly on her suspicions. Her face flushed in relief; once again she turned to Violette as though to say, "You were right! I need not have worried after all." Incidents of this kind reveal the tremendous popularity Violette enjoyed and the confidence she radiated.

The alarm went almost every night. They rushed from their beds, their eyes heavy with sleep. Often, struggling into their coats as they ran, they stumbled and fell into a cabbage patch in the darkness. Once, arriving during a raid, the battery commander, Major Naylor, saw Violette busy at her predictor, dressed in pale blue pyjamas and a pair of red slippers; from her shoulders hung her greatcoat; on the back of her head was perched her tin hat. At times the action lasted for three hours or more. The girls at the instruments had no cover at all and were liable to be hit by a falling bomb and by shell splinters—indeed one girl working a predictor in another battery was killed shortly afterwards in this manner.

Their time off was admirably divided between sport and other diversions. At first the girls kept to basket-ball and net-ball, but later they joined the men in their games of soccer. The evening dances were lively, but quite the gayest and most hilarious of their diversions were the concerts they put on themselves. Violette took part in almost all of them, singing at times (she had a pleasant little voice), or acting in some of the sketches, but often it was a solo dance of her own evolution, with exotic and acrobatic touches that were excruciatingly funny.

Not only on the stage was she diverting. Elsie Bean says: "Violette was always in the lead when it came to fun. She worked hard and she played hard. She was full of vitality. She always had to be doing something. I remember she started a class to teach us all French." She had to get the battery commander's permission to do that. It proved a most successful venture—men as well as girls went to it. They got both instruction and diversion.

The battery came to be regarded as a model one and there was a constant flow of visitors. The GOC-in-C, General Pile, came down to inspect them. Shortly afterwards Miss Rosita Forbes, well known for her travels in the Near East, in Afghanistan and in India, spent a few days with them so that she might refer to their work in the course of the lecture tour she was about to undertake in America. There followed a host of journalists and press photographers from London. The BBC sent a recording van and arranged a broadcast which showed the girls at work and at play, with a singsong in the canteen as the finale.

Early the following April Junior Commander Vida Torry, the battery's senior ATS officer, reported to Major Naylor that Violette had asked for her discharge as she was expecting a baby. Naylor says: "I had a chat with her before she left. She was of course very excited about having a baby. She had heard that her husband would be getting leave soon and returning from Libya to be with her. She hated leaving the battery—that was obvious—but she had no choice. She promised to keep in touch with us and to return as soon as her baby was old enough to be left. But long before that Violette volunteered for far more perilous duties.

"The battery was most distressed at the prospect of losing her, for she had become quite a personality in our small circle. But that she would come back none of us believed. A few, surprisingly enough, seemed to feel that she would be going on to do bigger and even heroic things. But of this, I am quite sure, she herself was completely unaware at the time."

Shortly after she left, the battery was moved to the gun site in Hyde Park in London and was visited there by the King and Queen, by Field-Marshal Smuts, and many times by Winston Churchill, the Prime Minister, whose daughter Mary had joined it by now as a subaltern.

CHAPTER SEVEN

TANIA

HER mother and father were, of course, greatly excited at her news and looked forward with an ecstatic eagerness to the arrival of their first grandchild. They had filled Violette's room with flowers for her home-coming and insisted on her having breakfast in bed for the first few days at any rate, since she was not prepared to let her mother wait on her. Noel, the third of her brothers, had gone into the Navy a few months before on reaching the age of fifteen. Dickie, seven now, was still in Hereford with Aunt Florence, away from the bombing, and Grandma Bushell had gone to live there too. So, with the two elder boys already in the services, there were only her parents at home now.

She had written to tell Etienne the joyous news as soon as she was sure, but with the delays to which their letters were subjected, it was only now that his reply reached her. He was overjoyed. He intended, he said, to do his damnedest to be with her when the time came. "Don't be surprised," he wrote, "if you find me standing at the door one afternoon when you answer the bell." He told her to find a place that could be a home for the three of them. A flat, he felt, would not be difficult to get, with London so empty. She had herself felt this would be the best course. Despite all the kindness her mother would shower on them and the discomforts her parents would gladly put themselves to, there was really not very much room in the Brixton house even with the boys away. She did not want her child to have the narrow, confined setting that she had herself known in her childhood. Things were easier now. There was the money from Etienne which the Free French paid her regularly. She talked it over with Mama, who agreed that it would be best from every point of view if she got a flat of her own.

Violette set out eagerly on the quest. She wanted it to be in town, for, although the child could not be kept there, or in Brixton for that matter, while the bombing continued, it would be better for her and for Etienne while he was on what would inevitably be a very brief spell of leave, to have it near the West End. She went first to Bayswater, which she knew well during the months she had lived there as a child. Not far from their old home, in a wide street known as Pembridge Villas, which sweeps towards Notting Hill Gate, she found a small and attractive flat and for some weeks she was pleasantly employed in furnishing it. Going from store to store, though furniture was not too plentiful, she got, mostly on hire purchase, beds and tables, settees, carpets and china.

The time of her confinement drew near. The child was expected very early in June. But there was no news of Etienne's home-coming. She knew from the newspapers something of what was going on in the desert, though not of course in how much of it Etienne was involved. The glorious successes achieved by Auchinleck in November had forced the enemy back to Gazala and eventually to El Agheila. But towards the end of January 1942 Rommel had managed again to win back most of the ground. There followed a pause. But, at the end of May, Rommel struck again.

During the first week of June she went into St Mary's Hospital in Paddington, and there on the 8th her child was born—a girl, small and dark as she herself was, and very like her, everyone said, but with just a look of Etienne. She named the child Tania.

Soon after leaving the hospital, urged not to keep the child too long in a bombing area, Violette took Tania down to Havant, not far from Fareham, where she had been working on the land during the first summer of the war. She had heard that a Mrs Margaret Edwardes had a small nursery for babies evacuated from various danger zones, and she went to see what the place was like. She found Mrs Edwardes charming and kindness itself. The house, Yew Lodge, was comfortable and everything was extremely well run. Violette stayed for some weeks with her and bought a pram in which she wheeled Tania through the surrounding country lanes, rich with the scent of summer.

Violette returned to town, greatly worried at not having had a letter from Etienne for some time. She did not know that he had been bottled up in Bir Hakim with the rest of the Foreign Legion. Bir Hakim lay less than fifty miles south-west of Tobruk. General Koenig was in command of the French forces there and British confidence in him and his men was very high. On the night of May 26th-27th, a few days before Tania was born, Rommel, attacking by moonlight, succeeded in encircling this stronghold. Its retention by the Allies was regarded as vital. The French clung on desperately, though attacked incessantly by air and by land. But, after a time, inevitably their supplies began to run out and it became increasingly difficult to replenish them. After a fortnight's most valiant resistance, it had sadly to be decided that Bir Hakim must be evacuated. So once again, as at Narvik, Etienne had to be withdrawn from a position which, despite many sacrifices, could no longer be held. The fierce fighting took a terrible toll. But, hard pressed as they all were, there was no chance of a respite, and the remnants of the Foreign Legion, after being speedily re-grouped, were sent to reinforce the greatly depleted strength of the Eighth Army.

It was not until much later that Violette learned of this. She heard too at last from Etienne. He went into lyrical raptures over the birth of Tania, asked endless questions and poured out his paternal longing to take the child in his arms. That this would be possible soon he still had no doubt, for, despite the critical situation in the desert, he seemed as confident as ever of coming home. "For Tania's sake, if no other—though I long just as much to be with you—they must, without more delay, grant me this leave—from compassion for a father longing to see his first child."

But, try hard though he did, Etienne was not able to get leave. Rommel's successes were causing the gravest anxieties. After entering Bir Hakim, he attacked the British forces to the north and turned our flank. There was a culminating tank battle which lasted two days. At its close, as Winston Churchill has recorded, the enemy were masters of the field. Home leave could obviously not be granted in these circumstances. Etienne wrote again to say that in three months perhaps it might be possible for him to be with them. That would make it early in October. More sanguine than that he could not be.

Violette returned to Havant. She decided to bring Tania back with her. The recurrent journeys to Hampshire took too long. She wanted her child nearer at hand. A friend of hers, Miss Maidment, who lived at Mill Hill, had offered to keep the child with her. She was young and gentle, and would undoubtedly look after Tania well. Moreover, Violette could get there quite easily and in no time at all. For herself, her plan was to live in the flat, for it was there that Etienne would be writing to her and that was where he would come, without possibly any warning at all.

The newspapers, however, offered her little hope. She read that the Eighth Army was in retreat again and had been driven back into Egypt. On its heels came Rommel with his Afrika Korps. The situation became increasingly grim. Auchinleck took up a new position 150 miles inside Egypt in the Qattara depression, and soon Rommel thrust at our forces there. So widespread was the general concern that Winston Churchill flew out to Cairo early in August to see for himself what could be done to halt the enemy. The chances of Etienne's home-coming now seemed exceedingly slender. Yet in September Violette heard that leave had been granted. He hoped to be with her early the next month.

Greatly excited, she busied herself in the flat, preparing his welcome. Provisions were bought. She planned to have roses in every room because of his great love of them. And friends were told to be ready for a party the moment Etienne arrived.

But the days passed without further news. A battle was expected almost daily at El Alamein. This was to be Montgomery's first great thrust and wisely he planned it with the utmost care. It was expected at the end of September, but it had to be deferred. Churchill cabled: "A victorious battle makes amends for much delay." He had to wait nearly a month for the attack, which was launched at last on October 23rd, 1942.

In the opening round of that historic engagement, which marked the turning point of the war in the desert, Etienne was severely wounded. An enemy bullet, fired it may well be by one of the Germans who had served with him in the Foreign Legion and had been allowed by the Vichy Government to join the German Army for this war in the desert, tore into his stomach and it was soon found that the wound was mortal. Etienne died of his injuries twenty-four hours later.

Violette did not learn of this until months afterwards. She waited, meanwhile, still hoping that his leave had merely been delayed by Montgomery's stirring successes, and that one day, quite unexpectedly, she would find him on the door-step. She continued to write to him. Her letters were wholly about the child, the progress Tania was making, her first smile, so radiantly lovely, her halting efforts to say "Da Da". She waited for his answers, but of course none came.

Living alone, she wandered often amid the scenes of her own childhood in Bayswater, revisiting the familiar streets, seeing again at every turning little sights that had once delighted her. But the old watchman, with a red lamp outside his shelter, was no longer there to offer her one of the sausages he was cooking for his supper, and, in the rows of houses around, the bombs had torn many gaps.

As the weeks passed she began to have doubts, wondering if he was wounded, if by some awful mischance something worse might have happened. She could no longer bear to be alone. She locked up the flat and went back to Brixton to live with her parents. Again and again she called in person at the Free French headquarters in Carlton Gardens to ask for news of Etienne. But they had none, no news at all of him. "We have your address. We shall write," they said, "the moment we hear."

At her father's urging, so as to take her mind off things, she agreed to go to the aircraft factory at Morden where he was working. They were glad of the extra help. She applied herself earnestly, though her mind was in a turbulence of uncertainty. The one encouraging thought, indeed assurance, for her was that he must have been taken prisoner, for that usually was when one did not hear. In the general confusion caused by Montgomery's magnificent advances, little could be known about prisoners. She clung to that one hope but, pursuing it by her inquiries at the Red Cross and elsewhere, she was able to learn nothing.

That, despite the doubts and misgivings that agitated her mind, she did her work well at the factory is supported by the evidence of those who worked with her. In no time at all she was put in charge of a section. At home, however, her father and mother were only too aware of her listlessness and her despondency. "If anything has happened to Etienne," Mrs Bushell told her husband, "it will be terrible for her."

The news came at last and its effect was shattering. Violette was unable to go on with her work and stayed at home in utter dejection for some days. Then quite suddenly she announced to her father: "I'm leaving the factory. I want to do more—much more in this war." Surely there was some way—she felt there must be. She wanted to fight with a gun in her hand—and the women's services did not let you do that.

What had she in mind, her parents wondered? For some weeks they were aware only of her restlessness. She went up to London day after day, came back late in the evening, when she came back at all. She was entirely uncommunicative as to what she was doing or trying to do.

"She'll settle down," said Mrs Bushell, trying as always to look at the pleasanter side. But Mr Bushell was not at all sure. He feared that, reacting to the shock, she had gone to the other extreme and was abandoning herself to a life of diversion—the theatre, dancing in the evenings, out till the dawn in night clubs. He didn't like it. He didn't like it at all.

CHAPTER EIGHT

THE INTERVIEW

THERE is no doubt that the shattering news about Etienne threatened to affect her outlook and her entire future. But she was not left to her sombre and melancholy reveries for long. A week or so later she received a brief and baffling letter signed 'E. Potter', a name she had never heard before. It invited her to come to an address in Sanctuary Buildings, Westminster.

She said nothing of the letter to her parents, although it was at their home in Brixton that it had arrived for her. On the appointed day, inquiring her way, she went to Great Smith Street, and found Sanctuary Buildings, a massive and hideous nine-story block of grey stone, not far from Westminster Abbey. She entered No 3, as directed in the letter, and was met in the spacious front hall by a man wearing the ordinary uniform of a commissionaire. There was nothing to suggest that the place had any link at all with the war, except perhaps in its aftermath, since it seemed to to be chiefly used for housing the Ministry of Pensions.

Violette asked for Room 531 and, after filling in a form on which she had to state her name and address, she was taken up by an attendant. Here she saw, seated at a table, a slightly-built gentleman in his early forties, wearing a quiet lounge suit. The room was starkly functional, for it was furnished, in spite of its size, with one plain deal table and two equally plain chairs and absolutely nothing else. The dingy cream walls were quite bare except for a large notice dealing with Air Raid Precautions; the windows were boarded up, either because they had been blown out or in expectation of being blown out. So the light came from one bright, naked electric light bulb in mid-ceiling.

Potter stood up, greeted her in a friendly, relaxed way, gave her the visitor's chair and sat down again behind the table. She still could not see anything about him or the room to suggest that his interest was connected in any way with promoting the war effort or that his work could be valuable or at all strenuous. Her anticipations accordingly dwindled.

But Potter was in fact concerned with the war in a very close and intimate way. He was not actually Potter at all, but Captain Selwyn Jepson, of the Buffs. Before the war he was a successful writer of mystery stories and the son of an equally distinguished writer, Edgar Jepson. Several of his books had already been filmed and later others were to be adapted for the screen by that mystifier Alfred Hitchcock. But he was not sitting in this uncomfortable room to discuss mystery stories, although one might say he was here to cause other people to live them. He had been seconded from the Directorate of Military Intelligence to an organisation as secret as the work it did.

It was his particular job to find secret agents. He had scouts on the look-out, but even they did not know for what purpose he wanted men and women with a knowledge of France and fluency in speaking French. From the Admiralty, the War Office, the Air Ministry, from the Central Bureau of Registration at the Ministry of Labour and National Service, and other less official sources, names were forwarded to him. In this instance he had heard of Violette from his liaison with the War Office. He had asked in the usual way if she might be sent up from her ATS unit for an interview, but had been somewhat taken aback by the reply. He was informed that, since her name had been passed on to him, she had been discharged from the ATS on compassionate grounds. Compassionate grounds? Security forbade his asking what these were, since that kind of curiosity from him might interest the ATS branch in his activities—and he did not want that. It could of course mean that there was something wrong with her health, or that she had been urgently required to help at home because of someone there who was ill and dependent on her. Actually her own physical fitness was absolutely essential, since the work for which she was required would be both tough and dangerous. However, his need being great at the time, he wrote to her at her home, a letter of sufficient vagueness to conceal its ultimate purpose.

He had two addresses at which he interviewed such candidates—this one at the Ministry of Pensions in Sanctuary Buildings and the second, a room at the Victoria Hotel in Northumberland Avenue, then occupied largely by the Quartermaster-General's directorate. There was a third address, a flat in Orchard Court, the large modern block in Portman Square, but this was not used for interviews, only for seeing agents who had already been selected and were about to begin their training; and every precaution was taken so that they should not meet those secret agents who had just returned from operations abroad.

This secret organisation had been set up very soon after the fall of France. In that grim summer of 1940, while many in Britain saw in the sad fate of the great French nation nothing but a fulfilment of their fear that the French could not really be relied on, there were others who regarded that judgment as unjust and severe. In their view, it was not faintheartedness or cowardice that had made the French Army crumble, but lack of tanks and aircraft to stem the formidable onrush of the German panzer divisions. They foresaw rightly that the people of France, who are intractable and unruly when driven, could not live tamely under the iron heel of Nazism, however masked by a show of correctness. This was soon confirmed. Of the British soldiers taken prisoner at St Valéry, some managed to escape and were greatly assisted in their journey across enemy-occupied France by the French people. They were given clothes, food, shelter, and even money. Again and again the people of France displayed their readiness to risk their lives in order to aid the cause of Allied victory. It was even more abundantly confirmed by the incessant flow to Britain of French refugees who were eager to carry on the fight under General de Gaulle. They reported that small groups were springing up in various parts of occupied France, resolved on resisting the enemy by whatever means they could. Some pounced on German sentries in the dark and slit their throats, for which many who were innocent paid with their lives in the heavy retribution exacted by the Germans.

It was with Churchill's famous directive to 'Set Europe in flames' that the work began of encouraging the many Resistance movements which were springing up all over Europe in the wake of the German advance. These movements, if haphazard and unco-ordinated, if left without arms and equipment, would have achieved only self-destruction. So an organisation was created in London to assist them. It was nominally under the Minister of Economic Warfare, but was answerable to its own Chief of Staff. Norway, Holland, Belgium, Yugoslavia, Italy and Greece each had their own section, but of them all France was by far the largest and most promising for such operations. Recruitment had necessarily to be conducted with the greatest care, since German spies were obviously infiltrating with the crowds of refugees from France.

General de Gaulle's Free French organisation also began to function in the same way but on a more limited scale. The two, however, were kept apart for security reasons, and only rarely had direct contact with each other or engaged in mutual activities. Yeo-Thomas, who was known as 'The White Rabbit', was exceptional in having first served with the Free French.

The French Section of the British organisation—its full title: 'Special Operations Executive' or SOE—was formed in February 1941 and came under the control of Captain Maurice Buckmaster. Buckmaster had before the war been working for the Ford Motor Company in Europe. He knew France well and was admirably suited for the work he was about to undertake. He had gone with the British Expeditionary Force to France as Intelligence Officer, had been evacuated at Dunkirk, and was about to return to France, for our army was still fighting at St Valéry, when he was sent with the de Gaulle expedition to Dakar in French West Africa. The plan was to rally the African possessions of France under the flag of freedom. But a leakage led to the Germans informing Pétain of it and arranging for him to resist de Gaulle's landing. Following an unfortunate scuffle outside Dakar, de Gaulle went on to French Equatorial Africa and established himself there. Buckmaster returned to England.

A few days after Buckmaster came to the French Section he was joined by Miss Vera Atkins, who also knew France exceedingly well. She kept in close and constant touch with the agents from the moment of their recruitment, throughout their period of training and even after their dispatch to France.

The earliest recruits were soon under training, each with his *nom de guerre*, and in the course of three months went from one specialised course to another until they were ready for 'the field'. They were sent to France in fishing boats, landed by submarine, or dropped by parachute. At first they had no reception committees to meet them but had to pick up such threads as they could, and they faced, of course, very grave dangers, not only from the vigilant Germans, but also from many French people, who were constantly being roused by the Vichy Government against Britain's attempts to bring the French Navy, and overseas dominions in Africa and elsewhere, into de Gaulle's fold. There was indeed a great deal of bitter feeling in France over the incident at Oran, where, to prevent some of the finest French battleships from falling into German hands, a British naval force went to beg them to join us. When this was refused, our warships opened fire to deny them to the enemy. A heavy engagement followed, in the course of which the French battleship *Bretagne* was blown up, the *Dunquerque* ran aground, and the *Provence* was beached by its crew. So great was the wrath of Pétain over this that in retaliation he ordered the bombing of Gibraltar. Many in France were sadly bewildered. They could not imagine what they had done to deserve these fresh misfortunes at the hands of their recent Ally. Fortunately these doubts were not generally prevalent. The majority of the people in France were clear in their purpose, which was to free their country from the Nazi oppressors. The earliest of our secret agents found sixty per cent of the people well disposed towards the Allied cause, quite a large number of these were in fact prepared to help us. Only about twenty per cent were decidedly hostile, a large enough number, amounting in all to many scattered millions. The remainder were anxious only to keep clear of trouble and would not take sides one way or the other, fearful not only of life or liberty, but of the confiscation of their possessions.

Moving with caution, our agents managed to weld the scattered and unorganised resisters into small effective groups. Each group, or circuit as it was called, needed a leader and as a rule the agent, trained to do so, took on that role himself. It needed also as an essential a small portable wireless transmitting set in order to keep in touch with the headquarters in London. Radio operators were already being trained in England for such work and small portable transmitting sets were being specially made for this purpose. Specified times were arranged for the transmission, generally twice a day. They were in code, of course. The voice was not used; the signals were in Morse. In London a group of operators, similarly trained, received these vital messages, giving information of inestimable value about war factories and railways and troop movements, and were sent in return clear directions for various forms of sabotage, which became in time a grave and baffling problem for the occupying Germans.

Our earliest agents, landing without any contacts at all, had to grope their way carefully. Several were caught and tortured by the Gestapo, who sought to wrest from them the secrets of their underground work. But those who escaped detection laid the foundations of a vast network that was in time to cover all France and was of the utmost importance in the conduct of the war. They greatly aided the Allied armies of liberation after the landings on D-Day, as will be seen.

The earliest agents had to make their own way back to England as best they could, coming across the Pyrenees and Spain or being picked up at night by a submarine or a fishing boat, if somehow or other they had been able to get a message home. But as each circuit was formed a more direct contact was established. Our agents landed by parachute on selected fields provided by sympathetic farmers. Reception committees were formed to guide the drops with prearranged light signals and, where the field was large enough and conditions favourable, it was sometimes possible to land a plane. Small Lysanders, able to fly slowly at low altitudes, were used for this purpose, and were guided in on a short wave signalling call. An almost regular ferry service was in time established in this way. Many French men and women, scientists needed for war work, and others being hunted by the Gestapo, were contacted by our agents and brought to England in the returning planes. It was a Scarlet Pimpernel service on swift up-to-date lines.

The Germans knew of course what was afoot. They had detector vans constantly on the prowl to locate the radio transmitters, catch the operators and learn from them by every means they could employ the time and place of these landings. Some operators were caught, others had to go into hiding for a time. And the landing-places had constantly to be changed.

As the field of operations widened it became obvious that more and more agents and wireless operators would be required; and it was eventually decided to recruit girls for such work. Vera Atkins says there were heated discussions when this was first suggested. But women were in fact ideally suitable, especially for such jobs as wireless operators and couriers, since they were likely to attract less attention in enemy-occupied country than men, of whom there were naturally very few about at the time: millions were prisoners of war in Germany, and, as those remaining had known jobs on farms or in factories, new faces in any area were all too noticeable.

The recruitment of women as secret agents began in the spring of 1942, just a year before Selwyn Jepson, as E. Potter, wrote to ask Violette to come and see him in Sanctuary Buildings. Sitting behind his bare table, with a single sheet of paper before him on which he pencilled an occasional note, he began his exploration in a quiet, gentle voice.

He says Violette looked older than the twenty-two years she gave as her age; she had a certain maturity of poise and expression that made her seem twenty-six or seven. She seemed healthy, even strong, and he soon brought her to the subject of her release from the ATS on compassionate grounds. He asked if she felt quite well again.

"Yes," she said, "thank you."

"Was it anything serious?"

"No," she replied, thinking of the near-to-breakdown stage she had recently reached on learning of Etienne's death.

"May I ask what was the matter?"

"My husband was killed at El Alamein. I'm afraid I took it rather badly."

This surprised him. He had been given to understand she was *Miss* Szabo.

"Were you married long?"

"No. In fact we were together for only a very few weeks."

"I'm sorry. How very sad . . . and now you're living with your parents?"

"Yes."

He went on to ask her about her life before the war and gradually learned more and more about her. He felt that her qualifications were excellent for the work he had in mind.

Then she asked a question. "What did you want me for?"

"I was thinking your knowledge of France and your fluency in French might be very useful."

"In what way?"

"Well," he said, "it comes under the heading of dangerous work."

She received this with the momentary silence to which he was accustomed. They generally guessed now, or came very near it.

"You mean—spying?" she asked.

"No. This is different, but in some ways the conditions are similar. It calls for special training as well as special qualifications, and, after that, it means moving about, living, and doing this particular job, in enemy-occupied territory."

"In France?"

"In France, where we are trying to make things as unpleasant and difficult for the Germans as we can. Sabotage in fact—from blowing up their troop trains and immobilising their commandeered factories to putting chalk in their ink." His eyes were serious in spite of the light note at the end. "And," he said, "they don't like it. They react violently and brutally."

He knew what he was talking about and so did she, now.

"That would suit me very well," she said without hesitation.

This bothered him. Immediate, unqualified, unquestioning acceptance was always disappointing. And yet there was nothing casual or irresponsible about her that he could detect.

"It would? Why?"

She thought, but only for a short moment, and said slowly: "I wouldn't mind dying the way he died."

This worried him even more. It sounded too much like self-immolation, not a motive to encourage and certainly not one in which to involve other people. An agent in these better organised days worked seldom on his own.

"That seems to put rather an emphasis on dying," he said. "We want our people to live, not die. To live and fight the war. So you see how difficult it would be to have anyone around who saw a situation as a possible means of rejoining someone she had lost through death."

"I did not mean that," she said. "You mentioned danger. I only wanted to make it clear that I am prepared to face danger—of that kind. It is true I have felt since my husband's death that I have little to live for. But if the work you give me is worth while in the sort of way his was, as a soldier, I shall have a great deal to live for, and if it ends as it ended for him—well, that's all right too."

There were times when the burden of this job he was doing was heavier than at others, and this was one of them. Humanly, he could have wished her less good-looking. She was too pretty altogether to talk of death, let alone consider it.

But he had to be reassured, and was. The clarity no less than the quickness of her analysis showed it was genuine. He felt she would make a good agent, even a very good one, if all went well. He asked her the next question. Had she anybody dependent on her?

She hesitated a moment. "Both my parents are alive," she said. But not a word came from her about her child. Had Jepson known that afternoon, he feels now, looking back on it, that he would have stopped the conversation there. "The loss of her husband outweighed everything, even her motherhood—desperation which I should have seen as weakness. But, as it turned out, she derived strength from her training and from integration with the small group of men and women with whom she was trained for the work. Indeed she reacted in this way to a remarkable degree and the death-wish business (which after all was in the comparative safety of her consciousness and not buried somewhere deep inside her) completely cleared up, and that was all I was really worried about.

"In the same way, as her preparation progressed, she was carried over the apparent indifference to the child by a true dedication to what she had chosen to do. It was bigger than she was, bigger than anything else. The self-immolation prospect disappeared. I am sure of that. If it came back it would have been only at the end, when it would have been a comfort and a strength. Nothing less."

But he did not know about the child until much later, by which time she had so convinced everyone of her enthusiasm and capabilities that no one could have been deterred from letting her go through with it. "Violette gave us all the belief that she would be successful."

He ended this first interview with her by saying: "I'd like you to think this over very seriously indeed, and let me know in about a week whether it's the sort of thing you want to undertake. I don't have to tell you that you must think all this over alone. The security on this is absolute."

"I don't need to think it over," she said. "I know it's what I want to do. I can tell you that now."

"Well, I'd like to think it over myself," he replied. "I'll write to you in about a week's time." His intention was in any case to obtain a full clearance on her from MI5 before he went any further.

He got up and held out his hand.

"May I," she asked, "have your telephone number?"

He gave her the general number of the Ministry of Pensions, and first thing the next morning she used it, the call being rerouted through at least three switchboards to his line at the Baker Street headquarters of the French Section of SOE.

"Have you decided?" she asked.

"Not yet," he replied. "As I told you, I'll let you know in about a week."

The call indicated her eagerness, but he knew of that already. He hoped all the same that it would not prevent her thinking it over seriously; he did not want her to have second thoughts against it, but he wanted her to have second thoughts before her final decision was made. His problem was that there were very few as qualified as she was among the many who passed through his net.

A week or so later, having received the all clear from MI5, he wrote to her from No 3 Sanctuary Buildings, in order not as yet to reveal any other address, and he still used his cover-name of Potter. A second interview was arranged at which he indicated that, although she obviously could not serve in France in uniform, it was important under international law that she should be given a Service position of some kind. He explained that in due course she would have to be enrolled as an officer in the First Aid Nursing Yeomanry, familiarly known as FANY. This was an independent voluntary corps of women, formed in 1907, the year the Territorials came into being: in that year women were also able for the first time to become aldermen and mayors. Those anxious to serve in this new corps were given instruction in First Aid and in riding. It was primarily regarded as an adjunct to the ambulance service and women were expected to go into the fighting line on horseback and bring back the wounded to the ambulance stations. They rendered admirable service during the First World War. Many displayed the greatest bravery under fire and won a number of decorations. Since 1939 the FANYs had been running motor ambulance units in Finland and in France; they also drove ambulances for the Red Cross, served in Forces canteens in Britain, and acted as chauffeurs for officers of the British Army. At the prospect of invasion in 1940 many were put on to packing explosives for the Home Guard or for dispatch to the underground forces in occupied Europe. To this extent their work was closely allied to the work Violette was now called upon to do. SOE was served by a Motor Transport Section of this service, and the machinery for enlisting the women agents into it was already in existence. It provided an excellent cover for them while they were training in Britain—and, when the time came for them to go into the field, it was still useful, since the FANYs were known to be serving in all the theatres of the war abroad and in none of the other women's services, recognised by the Army Act, was it permitted for women to carry weapons. So in due course Violette was commissioned as an officer in the FANYs. She was made a subaltern and wore one red 'raspberry' on her shoulder-straps.

Her parents meanwhile, completely unaware of these developments, could hardly be blamed for wondering why Violette was doing nothing after saying she wanted to take a more active part in the war. To them, though several weeks had gone by since she left the aircraft factory at Morden, she still appeared to be doing nothing at all. And in fact for some weeks, until she was finally accepted, she had been doing nothing. Since the news of Etienne's death, she had been living only on the small pension paid by the Free French. Out of this she had her child's keep at Mill Hill to pay for and there wasn't enough over for the rent of her flat and her own living expenses. Again and again she debated whether she should not give up the flat and go back to her parents, but, if the appointment came, the flat she felt would be a useful centre. The financial strain, meanwhile, was great. She was aware that, with the acute shortage of labour, it would be easy to find work at a more ample remuneration than she could hope to get for the dangerous work she was to undertake. But she preferred to wait, and eased the strain by taking on odd jobs, such as helping out for a few hours in a shop and being a photographer's model. The one thing she was determined not to do was to miss the opportunity of becoming a secret agent. So she waited. Her cigarettes she always got for nothing at the shooting gallery at Marble Arch where she had won them so often before.

Then at last came the appointment and she went down to Brixton in her new uniform. She looked very smart and everyone assumed that she would now be happy, having obviously found the more useful and active war work she wanted. But just how useful and active she was to be only she and a handful of people knew.

CHAPTER NINE

INITIAL TRAINING

EARLY in September Violette arrived at Sanctuary Buildings for her third interview and was taken by Jepson to Orchard Court in Portman Square. There in a four-roomed flat, which had been in private occupation before the war and was now sparsely furnished with a table and a few chairs in each room, various discussions seemed to be in progress. Some were busily talking in the kitchen, others in the bathroom. A group of about a dozen, about to embark on their initial training as secret agents, waited in what was once the drawing-room. They were all in uniform, the girls dressed as FANYs, the men in the uniform of some corps to which they were nominally attached. It was at this stage that Jepson introduced Violette to Buckmaster and to Vera Atkins, who had walked down the short distance of a hundred yards or so from the headquarters of SOE in Baker Street. There was a short impersonal talk on the aims of the organisation and the purpose of the training. Then each was allotted a distinctive Christian name by which he or she was to be known at the first school. That name would be changed as they progressed to further courses. This was done in order to make it difficult for other agents or unauthorised people to keep track of any individual members from one stage to the next. Violette, in the course of her training and her work, had in all six different names—Louise, Reine, Corinne and so on—but for the purpose of consistency and clarity she is called Violette throughout this narrative.

The talk over, the group, accompanied by two escorting officers, one for the girls, of whom there were only four, and the other for the men, set out by coach for Wanborough Manor, an attractive old country house standing in a very large garden a few miles outside Guildford. The nearest village was quaintly, and in Violette's case significantly, called Normandy.

Here they were received by Major Roger de Wesselow, tall, elegant, every inch a Guards officer, who was before the war head of an organisation connected with books on form in horse-racing. The new batch had the place to themselves. There was no overlapping with pupils from a previous group, for every month saw a fresh course begin. There was one training officer, two NCOs to assist him and the two escorting officers who kept the trainees under friendly but searching scrutiny and reported constantly to Jepson who was responsible for weeding out any who were unlikely to prove suitable. Everything mattered: all the personal idiosyncrasies, aptitudes or lack of them; temperamental reaction to their companions, to strain and tension, to success and to disappointment.

The house had large bedrooms, which they shared four or five to a room. The beds were most comfortable. The food, which was supervised by a French cook, was exceptionally good and plentiful. They were allowed special rations and the larder was stacked with a variety of good things not normally available at the time. As de Wesselow says, it was in some ways a drawing-room life. The aim was to put them all completely at their ease and in a relaxed mood, so that, at this early stage, many would be seen off their guard and much might be learned of their true spirit and outlook.

Violette and some of the others, despite what Jepson had said, were convinced in their own minds that they were about to become spies. But in fact, beyond the assumption of an alias and later the evolution of a new identity, with their normal backgrounds completely obliterated, there was nothing in the training approximating even remotely to any preconceived ideas one had of Olga Polowsky and other famous spies of song or story. To that extent it must have been disillusioning to some. They were told, of course, that on their behaviour and circumspection would depend not only the success of the operation they were to be sent out to undertake, but even the lives of their comrades. One had therefore to be secretive without being suspected and this undoubtedly offered some solace as being a little along the lines expected.

De Wesselow, assembling them, indicated that there would be lectures as well as both practical and physical training. They were taught map-reading, signalling in the Morse code, the handling of weapons, such as revolvers, rifles and hand grenades, a knowledge of explosives and their most effective application for purposes of sabotage, and they were put through the initial stages of parachute jumping, confined here chiefly to the art of falling without hurting oneself, a technique derived largely from the comedians of Fred Karno. Physically they had the usual jerks and drills—just the preliminary stages of toughening to test how much each was able to endure. They had to rise early in the morning and run before breakfast across the fields to the top of the Hog's Back. The more strenuous exercises included all-in wrestling, which brought a mass of aches and bruises. They played tennis and swam in the private pool among the pine trees. The evenings were diversified with indoor games designed to sharpen their sense of perception. They were given a quick glimpse of a tray littered with a variety of articles and had to enumerate afterwards what these were. This was followed by charades. Conversation at all times and particularly during meals had to be in French. All letters received and sent out were censored. The use of the telephone was absolutely barred.

At the end of the month, the course having been completed, all the candidates returned to their homes. Meanwhile at headquarters the reports on them were scrutinised and in those cases where there was still a doubt the candidate was discarded. Few indeed survived their first stage of training and inspection. Only the most alert, the most composed and the most resourceful were allowed to go on. Violette was overjoyed when, a fortnight later, she was informed that she was one of the few selected.

She spent part of her time off in her flat in Pembridge Villas. Almost daily she went to see her child at Mill Hill. Occasionally she spent a night with her parents in Brixton. Here endless questions were asked her. Being in uniform she was able to answer some of them. Dad was vaguely aware of the FANYs in the First World War. Not unnaturally he wanted to know what exactly Violette was doing. She explained that she helped in a Forces canteen for the most part, but from time to time had to drive a lorry to Nottingham or Bristol, taking stores—and that of course took her out of town for days on end.

"That what you've been doing for the past month?" he asked.

"Yes," she said, a little uncomfortably. She wondered if it sounded like a lie, for she had never before had to evade their questioning.

Dad looked at her doubtfully.

"I see," he said, "and I suppose you'll be off again presently?"

"Yes," she replied. "In about a week from now."

"And where's this canteen of yours?" He obviously had very grave doubts.

"Oh, at different places—Ealing—West Kensington—Birmingham. I have to go and lend a hand all over the place."

"I see." But it was clear that he didn't. In order to avoid further questioning, and also from a desire to see something of the others who were in the same service, Violette decided to live for the most part in town. Her flat was central enough and quite easily accessible. Almost every evening friends dropped in for a drink and a chat. They played the gramophone and danced, or they went out together for a meal to the Studio Club, across the Park in Knightsbridge. Occasionally in a party of four or six they went on to a night club, where they danced to popular rhythms of the time, including the one which was her favourite and was asked for again and again, 'I'll Be Around'. She had a record of it, made by the Mills Brothers, and often played it, all raising their voices as they joined in the chorus.

The second and far more strenuous stage of the training was in Scotland. The train journey was long and tedious. They had to change at Glasgow, go on in a small train to a little station near Mallaig, transfer to a lorry and drive the rest of the way along narrow, winding, bumpy lanes to a small country house at Arisaig on the Inverness coast which was to be their home for the next month or so.

Here they were put through the entire commando course. There was no let-up for the girls, they too had to do it all. For many miles around them were other training centres at which similar courses were being conducted for Norwegians, Poles, Dutch, Belgians and others training either to be secret agents or uniformed commandos. These groups were kept apart, of course.

The area was big enough to ensure this: the west coast of Scotland was sparsely populated and ideally cut off from the world; and the same instructors were shared with the minimum of travel. Amongst these were experts of all kinds—rock-climbers, explorers, big-game hunters, canoeists and judo experts.

It was a most strenuous, indeed a drastic course of training. Everything was stepped up. There was regular practice now with not only revolvers and rifles, but with Sten guns, Tommy guns and machine-guns, as well as a variety of French and German weapons in case these were all that came to hand in enemy territory, after possibly pouncing on a German and killing him. They used hand grenades and bombs too and a wide range of explosives during their exercises in sabotage. They learned to gauge the charge needed for blowing up a bridge, which varied of course according to the size of the bridge, as well as the more delicate ways of dealing with vital parts of machinery in a factory. During these exercises the air resounded with bangs all day long for miles around. They were taught canoeing and had to lay heavy charges at the bottom of the sea linked with electric wires to a detonator on land. A great diversity of most ingenious booby-traps had also to be circumvented.

They had to set out on long treks across the mountains, travelling often twenty-five miles in bitter weather, mist or rain, guided only by compass. Some got lost in the mountains and had to be rescued. They had to scale almost impossible cliffs, at first by day, then in dark glasses, and eventually by night, always burdened with heavy coils of wire, a load of explosives, hand grenades and guns. They had to wade across ice-cold rivers at two o'clock in the morning, sleep under the stars, however severe the night, and on a hill-top without blankets in the pouring rain. They had to climb walls and leap across from one roof-top to the next by day as well as by night. They had to shin up ropes and drain-pipes, break open doors of houses, blow out the front of safes. Progressively the training became more and more arduous until in the end they were sent on raids in which live ammunition was used. This was done to force them to utilise the best possible cover. As though all this was not enough, many diverted themselves in the evenings by forming raiding-parties of their own and trekked for miles across difficult country in the dark to relieve some other training camp of its gin and whisky.

Violette's conducting officer Peggy Minchin, who is now Mrs Turbett, remembers two things in particular about this period of her training. "One is how good she was at weapon training. She had the eye of a hawk and was very quickly extremely efficient with both automatic and Sten gun. I commented on this to her one day and she said: 'I only want to have some Germans to fight and I should die happy if I could take some of them with me.' She seemed quite determined to fight—she was always very single-minded about it.

"She used to entertain us, when we were doing our physical training, by literally tying herself into knots with acrobatic turns. But the other thing I especially remember about her training in Scotland was when two ropes were slung between trees about twenty feet from the ground. You had to place your feet on the bottom rope and hold on to the top one as you walked across from one tree to the other. I could never pluck up courage to try it. But it was just Violette's cup of tea. She would set out quite briskly along the rope, stop halfway and indulge in idle banter with the chaps below, while she swayed dangerously in the breeze, holding on by one hand and her toes.

"Though essentially feminine, there was something gallant, debonair and quite genuine about her. I shall never forget how gaily she crawled through bog and burns and heather during her field training and flung herself over the most hair-raising obstacles in our private assault course, being almost eaten alive by midges all the time."

Special instruction was given by the gamekeeper to His Majesty King George VI on how to take cover in open country, how to stalk and how to avoid being stalked, and, equally important, how to live off the land if one happened to be on the run. They learned how to catch rabbits and pigeons, how to strip the animals and prepare them for eating; what berries were edible and which should be avoided because they were poisonous.

In the final stage of this course each one in turn had to take charge of an operation in order to show his or her ingenuity and initiative in leadership. It was obvious that there would be a further weeding out. Violette, who had the good fortune to be brought up with nearly a dozen brothers and male cousins, was exceedingly efficient, and her admirable state of health enabled her to stand up to the great strain. She emerged in consequence from the course a fully-fledged female commando.

The next stage in her training was at the Parachute School at Ringway, a few miles south of Manchester.

The preliminaries here, before one actually attempted to jump out of a plane with a parachute, were further exercises in falling. One learned to fall with both legs kept close together and to roll over to the right or the left with both hands in the pockets. Falls of every kind were practised over and over again. There followed a series of exercises with the parachute harness strapped on, culminating in jumps from a lofty gallery in the hanger. The parachute itself was not used at this stage, control of the fall was maintained by a cable. It was almost a trapeze act, with the added complication of having to handle the harness. And so progressively until one jumped with a parachute first from a tower and then from a platform attached to a barrage balloon at a height of nearly 900 feet.

At last came the final phase, the drop from an aircraft. Whitley bombers were used for this. Few escaped the feeling of uneasiness, and even fear, as the doors opened and one dropped through space, wondering all the while whether the parachute would open and one would land safely. For all these tests a static line was employed. It was a length of cable attached to the parachute on your back, which tugged the 'chute open automatically and did not leave its manipulation to your fumbling nervousness.

Violette had to make five such jumps from the plane and was apparently not in the least bit nervous. But on her second fall, as she reached the earth, despite all her care in rolling over, her ankle got twisted and was badly sprained. One could see as she rose after unstrapping the harness that she was walking with a marked limp. The ankle was swelling rapidly and all further jumps were thereupon cancelled. She was sent home for rest and treatment.

She travelled down by train, her left foot in bandages, and went to Brixton to stay with her parents, whom she had not seen for more than two months. Their welcome was eager. Concerned inquiries were made about her ankle. But, from Papa especially, there was a questioning also about her long absence. He asked where she had been and what she had been doing. The only address they had was a box number at the post office in Wimpole Street. Her letters to them, postmarked West London, were brief and revealed nothing.

Once again she had to be evasive. She trotted out the old stuff about working in canteens and driving lorries and could see that it was not going down at all well. It made her embarrassed and self-conscious. It was not easy to lie to those one loved, and she hoped most fervently that it would not be so difficult when she was questioned by the enemy, towards whom of course her feelings would be violently different. After a time Papa abandoned his efforts. But, when dinner was over, he sat alone with her in the lounge and said he wanted to have a talk with her.

"I don't know what you get up to," he began, "but I know you are very pretty and that men have always been interested in you. Now don't tell me that you're grown up, that you've been married and have a child. That does not qualify you to do what you like. You should realise that it is very natural for parents to be concerned, especially in times like this. Your mother and I have had many sleepless nights wondering what you might be up to."

"Oh, Dad! How absurd! I'm not the first girl to join the Forces."

"I know that. And do you think what you're doing—canteen work, driving lorries, driving cars for generals and what not—is more useful—is helping to win the war—more, for instance, than your work in the aircraft factory?"

" I do," she said.

"Well, I don't," he countered with some emphasis. "And what about your time off? What do you do with that? You meet men, don't you?"

"I'm with men all the time, Dad. It's part of my work. There's nothing wrong in that."

"Don't you go dancing any more?"

"Yes—when I can. We danced at the ack-ack battery, you

already know about that—and we dance sometimes in the canteen after the tables have been cleared."

"And what about the officers? Do you go about with them?"

"Why, of course. I'm an officer myself now. We sometimes go in a party to the theatre and go on afterwards to a night club. There's no harm in that, surely."

"There could be. Look, Vi. I wish you'd live at home with us. Your mother and I would like that—instead of you rushing about all over the place."

"I can't. I've got to get about—it's part of my work."

"And get your foot into that ghastly state? Is that helping to win the war too?" He was getting quite worked up now.

"I told you. I twisted it jumping out of a lorry."

"You expect me to believe that?"

"Why are you so suspicious, Dad? What does the twisted ankle prove—that I've been having a mad flirtation with a colonel?"

"I don't know what to think."

"Oh, don't be so absurd. And please don't go on about it," she said. "I'm most dreadfully tired." She was about to rise.

"All right! All right!" he said finally, raising his voice. "You do what you like. But I tell you this. If you're not careful, my girl, you'll come to a bad end. You mark my words."

Her lips tightened slightly, but her face was like a mask. She leaned forward to pick up her handbag. With her thoughts elsewhere, she clasped it insecurely and, as it fell forward, it opened and almost everything in it was scattered about the floor.

Her father was too angry to help her pick anything up. So she got down on all fours herself and, moving carefully with her bandaged foot, retrieved her lipstick, the compact, her purse, which had opened out too, and she had to stretch for the coins that had rolled far away. Her father, relenting a little now, helped her to pick up the last few things.

She shut her bag, rose and, with a weary 'Good night', limped out of the room.

After she had gone he sat sucking at his pipe for a long time, wondering about her. There was nothing more he could say—or do for that matter. After all she was old enough: she was twenty-two—a widow—and a mother.

Mrs Bushell, having said good night to her at the foot of the stairs just as Violette was limping up to her bedroom, came in and sat with Mr Bushell, and they talked for well over an hour about her evasions and her vague excuses until they too, feeling tired, got up to go to bed.

As he moved towards the door of the sitting-room Mr Bushell noticed something lying on the floor, half hidden by the sofa. He drew it out and was startled to see that it was a parachute badge. He held it out in his hand towards his wife and tears began to course down his cheeks. Everything suddenly became quite clear. He could hardly speak, and when he did his words came with difficulty through his sobs. He had suspected the girl, challenged her cruelly. He had used many harsh, hurtful words—and all the while, with neither reproach nor rebuke, Violette had suffered it, without betraying her secret.

Mr and Mrs Bushell passed the badge from one to the other, wept a little, and were very proud of their daughter—and yet they could not understand what canteens and lorries or even First Aid, the normal work of the FANYs, had to do with jumping out of a plane by parachute.

"She'll tell us when she can," said Mrs Bushell, and, taking her husband's hand in hers, they walked together through a mist to their room.

At breakfast the next morning her father said, "How do you like parachuting, Vi?"

She flushed. "How did you know, Dad?"

He held out the badge.

"Thanks."

"It fell out of your bag."

They ate in silence for a while, then, unable to resist it, Mr Bushell asked: "Have you to do much more of it?"

Looking him full in the eye, all her evasions now behind her, Violette sighed with relief. "I can't tell you anything. I'm not allowed to, Dad. I'm under oath."

"OK, Vi," he said. "I can guess what the job is. I won't ask you any more questions."

And he never did.

CHAPTER TEN

FINISHING SCHOOL

THE injured ankle caused a break of more than a month in Violette's training. A doctor had examined it at Ringway and treated it; now a local doctor, to whom nothing could of course be revealed of the cause, came in from time to time to see it. When it was pronounced to be definitely on the mend, Violette went off to Bournemouth to convalesce. There, on the doctor's insistence that the foot should be given a complete rest, she went about in a bath chair as so many of the residents there do, but, since a span of half a century separated her age from theirs, many looked and wondered, glanced down sympathetically at the bandages and asked about the bombing in London, which seemed to them to be the cause of the injury. She kept up the fiction and adhered rigidly to the treatment, for it was her resolve to get fit as quickly as possible in order to resume the courses, at the end of which she would have of course to go back to Ringway for the rest of her jumps.

Late in November 1943, her foot being at last out of bandages, she went on to Beaulieu in the New Forest in Hampshire for her final training at what had come to be called the finishing school. The headquarters of this establishment, where the staff of instructors were housed, was in the home of Lord Montagu of Beaulieu, who was at the time only sixteen years old. He was away most of the year at Eton and came home only for the school holidays. The candidates were spread out in various country houses for many miles around, about twenty minutes or so by car from each other and often even further from Beaulieu. The houses stood in their own parks, some of them enormously large, and had been taken over from their private owners. The grouping was by nationality. To one house were assigned the Polish trainees, to another the Dutch, and so on. The French, being generally the most numerous, had as a rule two houses to themselves. As usual there was no contact between one nationality and the next—they were kept strictly apart. Often there were as many as a hundred men and women under instruction in the various houses.

This was the most vital stage of the entire course. It was no longer physical, but psychological, though no let up was possible in one's physical fitness: that had to be fully maintained. But here, in the main, the mind had to be reconditioned for the work that each secret agent had to undertake in enemy-occupied territory.

The staff of instructors numbered about twenty. Some were business men, others were travelling salesmen, schoolmasters, lawyers and journalists. One was an actor. Each of them was fluent in one at least of the European languages, in addition of course to French and German; and always among the instructors there were those who had a knowledge of the particular country to which some of the agents were to be sent—such as Greece and Norway and Yugoslavia.

The classes for the most part were small, consisting of only three or four pupils; occasionally there was just one pupil, for some of the instruction had to be given individually. Since hardly anything of this kind had ever been attempted before in any previous war, the bulk of the course had to be most carefully evolved, and it was constantly being expanded or modified to suit the ever-changing requirements of the situation as revealed by the experience of our agents on the other side.

The overall essential was to provide oneself with a completely new identity, one which would help the secret agent to merge entirely into the life of the district in which he or she was going to live. A cunningly forged identity card would be provided of course, as well as food coupons and clothing coupons. These were indispensable tokens. In addition one had to hold in one's mind the details of the entire life of the new personality—incidents, for example, of one's childhood and one's work (both fictitious), a familiarity with the fresh setting and with the events of recent years. The Germans had been in occupation for three and a half years. Their military police and the Gestapo, as one was aware, kept a keen, searching eye on all activities that seemed in the least unusual and were only too readily aided by French men and women who were anxious to curry favour. There were restrictions and regulations with which Violette would have to become familiar. There were all sorts of shortages, which did not necessarily correspond with those in England. As a member of the community, as one who was supposed to have lived there continuously, she would have to know something also about the trains and buses, both of which had been greatly reduced, and she would have to avoid showing any surprise with what was really unfamiliar. In this setting she would be not Violette Szabo, but someone with a new name, a new background, and a new job, an undercover girl, quite apart from her actual work as secret agent. She was told that it was not at all like assuming a role on the stage and learning lines that she could trot out as required. One could be a bit too pat, which, of course, one never was in real life. The date of one's birth one knew, but there were little incidents in one's actual life that one had to search the memory to recapture.

This assumed identity was rehearsed over and over again. In the small hours of the morning two men, taking on the role of the Gestapo, would enter the house in which Violette lived, shake her out of a deep sleep and question her closely. Slips were inevitably made the first time, and by many even at the second rapier-edged grilling. Violette fared no better than the rest. Imagine yourself trying drowsily, to put over a pack of lies to two keen-witted men with the power of life and death over you. It is not easy. Hence the need for the recurrent rehearsals. They served to make the mind alert, the tongue less hesitant, the manner less awkward and much more natural.

Another important lesson was on how not to attract attention to yourself. One began with the assumption that almost anybody might be hand in glove with the Germans. It might be a French girl, an old woman, a farm hand, an errand boy—the least likely passer-by or shopper might have a wary eye open to detect and to tell. It might be someone in a window across the road. So you had to be extremely circumspect and yet not show by a move or a glance that you were trying to make sure you weren't being watched. You had to walk quite unconcernedly and still keep your senses alert. If you felt you were being followed you had to know the best method of eluding the follower. That is what you were taught in this course and you had to put it into operation in a series of testing rehearsals. These were generally carried out at Bournemouth or some other near-by town. You were taken there by car and left at a street corner. Someone you didn't know was tipped off to follow you. You had, by applying the instructions received in the course of the training, to make your way back to your own house without being caught up by the man or woman who was following. This too was tried out again and again. In films the person under suspicion is generally seen standing flat against a dark wall, with both arms outspread and, presently, the pursuer goes by without noticing. That, by its very unusualness, would in fact attract attention if done in enemy-occupied territory.

These exercises began to square up with some of her ideas about spying. What was even more exciting was a reversal of the procedure when she had to be the active instead of passive person. She had to do the looking-out, the watching and the detecting. She had to seek for slips and false moves so as to determine which of the men and women around her were to be suspected. As a prelude to this she was taught, with photographs, charts and diagrams, the entire German military and espionage set up—the uniforms of the Nazi army, the air force and the police, all the German divisional signs, even the lorry registrations, and whatever had been discovered of the methods of the Gestapo, the Abwehr, who were concerned with intelligence and counter intelligence, and other organisations which wore no uniform, their mode of communication by codes and ciphers, their aim, and the mentality of the German intelligence men and women. These had to be known in order to be circumvented.

She had in these exercises to make contact for her part with people who were prepared to help secretly, and would have to be identified with the greatest possible care so that the enemy, having learned some of her plans, should not, by putting in a substitute, get her into their trap. The process of identification had to appear to be perfectly natural. The greeting exchanged might be overheard, so it had to be commonplace, yet it had to have inserted into it, in a way that would not make the eavesdropper prick up his ears, two or three significant words that had been agreed upon, and the response to the greeting would, in the same way, have to be identifiable by special words. Such a remark as "I hope your aunt is better" might evoke the very natural answer, "Yes, much better, thanks for inquiring"—but it would not perhaps be what you were seeking for purposes of identification. The phrase "Lovely day, isn't it?" would have to be discarded, since it might be raining at the time of meeting. It was by no means easy in view of all the pitfalls lying between a natural casualness and security. One had to smile, however serious one's purpose, and perhaps even laugh in order to be disarming, since people engaged in genial converse arouse less suspicion.

The passing on of messages, they were told, could be done in a variety of ways. By word of mouth was the most usual, but to indicate the exact location of a factory or the section of railway lines to be blown up, one had to supply a diagram or an address, and for this one had to resort to the use of paper. A trusted tobacconist or grocer or bookseller handed it on as a receipt or a bill—or it was scribbled on to the margin of a newspaper and thrown down casually on the café table at the moment you were leaving and the new customer, who was to be its recipient, was about to sit down.

Since theoretical instructions were never regarded as enough all this was put into operation in this country. Violette was sent to Southampton, where she had to go along the streets and try to spot those who seemed at all doubtful, to make contacts, to pass on messages—all without detection; and, since an extensive course in sabotage was included in the lessons, she was sent further afield to blow up a bridge or a railway line and try to discover military secrets at air or naval bases in England. The police were not tipped off in advance, and indeed only one high-ranking police officer in each area where these schemes were worked out knew what was going on. The agent would only reveal himself to this officer when all hope of escape was lost. Telephone contact with the police liaison officer at SOE then established his or her bona fides and release followed at once.

Violette was an extremely apt learner. She was at Beaulieu from the end of November 1943 until the first week in February 1944; then she went home to Brixton for a brief rest. She looked extremely fit and was in high spirits. A fortnight later she left for Ringway to complete her course in parachute jumping.

CHAPTER ELEVEN

READY TO GO

IT WAS at Ringway that she met Staunton. He was known as Captain Charles Staunton and was regarded as an Englishman. In fact he was a Parisian by parentage and by upbringing. His real name was Philippe Liewer. He was a journalist by profession and worked for the Havas news agency in Paris before the war. Sent to Munich in the autumn of 1938 to cover the famous meeting between Hitler and Chamberlain, which Daladier and Mussolini also attended, he was turned back at the airport by the Nazis and sent home in the next plane. On the outbreak of war he was appointed liaison officer to the British Expeditionary Force and, evacuated from Dunkirk in one of the little ships, was brought to England, but returned to France to see his wife. He had told her "I'll come back whatever happens to France." And he did, though, with the swift and dramatic developments, endless difficulties inevitably presented themselves and had somehow to be overcome. His wife, a journalist and a novelist who wrote under the name of Marie Louise Villiers, had left Paris, he discovered, and was at Nice. So to Nice he went to say his farewell. He found there, although the Germans were not yet in occupation of that part of France, a deep feeling of resentment against Pétain and Laval for allowing the Germans to take over half of their beloved country and hold in thrall the lives and happiness of the people. Staunton organised at Nice one of the first Resistance groups in all France. When Pétain's police discovered this, they arrested Staunton and threw him into a Vichy detention camp. It did not take him long to work out a plan of escape. Together with twelve other prisoners he was about to break out when two warders came up, not to detain them, but to beg to be allowed to accompany them. Not together, but split up into small groups of two or three, they crossed the Pyrenees into Spain, and from Portugal they managed to get to England. That was in the autumn of 1942. He contacted the French section of SOE and soon became one of Buckmaster's secret agents. He was given a commission in the British Army (general list), assumed the name of Charles Staunton and went into training for the work that lay ahead. But he missed Ringway. He did not like parachute jumping, explained his phobia to Buckmaster and was allowed to skip it.

He was in his early thirties, good-looking, of medium height, had an extremely alert mind and a fine organising ability. In March 1943, his training over, he was sent to Rouen which, because of its position so near the mouth of the Seine, between the two most suitable landing beaches for the Allied armies, was a most vital area. It was the centre of road, rail and canal communications. It was a port for sea-going vessels and a refitting depot for German U-boats, more admirably suitable for this purpose than Le Havre because it was further away from the Channel. Obviously much could be done in this key centre by careful organisation.

Staunton was landed by plane in a field near Blois, many miles to the south-west of Paris. He knew Claude Malraux, a brother of André Malraux, the famous French writer, and felt that by contacting him, he might be able to learn of some reliable people with whom he could get a Resistance group started in Rouen. Malraux said he had a brother there named Serge and suggested that Staunton should go and see him. In the succeeding months, Staunton, with the help of Serge Malraux, was able to build up a powerful underground organisation in Rouen. Normally Resistance groups numbered no more than five or six members, of whom none knew more than one or two, so that if caught and tortured they would be unable to give more than one or two away. But in this vital centre, taking in Le Havre and all the intervening country, Staunton was able to build up a vast network of little circuits, numbering in all ninety-eight underground Resistance workers. It took time of course. A wireless operator, Peter Newman, was flown out to him from England in April with his own small transmitting set. A special wave-length was allotted for his signals, a code was supplied, and the hours at which he was to send messages were allocated. Through Newman requests were sent for arms, explosives, and for an instructor to train the Resistance workers. The supplies arrived and with them, also dropped by parachute, came Robert Mortier, who was to be very closely associated with Violette's work later on.

Mortier was not his own name any more than Staunton's was. He was a Frenchman, born in Paris in 1923, the son of French parents, both of whom were teachers and had spent some years lecturing at the University of Columbia in New York. There his elder brother Jacques was born. Robert, called Bob even at home after his parents' long stay in America, was only seventeen when the Germans came to Paris. He was still at school; his parents were in the South of France. Studies, as may well be imagined, were greatly disturbed and, just before the Germans came, the schools closed down. Bob left Paris on a bicycle. The roads were blocked with traffic, which crawled at the pace of the slowest vehicles. There were children in prams, old men and women in donkey carts, others, bowed under their loads, moved along on foot, weeping as they went. At intervals German planes zoomed overhead, dropped their bombs and, as the people scattered into the fields or lay down in ditches, the planes returned and machine-gunned them. By the time Bob reached the south, France had fallen and he was as disgusted with the Pétain-Laval state of affairs as Staunton. His one resolve now was to get out and carry on the fight. He made his way to Marseilles, got a boat to North Africa, joined the French Air Force there, and was sent to Tunisia, where, to his disgust, the Pétainist influence was strong. He was determined to get out of this place too. When the Germans came to Bizerta, he borrowed his colonel's bicycle and cut westward across the frontier to join the Allies, who had landed on the day before at Algiers. He offered his services to a British officer he met in the street and, after the necessary security check-up, he was flown to Gibraltar and shipped from there to England. It was felt that he would be most useful as a secret agent and, after being given a commission in the British Army, he began his training, with an extended course in arms and explosives. It was in this capacity that he was sent to assist Staunton at Rouen. They worked well together.

In December Staunton, as he was leaving to return to England, said to Bob: "The man who has been forging all our papers for us was telling me that he has never seen a parachute landing. He has begged to be allowed to come along. I promised to take him, but as I won't be here for the next one, will you take him along with you? Let him see it all happen—the people sent over and the arms and explosives that are dropped." Then he added with a wink, "It'll be good for his morale."

Bob organised it with his usual care and precision. At a garage in Rouen, which the Resistance used as their headquarters, Bob arranged for a lorry on which to bring back all the equipment and stores that were dropped. He asked the lorry-driver to bring the truck to the garage not later than ten o'clock that night because of the curfew, which was at eleven. The man was late. Bob waited and as the minutes ticked by he got uneasy. At a quarter to eleven he decided he could wait no longer. There was just enough time to get out of Rouen without being stopped by the curfew patrols. Without the truck he could not of course bring back the stores. But the arrangements at the secret landing-ground had to be seen to. So he grabbed a motor-cycle that was parked in the garage and, motioning to the forger to jump on behind him, he sped out of town to the landing-ground near Elbeuf. There he would position the men with torch-lights, check over the stores and hide them until they could be collected the following night.

The motor-cycle, with the forger on the pillion, got safely out of Rouen just as the clocks were striking eleven. Bob was travelling along a deserted country road and had not got far when he heard a car coming up behind him. It was approaching at great speed and soon overtook him, then pulled up sharp and motioned to Bob to stop. Inside the car were the German police. Three men promptly leapt out.

The forger jumped off the back of the cycle the moment he saw the car stop. He scampered off the road and fled across the fields. The Germans fired after him, but the man managed to get away. They questioned Bob about him. Feigning ignorance, Bob said he had no idea who the man was; it was just someone who thumbed a ride.

"You have never seen this man before?"

"Never," Bob assured them.

They thereupon asked him what he was doing out of doors after curfew. He was ordered to remount his cycle and one of the German police got on the pillion behind him. With his revolver at the back of Bob's neck, the German directed him to turn round and drive back to Oissel, a little town four miles outside Rouen. The police car followed, its headlights turned on to keep the cycle in view. Obviously there could be no funny business.

Arrived at Oissel, Bob was surprised to see lights outside two of the buildings in the centre of the town. One he recognised as the town hall, the other, next door to it, was the police station. The German car now overtook the motor-cycle and made for the police station. Bob, feeling this was his chance, pulled up suddenly, swung the cycle round and as his passenger, who was thrown off, was trying to steady himself, Bob flung the cycle violently against him and ran.

Hearing the scuffle the Germans, who were just alighting from the car, blazed after him with their revolvers. Bob was shot through the lung, but dived into a dark side street and was surprised that the Germans did not come after him. Presumably they had emptied their magazines. But a moment later, with their revolvers recharged, the Germans came briskly down the side street. Bob by this time had dashed across a field and was lying in a ditch full of foul water alongside the railway lines.

With their torches, and later with two police dogs, they searched for him through most of the night, but by lying in the water he managed to escape detection. He lay there for some time after the German police had given up the hunt, his limbs frozen, a stinging, agonising pain in his lung; then, crawling and staggering, every step making his suffering unendurable, he succeeded somehow in covering the few miles to Rouen. Threading his way through the streets, with dawn just about to break and reveal his agony to the early passers-by, he reached at last the block of flats in which he lived. Even that was not the end of his torture, for he had to climb up five flights of stairs.

When he let himself in, the friends with whom he lived, roused from their sleep, were appalled at his condition. A doctor, who was also in the Resistance, was fetched at once.

After a very careful examination, the doctor shook his head and said he did not think Bob could live. It was indeed a miracle that he was alive now. They were all greatly overcome at hearing this. The doctor himself, who was very attached to Bob, spared two tablets of his precious sulphanilamide, knowing that they could not now be of any avail. It was an emotional offering to a dying man.

The friends were confronted now with a fresh and extremely grave problem. If Bob were to die there would have to be a funeral. The Germans would be curious. They would examine the body in case it was a ruse of some sort, and, discovering the wound, would pounce on the friends with whom Bob had been staying as a cousin. They would be grilled and tortured, perhaps even shot as members of the Resistance in this vital sector of Germany's coastal defences. They pleaded with the doctor, who was alarmed for himself too, but he said there was no hope at all.

Arrangements for the funeral were made with the utmost secrecy. They got two potato sacks, slit them open and stitched them together into one large enough to take the body, for Bob was exceedingly tall. They also got stones with which to weight the sack further and arranged with a friendly lorry-driver to call for the body just before dawn, take it well out of Rouen and drop it into the Seine, since it could not be thrown off a bridge in the town without attracting a great deal of attention.

The days dragged by, however, without Bob dying. The doctor came again and again, treated him, but there seemed to be no improvement. The lorry-driver got impatient, not knowing when he would be required. Then unexpectedly Bob began to improve. The doctor exclaimed with astonishment and relief. The 'cousins' exclaimed too and threw up their hands with delight. It was clear now that Bob would live. The doctor said it was the bitterly cold water in which Bob lay for so many hours that cauterised the wound and saved his life. Ten days later he was able to get up and join his friends at a New Year's Eve Party.

Shortly afterwards Staunton returned to Rouen. He was not expected back so early. He explained that, because of the weather, he had not got a plane to England on the appointed date in December, and would have to wait now for the January moon, for it was only by the light of the moon, within the span of a few days on either side of the full moon, that pilots on these secret trips were able to pick out the landmarks to the isolated fields used for landing.

Staunton was greatly concerned about Bob's condition and insisted on his coming back to England to convalesce. "You must get out, Bob. You've had a pretty bad time and, in any case, you cannot operate here. You are known to them. They would pick you up."

Bob agreed to accompany him. They set out together to get the plane in January, but once again no plane came. This time Staunton refused to let Bob return to Rouen. "You stay in Paris till the February moon. I'll join you there a little before that."

They got their plane on the night of February 6th, 1944, and were flown back to England. One of the first things Staunton did was to go to Ringway. "I must try the jump!" he said. "I can't bear these long train journeys half across France. The parachute brings you much nearer to your objective." And that was how he came to meet Violette.

When she and Staunton returned to London, Bob, who was resting for a while before going on an extended arms course at a school in Hertfordshire, joined them on their first evening in town. He found Violette delightfully refreshing. She was gay and amusing and, now that her ankle was all right, she was able to dance again. He thought she danced divinely. Evening after evening the three sat in her flat and were joined by others who dropped in. Among them were many they had met at one or other of their schools of training. Others were chance acquaintances in army or air force uniforms. They sat talking, drinking, smoking, singing the choruses of various songs, swapping yarns, laughing, while they waited for the next assignment, and varied it by going round to restaurants, cinemas and night clubs. Suddenly one of them would be missing. He had gone without a word, and as suddenly somebody else would loom across their horizon. Fresh friends were made almost every day. You met them at the Studio Club or on the crowded dance floor of the Astoria or one of the night clubs and it was possible that you would never see them again.

She met Harry Peulevé at a much earlier stage, long before her meeting with Staunton and Bob. He was dancing with the widow of a Battle of Britain pilot, an Italian girl whom Violette knew slightly. Harry, despite his name, was English. He was an officer in the British Army, tall, broad-shouldered and very good-looking. Violette was not in uniform at the time. Harry wondered what she was doing in the way of war work, but he asked no questions. Some nights later he ran into her in the underground station at Piccadilly Circus and saw that she had on the uniform of the FANYs. He pointed to it and she explained that she was working in a canteen. She asked if he was on leave. "Yes," he said. "My regiment is to go overseas shortly. Let's have fun while the leave lasts."

They saw a great deal of each other, at times in the company of others, but often alone. They went to the theatre or to a film, dined and talked till three in the morning. Some of her friends wondered if a romance was developing, for her eyes would light up when they danced together and in his there seemed to be more than just a passing interest. Yet neither told the other the truth about their work. This they were to discover some months later when they met under very different circumstances.

CHAPTER TWELVE

HER FIRST MISSION

STAUNTON, having brought Bob back, was eager to return to Rouen to expand the circuit, check over the details and assign the work that had to be done when the call for action came on D-Day, for that was when they would have to strike at the Germans from behind. It was obvious, of course, that Bob could not go with him. As the German police had caught him once and he had been seen and questioned by four of them his return would involve him, and others too perhaps, in the gravest danger. So it was decided that it would be better for him to operate elsewhere as soon as he was fit again and had completed his present advanced course of training.

Buckmaster felt that Staunton should not go back to Rouen either. Peter Newman, the radio operator, was nominally in charge of the British end there, under Serge Malraux, who controlled the entire circuit all the way up to Le Havre. Help would be sent to Newman during the March moon, but Staunton, Buckmaster insisted, should go elsewhere.

Staunton, however, did not share his view. He wanted to see to the Rouen arrangements himself, as he had started this circuit and knew all the people involved. Buckmaster eventually agreed that, provided Staunton did not enter the area himself, but operated from outside through a reliable, tough and fearless assistant, he could undertake the check in this dangerous area, the whole of which was most rigorously guarded by the enemy. The section formed a vital part of the Nazi Atlantic Wall. It was a forbidden zone, totally barred to all except the actual residents.

Violette, Staunton felt, would be his best emissary for this purpose. He mentioned her name to Buckmaster who stared fixedly at him for a while. "Do you feel you could trust her with your life?" he asked at last. "For that's what it amounts to."

"Yes," said Staunton, "I can trust her absolutely."

Buckmaster eventually agreed.

Violette herself leapt at the idea. In order that they should get to know each other better before setting out, Staunton suggested that he might come and stay with her at her parents' house in Brixton for a few days, and, with Mr and Mrs Bushell's consent, he moved in, occupying one of the boys' rooms downstairs.

Mr and Mrs Bushell realised at once, of course, that their daughter was to be sent abroad on what would be not only a dangerous mission, but might even prove to be fatal. They could not discuss or even hint at what was afoot and they tried hard not to show their grave anxiety. By their silence Violette could tell how heavily it was weighing on their minds. She said: "Don't worry, Mama. I'll be back—I promise you I'll come back. And I've been equipped with a wonderful new career. I shall do well at it when the war is over."

Smiling through the tears she was pressing back, Mrs Bushell asked, "And what is that?"—"A cat burglar," said Violette with eyes twinkling. "I can scale walls. I can crack through roofs and blow open safes. There is nothing in that line I can't do." And for the moment the anxiety dissolved in laughter.

Violette went along again and again to Mill Hill to see Tania. The March moon period drew near and the moment came to say good-bye. She and Staunton got ready. Papa asked if he could go part of the way with them. "As far as Victoria Station," she said and there they parted.

With Staunton she went to the headquarters of the French Section of SOE for final instructions. Their forged papers had been prepared and were handed to them. On her new identity card, most skilfully devised on the exact pattern in use in occupied France, she was Corinne Reine Leroy, the surname being her mother's before marriage; her profession, it stated, was *Secrétaire Commerciale.* The date of her birth was entered correctly—"26 Juin 1921", but the place of birth was altered to "Bailleul, Département Nord". Her nationality was put down as French and her domicile—64 rue Thiers, Le Havre, so that she might have a right of entry in the forbidden zone. The other entries read: Height 1 m.64, hair *châtain* or auburn, eyes *marrons*, face *ovale*, colour pale. The card bore her photograph, her fingerprint and her new signature. Her identity number was 98272. The card was rubber-stamped in the appropriate places with a very fine imitation of the Mairie du Havre stamper, overlapping both her photograph and the 15 franc stick-on stamp pasted under it. The date put on it was May 15th of the preceding year 1943 and it bore the correct rubber-stamped signature, authorising her to be in the forbidden *Kusten* zone or coastal area. Ration cards both for food and for clothing were also provided, with rubber-stamped dates in a variety of faded inks, put on crookedly (as they generally are) for the months when she was actually in England.

A further provision was a set of papers, made out in a different name, to help her to escape through Spain in case the Germans got on to her trail and the British were unable to come to her rescue. The name she was to use in Spain was Miss Vicky Taylor.

A postal address in Spain was also supplied, and a special code (which had to be memorised) provided such innocent words as *un*, *deux* and *trois* with special significance. *Trois*, for example, meant 'I have gone to my cachette, or hiding-place, as arranged. Come and get me out.' The name she was to use for these messages was 'Louise'. These changes of name were intended to cause confusion and so prevent a possible follow-up by the Germans.

A final check-up was now made on something that Violette and Staunton had been going over together for weeks, with large-scale maps and photographs. From this she had acquired a detailed knowledge of Rouen and of the surrounding countryside in which she was to operate—the names of the main streets, the turnings off them, the shops, the riverside *quais*, the cinemas, the public baths, the buses, especially the country buses of which there were now very few. She had been equipped with a clear and exact mental picture.

With Peter Newman in Rouen, London had been in close radio contact, working out the place and the hour for the parachute drop. Everything, London was informed, had been fully organised. The reception committee would be there, awaiting the arrival of Staunton, whose return they welcomed, and of Violette.

On the day they were to leave, London received a strange and startling message. It came not from Rouen but from a Resistance group in the South of France, the one headed by Serge Malraux's brother, Claude, whom Staunton had contacted on his first trip to France, before going to Serge in Rouen. The message, signed Catherine, claimed to be from a friend of Serge's who had managed to get out of Rouen and make her way down to Claude. She said that the Germans had arrested Serge and Peter Newman, had seized the transmitting set, found the code and had been sending messages in order to get Staunton and whoever else came out with him into their clutches. Catherine's message was brief and urgent. Its phrasing revealed her agitation and her acute distress. "For God's sake don't come," she urged, "or you'll find the Nazis waiting for you on the landing-field." Buckmaster was baffled. All their cautious spade work which had built up a powerful organisation to support the Allies on D-Day in quite the most vital area appeared to have been, if not destroyed, at any rate dented. How much of it still remained? What did these warning messages mean? Who was Catherine? The organisation knew nothing of her. Staunton said he knew her well. She had worked with him all the time he was in Rouen. She was one of the most loyal and reliable members of the vast team he had set up there.

The warning came only just in time. A few hours later and Violette would have been on her way with Staunton, without any means of being contacted and turned back.

Their departure was cancelled of course. They would have to wait now until the next moon in April. The place selected for the drop had to be abandoned. They would have to land at some distance from Rouen, possibly outside Paris. From there Violette would have to make her way up to Rouen in order to find out what had really gone wrong, who had been arrested, how much the Germans actually knew.

There was nothing for Violette and Staunton to do now but to wait for three or four weeks. She went to live in her flat. Friends dropped in. They talked and laughed and dined out. Often she spent the evening with Staunton. Bob joined them when he was able to get up to town. Harry Peulevé had apparently sailed with his regiment for she no longer heard from him or ran into him at their familiar haunts.

Quite unexpectedly she had been given this bonus of time with her daughter Tani and she made the most of it. The child was close on two years old—sweet, pert, talkative and happy. During the long months of training, broken by her period of convalescence, Violette had scarcely had any opportunity of being with her. Now she spent days on end at Mill Hill, leaving her address and telephone number at SOE headquarters in case there was a sudden chance to go.

She was beginning now to know her child. She found that instead of just an animated, smiling, cooing baby, Tania was an individual, with a personality and a will, and she wondered *if* anything happened . . . Quickly she checked herself. Of course she would come back. Of that she was quite confident—and they would have months together, years together once this war was over. She insisted on doing everything for the child herself—preparing her meals, carrying her up to bed, sitting beside her and telling her the most fanciful tales, drawn from books she had herself read as a child, and of the places she had been to, and especially of her own childhood in France. She promised to take Tania there one day—and fell silent as she realised that Etienne would not be with them now. "I'll take you to Paris," she said, wrinkling her nose at the child. "I'll take you to the Madeleine." She remembered stopping suddenly on the pavement and pointing up to it and asking her mother what it was—and also that it was there that Etienne had planned to take her . . . to give thanks . . .

These weeks were full of memories and of hopes. Then at last the call came. They were to leave a night or two before the Easter full moon, which fell on April 8th. Violette came up to town some days before in order to go over the plans again with Staunton in case there had been any changes, and to refresh her mind about the places and streets in the Rouen area, and to check carefully, although it had been done very thoroughly before, all the personal articles she was taking with her. The clothes she was to wear had been specially made for her by one of the very few firms engaged in making these clothes for secret agents in the style of the country to which they were being sent. On hers French seamstresses had worked so that none might detect any difference in cut or in size of stitching. The lining, the buttons, the braid used had all to be right. The jackets worn in France at the time were ten inches longer than in England and there were other minor but far from negligible differences. These clothes were given her some weeks before so that they might be worn and not look new. English laundry marks and name tags had of course to be obliterated. Her face-powder, her tooth-brush and tooth-paste, her make-up accessories, even her shoe polish (in case she had to clean her shoes after a muddy landing) had all to be such as one could buy in France at that time.

Violette was cheerful and quite calm when she reported at headquarters on the afternoon of the appointed day. Staunton had gone straight on to the aerodrome, but Violette travelled with Vera Atkins by car through the pale waning light to the secret aerodrome in Bedfordshire. As they passed through Mill Hill, Violette leaned slightly towards the window. Seeing that Vera had noticed it, Violette said: "It's where my child is." That was the only hint she gave that Tania was in her thoughts.

"I know she was devoted to her child," says Vera Atkins. "Every moment she could spare she spent at Mill Hill. But she said nothing more to me that evening about Tania. She just sat there calm and composed—the picture, one might almost say, of a poster girl, for she was really very beautiful—the sort of loveliness that churned up the emotions of every man. But she did not seem to be conscious of it at all. She never fussed about the way her hair was done or worried about her make-up. And, despite the havoc she caused among men, she was not in the least bit flirtatious."

Violette was conscious only of the great experience that lay ahead. In a few hours she would be in France. A year ago she did not think this would be possible in war-time. It was another world, remote, completely cut off, and impossible of access. . . . Not since that night, nearly five years ago, when she bade her aunt good-bye at Calais and scurried on board with her young brother to return to England on the eve of the war, had she seen the beloved countryside of France, and not since she was five had she been in Paris. Etienne had been there since the war—within a few months of their first meeting. Her thoughts roved over all this and the car journey was completed in silence.

They drove to a large and attractive country house near Sandy. It was an eighteenth-century mansion, a few miles from the secret airfield at Tempsford. The house stood well back from the road and was hidden in a wood. By the bar in the large lounge and also at the tables in the dining-room were a number of men, commandos, RAF pilots and special forces officers going out on various dangerous missions. Violette and Vera were the only women there. Staunton came in dressed in slacks and a leather jacket. Over these, before leaving, he was to draw on a flying suit, specially designed with a large number of zipped pockets into which were thrust a revolver, a knife, a small flask, emergency rations, maps, compass, a shovel and other equipment that might be needed if he ran into difficulties. In a belt, against his skin, he carried franc notes to the value of many thousands of pounds. Violette, similarly dressed and equipped, carried French money too in case they got separated on landing. Her francs totalled 100,000, which at the then rate of exchange were worth close on six hundred pounds. Secret agents were also offered what was known as an L pill. Its effect was lethal (hence the L) and it was provided in case, in a tight corner, or when facing acute torture, the agent felt he or she could not endure the agony any longer. The pill had to be secreted, generally in a garment, and had always to be at hand. It is a confirmation of Selwyn Jepson's ultimate analysis, following his initial fear that Violette might be suicidal, that she should have refused it. Self-destruction was not even remotely in her mind. Whatever came she was prepared to face it. She declined to take the pill with her.

A final examination followed. Their cigarette-cases were gone through for English cigarettes. Their pockets were searched for matches, forgotten bus tickets or stubs of theatre and cinema tickets. Their identity cards, their rations cards, their clothing coupons were all checked very carefully. Their suitcases, similarly inspected, had already been placed in the plane.

A car with the blinds drawn took them not only on to the airfield but right up to the plane. It was a Lysander, the smallest plane in use at the time, and known familiarly as a 'Lizzie'. It was revving up in readiness. Hands were shaken, good-byes said, and the two got in, sitting back to back behind the pilot. Slowly the Lizzie taxied and then took off, heading for France.

Going by Lysander meant that they were not going to be dropped but were to land. So they had no parachutes. The plane was no doubt required to do some Pimpernel work on the other side, to bring back agents, as in the case of Bob, or VIPs whom the Gestapo were after, as well as reports supplementing the brief radio messages. They crossed the Channel at a height of 3000 feet, then the plane dropped gently down to 400 feet, at which height it was almost impossible for the German anti-aircraft guns to hit it. Its speed was less than 200 miles an hour and, being very small, it was able to land on a field only 30 yards long. Soon the landmarks would be picked up with the aid of the moon, and as it neared the landing-ground, an ultra short-wave wireless set in the plane, called the S phone, would get the directional signal. They would then see the three or four small pinpricks of light flashed by members of the reception committee, carefully spaced out to indicate the size of the field.

The landing-ground selected for tonight lay hidden among farmlands between Chartres and Orleans. Before it could be reached the Lysander was spotted by a German fighter, and after a series of manœuvres was forced to turn off its course. The Messerschmitt with its great speed kept overshooting them and whizzed by again and again. It was obviously impossible in these circumstances to land, so the pilot turned back. Violette and Staunton, faced with having to wait in England for maybe a further month, wondered, as their plane climbed and recrossed the Channel for home, whether by some cruel fate they were destined not to carry out this operation. But after a while the German fighter gave up the pursuit and their plane, with barely enough petrol left, turned again and retraced its course towards the secret landing-ground.

Suddenly, below them, they saw the dim signalling lights of the electric torches. With the engine switched off, the plane began to descend cautiously, down and down towards the pale moonlit countryside, and in a few minutes was bumping gently along the uneven field.

Silently the men with flashlights ran towards them. As the plane came to a stop, first Violette, then Staunton descended down the steel ladder on the outside and were clasped in a welcoming embrace.

They all talked in whispers. Bicycles had been brought for the two passengers. Their suitcases were taken out of the plane and strapped on to the backs of the cycles: in Violette's case, as she had two suitcases, one of them had to be strapped on to her back. They then set out through the night on a long cycle ride of more than twenty miles. It was not wise to try to go as far as Paris because of the curfew, so they spent what remained of the night in the home of one of the Resistance workers. Supper was insisted on by their host and hostess. A couple of sandwiches and a swig of coffee from a flask in the plane, although it was better coffee than one could get in France at the time, was not considered enough, not by French standards. In any case a meal had already been prepared. In the kitchen, spread out on a table covered with a checked tablecloth, spotlessly washed and ironed, were dishes of delicious *hors-d'œuvre*, the onion soup was being warmed on the stove, and large steaks had been prepared too, for outside the big towns there was plenty of food in occupied France, especially in a farming area such as Violette was in now. They ate well; the coffee they had brought along from England was enjoyed by all and was followed by a strong cognac.

They slept late the next day and then took a train into Paris.

CHAPTER THIRTEEN

ON THE NORMANDY COAST

STAUNTON had an aunt in Paris in the Rue Sts Pères, leading from the Boulevard St Germain to the left bank of the River Seine near the Pont du Carrousel. Just across the river were the Tuileries Gardens and the Louvre. So it was extremely central. Staunton arranged that Violette should live there with her. He himself went elsewhere, for, if the Germans were after him, it would have endangered Violette and his aunt too if he was found there.

Violette had of course been schooled fairly thoroughly in the names of the streets in central Paris. She went exploring on the first day with Staunton's aunt. She glanced at the Eiffel Tower, black against the grey sky. They walked up the Rue Royale, she saw the Madeleine again and her mind was filled at once with thoughts of Etienne and Tania. The streets swarmed with Germans in uniform. Others, unmistakably German, wore ordinary civilian clothes. They were for the most part industrialists hurrying about their affairs or out shopping, for the shops still had much to sell despite the German depredations during the four preceding years. She saw scarcely any motor-cars. Most of the French men and women went about on bicycles. There were bicycle taxis, quaint contraptions that the driver worked with pedals while the passenger sat alongside in a small covered sidecar. There were no buses. The Métro was still running and it was the principal means of transport for long distances.

In a restaurant in the main Boulevard des Capucines, Violette used her forged ration cards for the first time. The meal was expensive and the choice was extremely restricted. Later in the afternoon, as had been arranged, she met Staunton in the Luxembourg Gardens and they talked as they walked along the well-kept paths.

He arranged that she should go to Rouen the next day by the morning train. The distance was about seventy-five miles and the journey now took nearly two hours. Staunton said: "When I went there for the first time to start the Resistance group, I was sure of one contact. I had Serge Malraux. But you have no contacts at all and not even a wireless transmitter to keep you in touch with London. You have just nothing. I've prepared this list of the people who used to be in the group—but we have no idea if they are still there or if they are still with us. You'll have to memorise all this and destroy it. You can't take the list with you. All that you can be sure of is that you are going into great danger. You will hardly be able to move without being watched and followed. It's a pity you have to go alone. But if I came along, it wouldn't help, it would only increase the danger."

"I understand," she said.

"Still want to go?" he asked.

"Yes," she said. "I still want to go—and you may be sure——"

"I know," he said, patting her arm. "I know."

He then gave her one last word of advice. "Try not to say very much."

"You don't imagine I'll . . ."

"It's not that," he said, "but you have quite a marked English accent."

"I have?" She was very surprised.

"Didn't you know? You could get away with it if you said you were from Alsace Lorraine. But the Germans would expect you to know German then. So"—he winked—"don't say much. It's the French who would spot you and you never know which of them you can trust."

Staunton himself was going into other areas to give final D-Day instructions. All would have to play their part when the Allied landings were made. We needed every act of sabotage and organised destruction behind the enemy lines to coincide with these landings. He asked Violette to meet him in the Luxembourg Gardens at the end of the month.

That night she walked alone along the *quais* on the left bank. The river looked lovely in the soft moonlight. She could hear the heavy stamping feet of German sentries. From far away came the sound of flak—heavy flak, firing no doubt at British planes—and she thought she heard even further away the sound of bombs exploding. In her mind she reversed the position and saw herself serving the anti-aircraft guns near Liverpool. Now it was our own planes that were overhead.

In the morning at the Gare St Lazare, as she walked along the platform to her train, she noticed many of the Germans turning to stare at her. For a moment she felt uneasy; was there something wrong about her clothes? But she saw in their widening eyes a stare of appraisal and she walked on unheeding. The train was as crowded as trains were in England in war-time. She had been told that certain compartments were reserved for the Germans. As she passed one of these a German officer bowed and pointing to the door said, in very guttural French: "Why not come in here, Mam'selle? You won't find a seat anywhere else in the train." Smilingly she accepted and found herself in a carriage full of German officers in uniform. They all rose to offer her a seat. She chose one by the window. Cigarette cases were then whipped out. She smiled as she took one and a colonel gave her a light. She enjoyed seeing so many German officers hopping around in respectful attendance. Wouldn't Mama laugh if she knew! And Winnie too! Then she remembered what Staunton had told her. She must not talk. So she kept to just '*Oui*' and '*Non*' and '*Merci*'.

It was a long and fairly silent journey. Only her recurrent smile kept the atmosphere friendly, while through her mind raced bitter, resentful thoughts as she remembered Etienne's death at El Alamein, caused by men like these. But she must not think, she told herself. The hardening look in her eyes would give her away. So she smiled again and turned to stare out of the window at the slightly battered countryside, though much of it looked lovely with the coming of spring.

Rouen once belonged to the English—she had been told all this before she came. Hundreds of years ago the English kings also ruled over this part of northern France, English families lived for generations in this charming old town and to this day many of the names are English, though the people who bear them may no longer be conscious of the link. Violette felt that the town, large, modern and industrial though it was, still retained its charm and beauty in the ancient streets and houses at its core. There were *quais* alongside the river, the same river as in Paris, and a most impressive cathedral. She saw the old tower in which Joan of Arc was once imprisoned; from here she was led out daily by the guards to be questioned by her inquisitors, and later, in this market square, she was burnt at the stake.

One of the first things Violette noticed in Rouen were posters in the streets of two 'Wanted' men. On these were pictures of Staunton and Bob Mortier. They were hideous pictures, making the men she knew so well look like criminals. Under each picture was an X, followed in Staunton's case with the words 'Known as Clément' and in Mortier's—'Known as Mollier, R.' They had got the correct field names but didn't know who the two men really were. Staunton obviously could not have come here without the risk of immediate arrest.

The place bristled with armed Germans. There were machine-guns at almost every street corner. Platoons of German troops marched and stamped through the streets. The vigilance was astounding. There was an air of tension, a nervous awareness that D-Day could not now be far away. They knew too that the Allied landings would be made on the beaches on one side of Rouen or the other and they were determined to deny us any help from inside. Nothing of which they were not fully aware could be allowed to go on. Everything had to be harnessed to the war effort, theirs not ours.

What was left of the Resistance here in the *réseau*, as it was called—that was what Violette had come to find out. Were there enough there to give effective help on D-Day? We had to know what we could rely on and what we should have to write off.

It was difficult for her to know where to begin. She had memorised the list Staunton gave her and, wondering what might be her best plan of inquiry, she had decided to see the wives of the men who had worked with the Resistance. Even this was not easy. The women would be suspicious. Some of them, with their husbands in German prisons, might be hostile, might even, though she hardly liked to harbour the thought, give her away to the Germans in return for some concession or favour or possibly the release of their husbands. She would have to be extremely cautious. It was obvious that she could not visit these women in their homes; and it was difficult, without knowing what they looked like, to make any contact with them in the streets.

She made her way first to the garage which Staunton and Mortier had told her had been their headquarters. It was here that the arms and explosives dropped by parachute by English planes were stored behind a false inner wall. One night, just before the Germans arrested Mortier and in the subsequent chase shot him through the lung, a British bomb, falling nearby, blew in the protective wall and left the secret hoard entirely exposed. Arriving there early in the morning, Mortier and other Resistance workers were horrified to see how near the Germans were to discovering their dangerous secret. A new inner wall was built with amazing speed, while garage hands casually guarded the entrance.

But even here Violette was not at all sure which of the old workers remained. Did that man with a wide brow fit in with one of the descriptions Staunton had given her? Or the man with the béret over his left ear? Or the man with blue eyes under shaggy eyebrows? She went in and asked one of the attendants if she could hire a bicycle. She would need one of course. It would be her only means of transport. The man looked her up and down. They did not have one, he said—not one they could spare. She said she'd look in again. And so, making her moves with the utmost circumspection, working in quite casually the password in use only a few weeks before in this area, in the hope that it might evoke a response, she was able, bit by bit, to pick up the threads.

She was appalled by what she eventually discovered. She found that of the ninety-eight members of this Resistance group more than ninety had been traced by the Germans and taken away as prisoners. What had become of them none knew for certain. Some, it was thought, had been sent to Germany. Others were in various prisons in northern France. Roger Mayer, a schoolmaster, who had been in charge of a group at Le Havre, had been taken off to a German prison camp. His wife, however, managed to get out of Le Havre and was now living in Paris. Some of the other wives were still about and it was possible in time for her to contact a few. She contrived even to get into Le Havre. The forged papers with which she had been equipped in London were not considered safe for use in this closely guarded port of the Atlantic Wall; so new papers were obtained for her, the actual forms, and in these her name was entered. She found there a feverish activity. The formidable line of coastal batteries was constantly being strengthened, fresh strong points were being added even now at this late hour. The beaches had live minefields. Even the sea was mined for miles. The Germans were aware that it was a race against time and Rommel came down for periodic inspections from his headquarters at La Roche-Guyon, midway between Paris and Rouen—the same Rommel whose army had been responsible for Etienne's death in Africa.

Violette was stopped and questioned repeatedly and her papers were subjected to constant examination. There were moments when she was sure she was being followed, but she managed each time to elude the pursuer, practising the art she had learned just across the Channel, and she wondered if the seagulls flying overhead had seen her at it there. Twice she was placed under arrest and taken to the police station for prolonged questioning. On the second occasion she was held there for nearly five hours. The Gestapo seemed not at all satisfied with her answers. Was this to be the end of her activities? And what would be her chance of escape from here? She thought of Bob's awful ordeal, thought also of the ninety or more who had been taken away from here and were now in various prisons, many of them in Germany. There appeared to be little hope for her. Again and again the Gestapo questioned her. But Violette, who had a nimble mind and was convincingly inventive, did not panic for a moment. She had shown in childhood her resource in the face of baffling difficulties; and now, by using her wits, by feigning a most charming innocence, she succeeded in making it impossible for them to link her in any way with subversive work. So they let her go.

Night after night Le Havre and Rouen and the adjoining coasts were heavily attacked by Allied bombers. Only a part of this was the selected area for the D-Day landings, the rest was attacked merely to mislead the Germans. All the main roads, railways and bridges for miles around were heavily bombed too in order to disorganise all the approaches and impede the bringing up of reinforcements.

Violette stayed in the area for two weeks. She was on the move all the time, spending a night first with one, then with another sympathiser. How many of these would be prepared to render active aid at the vital hour it was her purpose to ascertain.

Seated in Rouen one evening, in a back room behind locked doors, she heard for the first time one of the BBC's news broadcasts, which were sent out nightly at 7.30 and 9.15. They couched last-minute instructions in the most innocent phrases. Some were as simple as 'the cow jumped over the moon'. Single words, sent in from France, were inserted into the programme on three consecutive nights in order to indicate to the hesitant that the plans being made had the full authority and support of London; and by a similar method it was possible to prove, when, for instance, a substantial sum of money was required, that the agent had been authorised to raise it and that it would be refunded in full after the war. Behind all this seemingly childish nursery talk lay the entire might of the Allied forces preparing for the liberation of Europe. Plans for sabotage were indicated or confirmed in this manner. Parachute drops of arms and men, and the despatch of planes to rescue patriots were also, if necessary, adjusted by such simple pre-arranged phrases; and so 'Aunt Louise is better' might easily mean that the drop would take place that very night.

The Gestapo knew of this, of course. It was their purpose to prevent people listening to these broadcasts, not merely because they did not want them to learn the truth about the progress of the war, but because of the vital instructions hidden in some of the silliest phrases, which of course the Germans could not themselves decipher, but they knew the disastrous effect these had on factories, railways, and generally on the Nazi war plans. That is why they burst into people's homes during these hours of transmission: it enabled them incidentally also to discover who the listeners were and, in an area such as Rouen, everyone in the room was rounded up and placed under arrest.

Her inquiries over, she returned her bicycle to the garage and, making sure that she was not being watched, tore off one of the small posters in the street with the pictures of the two wanted men who were her friends. Imagine yourself doing that even in England. Then she took a train back to Paris to report to Staunton at the time and place arranged.

He met her again in the Luxembourg Gardens, where, as they walked, she told him all she had learned. There were many in Rouen and a few in Le Havre, she said, ready and eager to assist in every possible way. They awaited instructions and Violette was ready to return and assist them.

Staunton reflected in silence for a while. "I'm afraid," he said at last, "there won't be enough time to get it all going again. We would have to start completely from scratch. We shall need a radio operator, an instructor, more arms and explosives—for all that we have assembled so painstakingly there over many months has gone—all of it. It would take weeks—many weeks. And D-Day is not so far away now."

"But surely," she said, "if a start is made . . ."

"There isn't the time," he repeated. D-Day was in fact less than six weeks away. "But," he added, "at least we know how things are there. We can't call on Rouen, but, as a result of what you have learned, we shall be able to draw on other nearby organisations and fly in people for special jobs, like points to attack and bridges to blow up, when the landings are made. Thanks, Vi. You've done a fine job of work. No one could have done it better."

"What do we do now?" she asked.

"Well—we'll have to be going back."

"When do you think that will be?"

"As soon as we can get a plane. Possibly in three or four days. I'll get through to London this afternoon and see what can be arranged. Take the next two days off. See something of Paris. Go shopping. I'm sure there are one or two things you'd like to buy. Any money left? Well, don't worry about that. I have some over. You've earned the break. Meet me here again in forty-eight hours."

Violette was very tired. The strain of her two weeks in the heavily guarded coastal zone in Normandy, on the alert all the time without any let up, had begun to tell. She was staying again in the Rue Sts Pères with his aunt and when she left Staunton she went straight to bed. In the evening she and Staunton's aunt sat at a table on the Champs Elysées and ate a sandwich with their coffee.

Out shopping by herself the next day, she went to Molyneux, the famous couturier in the Rue Royale, which, despite the German occupation, was still carrying on. The bill head proclaimed quite bluntly that the firm had a branch open in London. Here she bought, as her bill dated April 28th, 1944, shows, three dresses and one very attractive jersey. The bill, made out to Mademoiselle C. Leroy, states that one of the dresses was of black crêpe de chine—it was draped with a lace neckline and cost 8500 francs. There was, of course, no official rate of exchange between England and France at the time, but the franc was worth much more than it was later: at the pre-war rate of 176 francs to the pound, the cost of this dress works out at nearly £50. Another of the dresses is set down as '*en écossais*': it was a red plaid dress. The third was of silk print. The jersey, described as a golf jersey, was yellow in colour. The total bill, with a purchase tax of 11 per cent, a municipal tax, and a 'Taxe au profit du secours national' of 5 per cent, came in all to over £200.

The dresses were fitted. Slight adjustments were required. "Will Mam'selle come back?" she was asked.

"How long will they take?"

"About three days."

"Can you do it in two?" she said. "I have to go to the South to join my parents."

"In two then, Mam'selle. In the afternoon."

She would have liked to have bought a dress for Tania. Dared she order one here? The risk was great. The 'Mam'selle' had been used repeatedly by the salesgirl and it was stressed even on her bill. There would be questions such as, "Can you bring the child in for a fitting, Mam'selle? . . . Next week perhaps?" More questions and Heaven alone knew what else.

Walking on towards the Madeleine, which rose in massive magnificence before her, she could almost hear Etienne speaking to her. Her eyes began to fill with tears, she felt she could not keep them back. Hurrying her pace a little, she climbed up the wide flight of steps, swept past the fluted pillars and, plunging into the church's dark interior, got down on her knees and buried her face in her hands. She stayed there for a while, alone with her thoughts of her husband and her child, praying that Tania was well and did not need her. She felt so desperately cut off. No news could be got through to her if the child was ill. She thought of the mother in Rouen in the house in which she had been staying who had to dash out in the middle of the night for a doctor.

She rose, feeling utterly desolate, and walked slowly out into the sunshine. At the side of the Madeleine, leaning against the church, stood the gay stalls of the flower market, with their gorgeous display of spring blooms. Among the daffodils and the tulips were early roses such as Etienne never failed to buy for her. She went to the stall and bought herself three roses. With them in her hand she crossed the road to the Trois Quartiers to get some little trinkets for her mother, for Vera Atkins and for Tania. But she hardly glanced at the varied display as she swept past the counters. Walking boldly up to an attendant, she asked where she could buy a dress for a child aged two. She was directed to the second floor. The choice was restricted. There were not many children in Paris now, she was told. The miniature dresses in pale blues and pinks fascinated her. In her mind she dressed her child in each of them in turn. As the attendant's voice brought her back to reality, she asked: "Have you nothing smaller? It's for a girl not quite two."

"No, Mam'selle," the attendant said. "We have not much these days. This—and this one here—*très, très gentil.*" They were all for girls who were older. She selected one at last. It was of gay flowered silk, with tiny pink and blue flowers and green leaves against a white background, and had a smocked bodice; in it she felt the sallowness of Tania would be set off to perfection. But she would have to wait a year or two before she could wear it. When she was four perhaps. Violette saw herself leading the child by the hand as they set off together for perhaps her first party.

"I'll take that," she said. Her heart was lighter now. She felt more cheerful. For her mother she bought some perfume, a compact, a pretty scarf and a pair of black gloves; for Vera Atkins she got a pendant brooch with three small and one large cluster of red and green enamel beads, a pearl at the end of each cluster.

The next day, when she saw Staunton, she learned that they

were to be picked up the following night by a Lysander from a field near Blois. That would mean leaving Paris by train in the afternoon. It meant also calling for her dresses at Molyneux a little earlier than arranged.

They were met at Blois station by two men with bicycles. They had to pedal through the darkness for an hour with their suitcases strapped on behind them, and in her case also a large box containing the purchases she had made. The patriots with flashlights said their farewells and guided the plane out.

CHAPTER FOURTEEN

HOME

THE flight home was smooth and without incident. The Lysander landed at Tempsford aerodrome shortly before dawn and a car brought them into London.

Staunton accompanied Violette to her parents' home in Brixton. The neighbourhood had not yet begun to stir. All was still in the house when the bell rang. The Bushells, wondering who could have rung it at that early hour, turned over in bed. Mr Bushell looked at his watch. Mrs Bushell, almost aware who it might be, got out of bed and went to the front door. Her hair was in disarray. She was tying the cord round her dressing-gown as she slid back the bolts. When the door opened she saw only a man standing there. "I've brought your daughter back," he said. Craning forward she saw Violette leaning wearily against the wall. "She was all in," says Mrs Bushell.

"Just put her to bed," said Staunton. He declined the invitation to come in for a cup of coffee.

Violette said: "I could sleep for a week."

"Come up to bed, darling." With her arm around her daughter's waist, Mrs Bushell led Violette into the house. They were confronted by the entire household in the hall. Mr Bushell was there and his sister Florence, who had come up from Hereford to meet her son Norman, home on leave from the Navy; and Norman was there too—all avid to see and to greet Violette.

"All right," she said. "I'll have a coffee with you before I go up to bed."

They sat in the kitchen and in their eager questioning kept her talking for two hours. She said nothing of Rouen or her work, merely that she had been in Paris. She could not resist telling them of the Germans who kept offering her cigarettes and insisted that she should share their compartment in the train. She did it with vivid mimicry, imitating their clumsy French accents, their heel-clicking and bowing and their heavy politeness. The suitcases were then brought in and unpacked. The Molyneux dresses were greatly admired. Mama fingered the material, examined the cut and the finish. They all cooed over the dress she had brought back for Tania. Mama was especially thrilled with the gifts Violette had got her. She tried on the Paris gloves, sniffed the perfume approvingly, gazed with admiration at the compact. To Aunt Florence Violette gave one of her own bottles of perfume.

By now the feeling of acute fatigue seemed to have left her. She refused to go to bed. All she wanted was a bath. After it, she was glad to be able to put her uniform on again and made her first call at the headquarters of the French Section of SOE. There she ran into a secret agent who was getting ready to leave that night for France. "May Day," he grumbled. "Everybody else has today off—only you and I have to work."

"Mine's finished," she said. "I just got back."

Staunton came out of an inner room. He had just handed in his report. "I've arranged for Bob to dine with us at the Studio Club tonight. I hope you can join us there?"

She said she would be delighted to. "I may be a little late. I'm now off to see Tania." A glow of happiness lit up her face.

All that afternoon she spent with her child. It was a joyous reunion. All the pent-up emotion poured out of her. She told the child of the dress, of the Eiffel Tower, of the Madeleine, and of the wonderful places she was going to take her to when the war was over.

In the evening Bob and Staunton had to wait the best part of an hour for her. "I'll never forget her entry," says Bob. "Everyone turned to stare at her. She looked radiant and very lovely. She had on a red dress she had bought in Paris"—it was the *robe en écossais*. "She was wearing a pair of new earrings she had also got in Paris—they were bunches of red flowers dangling from a gilt chain—and, though she was very sparing as a rule with perfume, that night she seemed to have splashed it on because it was something one could no longer get very easily in England. All the women in the room raised their nostrils to breathe it in and shut their eyes in ecstasy at the heavenly scent. She really looked wonderful."

As she took her seat Violette, her eyes dancing, said: "Wouldn't they be startled if they knew where I have been and where I got it all?"

In Paris now, as they all three knew, though the shops were filled with novelties, one's freedom was greatly restricted. Food and wine and even cigarettes were rationed, one could not dance (the Germans had banned dancing), nor could one move about the town freely at night because of the curfew. After midnight, if you happened to be in a night club, you had to remain there until five in the morning when the curfew ended.

She told Bob of her visit to Rouen and showed him the poster she had torn off the wall with his picture on it.

Bob smiled and shrugged his shoulders. "Well, I'm ready now to be sent off somewhere," he said.

"Don't be surprised," she said, "if I'm back there before you." In point of fact they were all three to make the next trip together in five weeks, but they did not know that yet.

She danced with Staunton and later, while on the floor with Bob, he tipped his head towards the band to draw her attention to what they were playing. It was 'The Last Time I Saw Paris'. She looked up at him and smiled.

They went on afterwards to a night club where they stayed till the small hours. Neither Violette nor Staunton seemed to be tired. But they slept through the bulk of the next day.

Her cousin Norman, whom she had not seen for two years, insisted that it would do her a world of good if she came back to Hereford for a few days with him and his mother. She agreed readily and they left a day or two later. There was a fair at Hereford. They went on the roundabouts, to the shooting gallery, where again she won all the prizes, rode in the bumper cars and discovered afterwards that in the course of these boisterous diversions she had lost one of the red flower-earrings she had brought back from Paris. They searched but it could not be found. Her Aunt Florence still treasures the remaining earring, which she insisted on keeping. "Violette used to cook some of our meals," she says. "I remember one night when she was frying eggs. The house was full of a burning smell. She had forgotten to use any fat."

After a week she and Norman, who had to rejoin his ship, came back to town by train. "There were two soldiers in our carriage and Violette and I played pontoon with them for the whole of the journey. She was not normally lucky at cards, but on this occasion she won all the time and was a considerable sum to the good when we arrived at Paddington. She refused to keep it, however, and divided it equally between the two soldiers.

"I spent two or three days in London before going back to sea. Violette knew London well of course, and we had a couple of quite hectic days and nights, finishing up always in a night club, where we danced. She was wonderful company. One evening she stopped our taxi, jumped out and spoke to two men in a car. She did not say who they were, but I guess they were connected with her work, of which she never talked at all." They were in fact Staunton and Bob.

She was fond of staying up late at night, of having lively company around her, of listening to music, and dancing. She did not drink much or smoke heavily. But the need for a release of tension was prevalent in war-time, especially among those serving in the forces. Her mother says: "Violette did not like drink and she smoked very little. One night she took her brother John, who was home on leave from REME, and a young Norwegian named Eric, who was a secret agent, to a night club in Soho. Both boys were over six foot tall, and you can just imagine Violette having to bring them home in the small hours of the morning with one boy on each side of her, holding on for support to this tiny girl. All Violette said afterwards was: 'Somebody had to stay sober or we'd never have got back.' "

As a rule she lived in her flat now, but from time to time spent a night or two at Mill Hill with her daughter. There was a lull in enemy bombing and the buzz bombs had not yet begun to come over. So occasionally she brought the child up to London for the day, took her shopping, and twice took her to SOE headquarters to show her off with pride to Bob and Staunton and the others.

She was told that plans were in progress for the next mission. "You don't have to go," said Buckmaster. "You've done your share—and a fine job it was too. You showed pluck and coolness and great resource."

"Don't you want me to go?" she asked.

"Well, yes. That's up to you. But I feel you ought to know that this time it's going to be much more dangerous."

She smiled. "If I can be of any help, I shall be glad to go again."

Staunton said to her a day or two later, "There's a thought that Bob and I and you might go together. It's going to be very dangerous. Although you've said yes, you can still change your mind, you know."

"Are you trying to drop me?" she asked.

"No. It isn't that."

"What is it then?"

"Just suppose you didn't come back."

"Tell me just this," she said. "Do you think I am capable of. . ."

"There is no question of that," he interrupted. "You are the one person I feel I can rely on absolutely to do the job."

"Then it's settled," she said. "There's no need for either of us to say any more. I'll come."

He smiled at her. "Good," he said.

"When do we go?"

"At the next moon."

The next moon, the June moon, for which D-Day had been planned too, was less than two weeks off. Many of the people she knew seemed to be away. She ran into very few of them now. The pretty Italian girl she had once seen dancing with Harry Peulevé told her that he was still out of town. "He has gone abroad with his regiment," she said. Where to she did not know.

Violette began to prepare for her own departure. She had a photograph taken of herself. It was not in uniform, but in the pretty black dress draped with a lace neckline which she had bought at Molyneux in Paris. Giving it to her mother, she said: "I like this picture. It's the best one ever taken of me. I'll get some extra copies to give to my brothers, my cousins and a few friends."

Mrs Bushell stared at her for some moments, wondering if

there was some sort of presentiment in her mind. Violette merely smiled and wrinkled her nose at her.

A few days later she told her mother that she had made her will. There wasn't much in the bank, just the hundred pounds or so that Etienne had left her, to which had been added her own small salary for the weeks she was away. It would of course continue to be paid in regularly while she was on her next mission. She wanted all the money to be kept for Tania. She also handed her mother the gold bracelet which was Etienne's wedding present to her, an attractive vanity-case she had received in advance for her birthday in June, and her wedding ring. Her engagement ring of emeralds and diamonds she retained. "I'd better keep this," she said. "If I am on the run I should be able to raise some money on it."

She asked her father to dispose of her flat and its contents.

There was some money still to be paid on the refrigerator and the furniture, but Mr Bushell managed to clear it all up and to have £70 over to pay into Violette's bank.

All this made Mr and Mrs Bushell more and more uneasy. It was as though Violette felt uncertain of the future.

She then looked up her friends as though in farewell. She dropped in on Winnie Wilson, who had married two years or so before and was now Mrs Sharpe. "I was doing my washing when Vi dropped in. She was wearing a black cape and a black skirt. With her high cheek-bones she looked very striking. She came to invite my husband and myself to the pictures and stayed only a few seconds, as she was obviously very pressed for time. She insisted that we should be her guests at the cinema. Looking back on it, I realise it was her way of saying good-bye."

Again she went up to Mill Hill for a night or two. Mrs Bushell, who was constantly visiting Tania, promised to keep in the closest touch with the child. On June 4th, just before going to headquarters in readiness for her second mission, Violette went to Mill Hill again and found her mother already there. Mrs Bushell could tell from the warmth of her manner that this was the moment of parting. Violette said: "You are not to worry, Mama. I shall be all right—and if anything should happen, well, Tania will get a good pension. There's a bit in the bank, as you know, and I've made you my executrix. So Tania should really be all right.

"Now there's just one thing more I want to say to you. Things may become difficult out there. I may be on the run and the Germans may be on my track. It may be impossible for me to get back—may even be difficult for me to write. But don't worry, darling, if you don't hear. I'll try—I promise I'll try somehow to get a message through. There may be a way. One can never tell.

"There's just one thing I *don't* want you to do—for Heaven's sake never try to find out where I am. Don't make any inquiries. If you do anything at all, one never knows what it might lead to. It will only add to my danger. You can't help, you know. If you think for a moment you'll realise that you can't really help at all. So don't make a move of any kind. Will you promise, Mummy darling? Just wait until the end of the war—you may have to wait that long. I'll do my damnedest to get back if I'm caught. I'll escape somehow—and quite suddenly you'll find I'm back with you in England."

Her mother's eyes were filled with tears. She did not know what to say. Violette fell silent for a while, then she added, as though thinking aloud: "If they torture me—I wonder if I'll be able to stand it. People do. I hope I will. I think I will."

Mrs Bushell pressed her face against her daughter's. Tania came out to join them.

"You promise?" Violette asked.

Mrs Bushell nodded very slowly.

Then, kissing them both very fervently, Violette moved quickly to the door; but turning there she came back, seized Tania and clasped her close, and kissed her again and again. She broke away at last, hurried up to town and reported at headquarters. There Vera Atkins was waiting with a car to take her to Hasell's Hall, the lovely old Georgian house at Sandy in Bedfordshire, which stood back among the woods and was used as a club house and dormitory by the secret agents and others setting out on special missions.

CHAPTER FIFTEEN

HER SECOND MISSION

THAT, though they did not know it, was the night selected for the dispatch of the mighty armada taking the invading Allied armies to the coast of Normandy. They were to land to the west of Rouen. But the weather all that day had been appalling, typical of December rather than June. At 9.15 that night, at a conference at Eisenhower's headquarters in England, the position was carefully examined. The experts said the weather was likely to remain rough for an indefinite period. Only a slight, temporary improvement was expected on the morning of June 6th. Eisenhower, who was opposed to postponing the invasion, decided to use this brief improvement. The invasion was accordingly fixed for the early morning of June 6th, which meant a delay of only twenty-four hours.

When Violette arrived at the country house at Sandy, she learned that they were to fly in an American Liberator. An American wireless operator named Jean-Claude Guiet was to be the fourth member of their party. Guiet was only twenty years old. Both his parents were French. He was born in America and spoke French with not the slightest trace of accent. He was tall and dark and quite good-looking. He held a commission as second lieutenant in the United States Army, but like the others he was not in uniform tonight. Violette had on slacks and a leather jacket cut in the French style. The men were in velvet trousers and jackets. All looked very French in their appearance and their bearing. There was, of course, the usual very thorough inspection of their clothes and the contents of their pockets.

As they assembled for dinner and the introductions were made, Vera noticed again that Violette was the only girl going out on an operation. All the men in the room, of whom there were a large number, including swarms of Special Air Service boys, who were known as 'Jedburghs' (they were to land behind the lines in uniform) turned to look at her, some with admiring eyes, others with a certain misgiving, as though wondering what on earth this pretty little thing thought she was up to. Vera Atkins says: "There was great tension in the room that night. All the boys were going out on various operations. You could feel the jumpiness of their nerves. Astonishingly, Violette alone was perfectly calm and composed. I was very struck by the contrast."

In groups, as they were called, the others left their tables and set out by car for the aerodrome. Presently it was time for Staunton, Violette and their party to go too. They got up and, accompanied by Vera, made their way to Tempsford, with the blinds drawn as always so that even the ground staff should not see the secret agents.

The Liberator looked enormous after the tiny Lysander in which she flew out before. There was a crew of seven, all Americans in uniform. At the back of the plane where they were to sit behind the bomb racks (only tonight the plane carried not bombs, but containers filled with arms and explosives which were to be dropped with them), there was room just for the four, apart from the rear gunner and the dispatcher, whose task it would be to attend to their jump. These men too were Americans and in uniform.

The parachutes, which were not the ordinary service parachutes but very much larger ones made especially for airborne troops, since they were to be used as a means of transport and not as a lifebelt, had already been placed in the plane. Wearing their flying suits, with the zipper pockets full of weapons, rations, maps and compass, the four got in. Vera said her good-byes. The engines were revved up and the plane began to throb. Just as it was taxi-ing along the runway a man came out with a message. It said that the weather ahead was very bad. A postponement to the next night was thereupon decided. Frantic signals to the Liberator brought it to a halt and the four passengers got out again. Vera says: "On their faces one could see their acute disappointment. It was the most awful anticlimax—to say good-bye, to get into the plane, to be on the point of taking off and then to troop out again, get back into the car and drive back to the house."

In the common room at Hasell's Hall, some smiled, others exchanged whispers which might have been a little contemptuous, but Violette did not turn a hair. She walked straight past them, accepted a cigarette from Bob and had coffee, while Vera arranged accommodation for them for the night. The three men slept together in a room on the first floor. Violette had one to herself a few doors away.

Vera returned to town and rejoined them the next morning to make fresh plans for their departure. She found Violette engaged in a brisk game of ping-pong. "I have never seen her look more beautiful," says Vera. "She had on a pair of white marguerite earrings which she had bought in Paris. Her dress had a plunging neck-line. She wore no stockings, but just a pair of bright sandals. She made a really striking picture—her well-chiselled features, her high cheekbones, her eyes bright and lively, her hair so pretty: a lithe, girlish figure, young, strong and supple, she was bursting with health and pulsating with vitality, all of her just coiled energy." Again she was struck by her amazing calmness. "If she had any premonition about the future she certainly did not show it."

The three boys, with time on their hands for the rest of the day, borrowed a car and, taking Violette with them, motored, not into Bedford which was only ten miles away, but into Cambridge which was twice as far. There they had lunch and, though the day was grey and uninviting, spent the afternoon boating on the river. They came back in time for dinner and went through all the previous night's formalities of departure—the inspection of their clothes, the careful search of their pockets. Then they set out again for the airfield.

This time the plane took off. It was the night of the invasion, but they were unaware of it. Enclosed in the back of the plane they saw nothing, but the pilot and the others in front saw the greatest armada of ships ever known to history proceeding across the Channel. It was a breath-taking sight. All round them the air was thick with planes. Every aerodrome in Britain was in use that night. In an endless stream they flew, all going southward. Three airborne divisions were to follow them and seize objectives at Caen and elsewhere behind the enemy lines.

The Liberator flew high over the Normandy beaches, then, descending, made for the heart of France. It picked out the landmarks and located the landing-ground, which lay hidden amid the low hills to the south of Limoges. Again and again it circled the dark hills and fields looking for the small signalling lights, but the crew saw none. So no parachute drops could be made and the plane had to turn back. Once again they returned to the Tempsford and drove back to the club house. Wearily, for it was only an hour before dawn, they went up to their beds, the men together again in one room and Violette by herself in another.

At five o'clock in the morning the men were shaken out of their deep sleep and told to get up. "It's time, sir. Come on," called the batman.

"Why?" asked Bob.

"What time is it?" inquired Staunton.

Guiet, the American, just turned over and groaned.

"It's five o'clock, sir," said the batman.

At this pandemonium broke loose. "What the devil do you mean by waking us up at five in the morning?" . . . "What's the big idea anyway?" . . . "We're not wanted until the night."

The batman walked to the door and brought in the notice pinned to it. It stated: "Urgent. Please call us at 5 a.m. sharp, without fail—and see that we are up."

The boys jumped out of their beds in a fury. They deduced, rightly, that Violette had put the notice there. So they stormed into her room and shook her into wakefulness, then dragged her out of bed, poured a volley of angry oaths on her head and returned to their room.

At seven o'clock the boys were awakened again—this time by Violette herself. She had not gone back to sleep, but had dressed and gone down for breakfast. She went now from one bed to another, calling out in an excited voice, "The Invasion! We've landed. Come on, get up."

"Oh, for Heaven's sake . . ." groaned Staunton.

"Get back to your blasted bed and go to sleep," said Bob, throwing his pillow at her.

"It's true," she said. "Look!"

She had brought the morning papers and in a moment they were all poring over them, reading the thrilling details of D-Day.

They dressed speedily. They were anxious to be off. But they had of course to wait until the night.

Vera Atkins was already there when they got down. The reception committee near Limoges had got through during the small hours. German patrols, it appeared, had been on the prowl. In the circumstances, of course, no landing signals could be given.

Once again they went to Cambridge for the day. It was warm, though not sunny. They swam in the river, played tennis, and at about eleven o'clock that night, after still another inspection of their clothes and their pockets, once again they got into the Liberator and this time all was well.

The flight out took four hours. Violette and the three boys sat uncomfortably on the floor of the plane and played gin rummy. The American dispatcher marvelled at their composure. He beckoned to the rear gunner, who wrinkled his chin in confirmatory surprise. With Violette leading them in song, they raised their voices and yelled the tuneful chorus of 'I'll Be Around', which they had come to regard as their theme song. This convinced the Americans that the four were quite mad. At about two o'clock they helped themselves to rum and coffee from their flasks. An hour later they were over their objective.

The signalling lights were discernible quite clearly below. The dispatcher got the four into position. They put on their parachutes; the static line of each was clipped on to one of the rings attached to the walls of the plane. There was no hatch for them to jump through, but a hole had been cut for this purpose in the floor of the Liberator. The lid was lifted off this and Violette, as the first to go, sat on the edge of the hole, with her legs dangling into the rushing wind below. For a moment she clung with her hands behind her, then she let go. The line drew taut and tugged open the 'chute. Staunton had by now taken her place, next came Bob, then Guiet. Slowly the four swung down to the earth. Taking another run above the field, the Liberator dropped the containers that held their suitcases, then four further containers, each containing Sten guns, Tommy guns, hand grenades, ammunition and explosives. The big plane then turned and made for home.

But instead of a reception committee of three, the four descending from the plane saw thirty men running across the field towards them. Remembering what nearly happened at Rouen and the cause of their turning back the night before, they wondered if it might be the Gestapo. Before they reached the earth they were seized by their feet, dragged down and covered with embraces and kisses. It was a most fervent welcome. No whispers here, they talked in their normal voices. Their torches were kept alight. A large car had been brought to take back the visitors and a lorry for the weapons and supplies.

They were now in the Maquis country. The people here had an arrogant confidence in their numbers and the utmost contempt for the Germans. They had been greatly heartened by the Allied landings in Normandy a few hours before, for they saw that the day of their deliverance was very near. They laughed and jested as they drove along the dark country roads, proclaiming proudly that there wasn't a German around for miles. The Germans as a rule kept clear of the Maquis areas: they found them difficult to control. But every now and again they made a sweep through this hilly, wooded country. Had they come again unexpectedly tonight there would undoubtedly have been a fight, for the reception committee had brought their guns with them. But the car and the lorry got through unchallenged to the little village of Sussac, where the visitors from England were to stay.

They were housed above a grocer's shop in the centre of the village. Once again Violette got a room to herself. The boys shared. The people did everything to make them comfortable. There was plenty to eat in that country area, where cattle abounded. No ration cards were required. The Maquis ran the place their own way.

All voices in the house were hushed that night so that the guests should get a good night's rest and there was no question of getting up for breakfast. It was brought to their beds.

CHAPTER SIXTEEN

THE AMBUSH

VIOLETTE and her party arrived at Sussac in the small hours of the morning of June 7th, 1944. The Allied landings of twenty-four hours earlier had already established a foothold in Normandy and the Germans were rushing troops at reckless speed from all parts of France and Germany in order to dislodge them and drive them back into the sea. For months all the valiant endeavours of the French Section of SOE had been directed to the one end of preventing the German divisions from getting there now, or at any rate hampering and delaying their progress. Every group of Resistance workers behind the enemy lines had been allotted a specific task. Roads and bridges had to be blown up. Acts of sabotage had been arranged at factories and on the railways, at lock gates and at power stations. It was their purpose to cause the greatest possible destruction and to create a confusion that would distract and bewilder the enemy. Staunton's task in the Limoges area was to harness the Maquis most effectively to this same end.

He saw around him vast sections of Maquis, numbering 3000 men in all. They were spread out across a hundred miles of country from Sussac northwards to Châteauroux. Through this great expanse of wooded land the Maquis roved as they pleased, save for occasional raids by detachments of heavily armed Germans. Two main roads to Normandy ran through this region—one from Toulouse, the other from Bordeaux. In its midst was the large industrial town of Limoges, which was completely under German control. The town was heavily guarded by German troops. There were road blocks at all points leading into the town and passes were required to enter and leave it. The Gestapo also had their headquarters for the area in Limoges.

Around Sussac were the Haute Vienne Maquis, numbering

about 600. On learning of the Allied landings, the 200 gendarmes Pétain had in the area instantly joined forces with the Maquis. One of the chief figures in this group was a young man known by the code name of Anastasie. His real name was Jacques Dufour. He was tall, dark, heavy-browed and had sparkling eyes. He was born at Salon-la-Tour, a village not far from Sussac. For his daring exploits against them, the Germans had singled him out as 'the greatest bandit in the Limoges area'. They knew his real name and were determined to get him. A large sum of money was offered for Anastasie alive or dead and the Germans had even rounded up some Dufours who had a hotel in Salon-la-Tour, but were in no way related. To the south were the Corrèze Maquis, to the east the Creuse Maquis. Others stretched westward into the Dordogne.

For the most part these Maquis were farm hands and peasants. There was a sprinkling among them of Spaniards who had fought in the Civil War and refused to live under Franco, and just a handful of Poles. They dressed themselves in any uniform they could find or devise and looked like assorted figures out of a musical comedy. Some had gay jackets with gold epaulettes and wore feathers in their hats, others went about in khaki shorts or wore a khaki béret with their workaday corduroys.

Staunton says in his report: 'When I left London I was given to understand that I would find on arrival a very well-organised Maquis, strictly devoid of any political intrigues, which would constitute a very good basis for extending the circuit throughout the area. On arrival I did find a Maquis, which was roughly 600 strong, plus 200 French gendarmes who joined up on D-Day. But these men were strictly not trained, and were commanded by the most incapable people I have ever met, as was overwhelmingly proved by the fact that none of the D-Day targets had been attended to and that each time it took me several hours of discussions to get one small turnout, either to the railway or the telephone lines.'

The members of this force were indeed highly individualistic. When arms and explosives had been dropped to them in the past, instead of guarding them for co-ordinated and advantageous use on selected targets at the arranged signal, their one resolve had been to settle the war there and then by themselves. Buckling on their equipment and shouldering their rifles they set out in immediate quest of the enemy, provoked a battle and, having neither discipline nor a plan of campaign, suffered heavily in such engagements.

Staunton realised that his task was not going to be easy. In Rouen, starting from scratch, he had been able to recruit men and women who were willing to serve and to accept both discipline and training. Here he found disorganised bands who wanted only to go their own way. No doubt all the other groups of Maquis around here were similar in composition and attitude. At the head of them all, with the entire force of 3000 nominally under his control, was a remote figure in Châteauroux. 'The Chief of this Maquis,' states Staunton in his report, 'a man who calls himself Colonel Charles, was by trade a saxophonist in a Bal Musette; a soldier of the second class with no war experience. He had been for Hector, Samuel and Anastasie (the leaders of the separate sections) their only contact with the neighbouring Maquis, which none of these leaders had every really visited, relying on Charles for their information.'

Staunton, who had come here with his team for the express purpose of organising and directing them, was resolved to get the entire Maquis force into immediate action. The German divisions were already on the march, so not a moment could be lost. Had Hitler listened to what Rommel had been urging for many months, these scattered divisions would already have been in the north, for that obviously was where they would be needed. But Hitler had an eye on the possibility of a landing in the South of France (which did indeed come not long after Normandy) and he felt that, by keeping his army dispersed, he would provide them with greater mobility and striking power. The most formidable of these divisions in the south was the Das Reich SS Panzer division stationed at Toulouse and already on its way to Normandy to aid the hard-pressed German forces there. Soon it would be entering Maquis country. That was the time to strike and strike hard.

Staunton called an immediate council of action. Anastasie, as the chief of the local Maquis, listened attentively and expressed his readiness to co-operate to the full. What they had needed was a plan of operation. Now that the Allies had landed and things were moving so fast, the Maquis, he said, could be relied upon absolutely to strike at the enemy whenever and wherever required. He knew the country well—they all did. He would get his men into position at points of vantage with their explosive charges, their hand grenades and Tommy guns. "You can rely on us. The Das Reich division will never through," he said. The words, Staunton felt, had the swagger of the Maquis, but the spirit was there, he knew.

He thanked Anastasie. "That takes care of this territory. Now what about the others?"

"They will act too. I am sure of it," Anastasie said. "But we must take the plan to them—and it will have to be explained to them very carefully. We must send someone . . ." He glanced round the room.

"Violette will take it," said Staunton.

Anastasie looked at the girl. "Good," he said. "I will take her along to the Maquis nearest to us in the Corrèze."

"We need you here," said Staunton.

"But someone must give the girl the backing of our authority. They know me in the Corrèze. I will hand her over to Samuel, who is the leader there, and I shall be back in three—at most four hours."

"All right."

"She will explain the plan of operation—and Samuel will take her on personally, like me, to the next group of Maquis in the Creuse area. And so on, till in the end she gets to Colonel Charles at Châteauroux and tells him how we have decided to act."

"That sounds fine," said Staunton. "But remember there's a price on your head."

"Oh, I shall be all right. I'll be back in the afternoon," Anastasie assured him.

Turning to Violette, Staunton added: "Whatever happens we need Anastasie here. I want you to remember that. He is vital to our plans."

She nodded. "I understand."

Anastasie got busy at once. Things had to be got going quickly. On the morning of June 10th, that is to say three days after

Violette's arrival, all was ready for her to start on her mission. The Maquis had collected in the preceding months vast stores of arms and explosives which were secreted in various dumps. They also had quite a number of motor-cars. Most of these were driven by wood fuel, but for this journey they brought out a large black Citroën and filled it up with petrol. The party assembled in the small square in Sussac in front of the grocer's where Violette, Staunton and the others lived. Violette was dressed in a light tailored suit, flat-heeled shoes and no stockings. She took a small suitcase with her and her Sten gun with eight magazines of ammunition. Anastasie, who had on his corduroys and a leather jacket, took his Tommy gun. It was a warm day, though the sun was obscured by clouds. Indeed the sky looked threatening, as though a storm might blow up at any minute.

The two got into the car and with a resounding cheer and a volley of good wishes set off at about half-past nine. Anastasie intended to take her to Pompadour, a charming little village about thirty miles away in the very heart of the Corrèze country. Pompadour is dominated by the fifteenth-century castle from which Antoinette Poisson, the mistress of Louis the Fifteenth, took her name.

The journey there was not expected to take much more than an hour. Almost all of it lay through narrow winding country lanes, not leafy but flanked by rocks and scrub. But they would have at some point to cross the main road from Toulouse to Normandy, and it was very possible that here they might encounter a Nazi division moving northward to Normandy with its tanks and fleet of lorries carrying supplies.

Anastasie had arranged to pick up on the way the son of a doctor who lived at La Croisille, about four miles from Sussac. The boy, who was not quite twelve years old, was going beyond Pompadour and was delighted to get a lift in the car, but brought his bicycle for the journey back. Violette and Anastasie helped him to rope it on to the side of the car. They placed it against the side Violette was sitting, so as to leave the door to the driver's seat clear. The boy got in at the back. The two in front kept their guns handy just in case there was trouble.

Anastasie decided to cross the main road at Salon-la-Tour.

He felt it would be an advantage to go through a village he knew so well. The people there, with whom he had lived since his childhood, would readily inform him of any activity by the Germans along the main road.

They sang, as they went, French songs that they all knew. As they passed under the railway bridge and approached the quiet sleepy little village of Salon-la-Tour, the storm clouds overhead descended in a heavy but brief downpour. Their lane swept westward and Anastasie pointed eagerly through the rain at the church, the huddle of white houses and the ivy-clad tower from which the village gets its name. "Look," he said, "I climbed up to the very top of that when I was nine and took lots of photographs with my small box camera."

They peered at the rain-slashed landscape on the right. "That's where I used to live. I'll take your right past it. On this other side, beyond the farms, is a little stream where my sister and I used to come and fish as children. We once saw a snake swallow a frog there."

The boy said: "It's going to be pretty slippery cycling back."

"Nonsense," said Anastasie. "Here's the sun trying to break through. This storm will be over in no time."

They went on towards the village street, beyond which lay the main road. Suddenly Anastasie pulled up. With lowered voice he said, "There's something behind that hedge—the further side—right in that field beyond."

"They're Germans," said Violette. "You can just see one of their caps."

The boy leapt out of the back of the car and ran into the nearest field. Anastasie got out too, Tommy gun in hand, and flung himself into a shallow ditch at the side of the road. Violette had to squeeze herself past the steering-wheel of the car. Seizing her Sten gun, she crossed the road to a tree. "Run," she called to the boy, but he was already scurrying fast across the fields.

Instantly the Germans began to shoot from the further side of the hedge. Violette turned her gun on them and blazed away too.

"Are you mad?" cried Anastasie. "Get down here. Come on. You haven't a dog's chance out there."

With a quick glance towards the boy, who was tearing towards home but was not yet out of sight, she sent a further burst of fire at the Germans.

"For Heaven's sake," shouted Anastasie. "Come down here."

"All right. All right," she cried. She crossed the lane, looked at the ditch. "That's not going to do much good," she said.

The Germans had by now emerged. There appeared to be about thirty of them. She saw that it was better to leave the lane and dash across the fields, where they might have a chance.

"This way," she said, prodding Anastasie with her foot.

Crouching, for the Germans had begun to fire again with their very rapid Schmeissers, Violette crept along the ditch to the wooden fence of a farm-house and leapt over it. Anastasie followed instantly and they both flung themselves down on the wet earth. A woman tending her cows turned to see the cause of all this startling activity. She was caught in the German line of fire and was killed instantly.

The storm had by now blown over and the sun was out. Anastasie motioned to Violette, both rose quickly and ran forward. The bullets flew around them. One tore through Anastasie's jacket but did not even graze his skin. Both were running hard. Violette dashed out of the small field, crossed a narrow farm track and entered the yard of the adjoining farm, with Anastasie close at her heels. The farmer, who had come in to get a jacket because of the storm, gazed with alarm through his window at the fleeing figures. He saw Anastasie stuff a piece of paper into his mouth and, running to the further hedge, leap across it to the wide sloping meadows which swept down to the stream. Violette sped after him. By the time the Germans came up the figures were out of sight. Calling angrily to the farmer, they demanded the way the fugitives had gone. He said, being indoors and they tearing by so fast, he couldn't exactly tell, but thought they had gone that way. He pointed in the wrong direction.

By now still more Germans had come up. They were in fact the advance guard of the Das Reich SS Panzer division, sweeping the villages to make sure the division could proceed along the road unhindered. Four hundred strong, with armoured cars in support, they were clearing the surrounding countryside of

Maquis assailants who, they felt, might be lying in wait with hand grenades and Tommy guns. Into the farmer's yard they poured in groups of twenty and fanned out, some taking the direction indicated, others tearing through the hedge to the meadows which sloped down to the stream. They were all heavily armed. Two armoured cars now appeared travelling along almost parallel farm tracks.

After some moments Violette and Anastasie, having waded through the stream, emerged, wet and out of breath, and could be seen dashing up the further slope towards a distant cornfield. Instantly the entire German advance guard dashed after them and the armoured cars turned and bounced along their tracks which, they all knew, converged at the far end.

Bullets began to fly fast now from the machine-guns of the two armoured cars and the Schmeissers of the pursuing Germans. Violette received a slight flesh wound in her left arm. In a moment the two distant figures were lost in the cornfield amid the tall golden corn. They knew, since both had been well trained, that their progress would have to be zigzag or the bending corn would leave a revealing trail for the marksmen.

The German volleys continued, tearing into the corn.

"All right?" called Anastasie, who was a few yards in front.

"Fine," she called back.

"I've swallowed the code," he said. "So all's well."

Then suddenly Violette fell. Anastasie turned back in alarm and found her lying on the earth.

"It's nothing," she said. "Go on. I'm doing fine."

It was not a bullet, he found, that had brought her down, but her ankle, already damaged during her jumps at Ringway; it gave in the swift zigzagging to right and to left.

He picked her up in his arms, but she struggled hard to get free.

"Don't be a damned fool," she said. "We can't both be saved. You won't stand a chance if you're caught. Besides, you've work to do. Go on. Get out."

He carried her while she struggled. She beat hard against his shoulders with her fists, kicked and wriggled. The bullets still breezed past them and the chattering guns came ever nearer.

With a final desperate thrust Violette succeeded in bringing them both down. As they fell amid the corn, with her Sten gun clutched in her hands, she crawled to the edge of the cornfield, clamped a new magazine in and, crouching, limped her way to an apple tree.

She was an easy mark now. The bullets pinged and spat up spurts of earth. It was a miracle that she was not killed. She stood up, cocked her gun and began firing at the oncoming Germans.

"Run!" she called. "Run! For God's sake, make a run for it."

Some Germans were seen to fall, whether killed or wounded none could tell.

Anastasie saw that it was utterly hopeless now to go to her aid. "It's your last chance," she called again. "You can just make it." With that she pressed a fresh magazine into the gun and resumed her firing.

Anastasie rose, glanced about him like a hunted animal, and with a last burst at the Germans from his Tommy gun, ran out of the cornfield to the road at the top. The two armoured cars were not far away now. Both were making for the same point. There was just a chance that he would get there first.

Crouching, half dropping with exhaustion, he ran on and reached at last the railway bridge at the top and the small farm-house beside it. At the corner of the road, by the bridge, lay a pile of logs. Anastasie decided to worm his way into their midst. They should with luck provide him with enough cover. From the window of the farm-house the farmer watched with apprehension. At other windows stood his wife and two daughters. They knew Anastasie well. Both girls had been to school with him.

Quickly the girls came out. They piled the logs upon him and had just got him covered up when the first of the two armoured cars turned towards them. With the greatest alarm suddenly one of the girls saw that Anastasie's foot was exposed, so she sat down on it.

The Germans leapt down from the car and started their questioning. The girls admitted they had seen a man run by. He had leapt, they said, down to the railway lines.

Meanwhile, swarming across the fields, shot at continuously as they came, the Germans, numbering many hundreds, firing all the time, closed in on Violette. By now all the magazines of her

Sten gun had been emptied. As they came to take her she fought them with immense strength for one so small. She kicked and struggled and struck at them with her fists, and bit their hands as they seized her. But she was no match for so many. Two Nazi soldiers eventually succeeded in pinioning her by the arms and half carried, half dragged her to the top, for she was utterly exhausted and in great pain.

They brought her, hot and dishevelled, to the heap of logs under which Anastasie was hidden and stood within a pace of him. The second armoured car now came up. A young officer, eyeing Violette with admiration, said: "I like your spirit. You put up a wonderful fight—right up to the end." Then, motioning to his men to let go her arms, he took out his cigarette-case, selected one for her and stuck it between her lips.

Some weeks before, while travelling with Germans in the train to Rouen, she had to appear to be affable in order to allay suspicion. But now the mask was off. She was no longer prepared to engage in an exchange of courtesies. She spat out the cigarette. Her eyes blazing with fury, she said: "You dirty cowards. You filthy German swine. I don't want your cigarettes——" and with that, leaning forward, she spat full in the young officer's face.

His eyes narrowed. Drawing his handkerchief, he wiped the spittle off his eyes and cheek. Then suddenly he threw his head back and laughed.

"All right," he said. "Take her away." He motioned towards the nearer armoured car. The two soldiers seized her and lifted her on to it. She refused the seat offered her.

The officer sprang on to the car himself. Hundreds of German soldiers meanwhile were swarming across the railway lines and beating the bushes in their search for Anastasie.

"We'll be back presently," the officer told the farmer, who was now standing at his door. "Get inside all of you. Not one of you must leave the house."

The girl sitting on Anastasie's foot hesitated for a moment. "Go on, get inside," the German officer commanded.

"All right, I'm going," she said casually.

She began to rise. With her body still covering the exposed foot, she waited until the armoured cars moved off. She heard

Violette say: "Will you tell your men to let go my arms? I'd like to have one of my own cigarettes."

As the two armoured cars turned into the village street hundreds standing at their windows saw her go by in the leading car, with a cigarette between her lips, shouting death and damnation to the Germans. "Your fate is already sealed. The end is drawing near. It won't be long now. Then you swine will get your deserts in full."

Many Germans were seen to fall when they closed in on her, for they presented a wide semicircle which she raked with her gun. But none can tell the exact number, as the entire village remained behind closed doors for the rest of the day. No bodies were found. The Germans were not likely to leave their dead and wounded on the fields for the villagers to dispose of.

Anastasie lay under the logs for many hours. By adjusting one of the logs after the Germans left, the girls were able to keep the foot concealed until night fell. Then they came out and took him into the house. The farmer's wife had prepared a meal for him. He ate it ravenously. "If I live a hundred years," he said, "I shall never forget today." But as things turned out he was killed the following year in Indo-China. His body was brought home and lies in the little cemetery within sight of the fields across which he and Violette were pursued for close on two miles, fighting all the way.

In Salon-la-Tour even now they talk of that heroic day when '*la petite Anglaise*' held four hundred Germans of the Das Reich SS Panzer division at bay, with a complete disregard of all personal risk. It gave the boy they knew his chance to get away. Of the girl's real name they are unaware. They heard later that it was Corinne. That was the name entered in her forged papers. By it she is still known in the area.[1]

[1] Later that afternoon another detachment of the Das Reich SS Panzer division, or it may even be the same detachment, went to Oradour-sur-Glane, not many miles further along the road, and massacred the entire village of 600 men, women and children to emphasise their determination to get through to Normandy. They never got through. It has been thought that Violette's shooting down of so many Germans may have been the cause of their savage revenge at Oradour.

CHAPTER SEVENTEEN

TO THE RESCUE

STAUNTON learned of the ambush through the doctor's son. The boy returned to La Croisille very late in the afternoon, footsore and frightened. With his bicycle still roped to the abandoned car, which was found later riddled with bullets, the boy had to walk the nine miles to his home. The doctor, mounting his bicycle, took the news on to Sussac.

What the outcome was Staunton did not know. Neither Anastasie nor Violette had returned. Had they been killed or were they lying injured somewhere? He decided to set out at once and find out. His inquiries had to be made with the utmost discretion in case Violette and Anastasie were in hiding.

As he approached Salon-la-Tour late that night he was told that both had been taken prisoner. This report had been deliberately spread by the Germans, who said: "We caught the boy later in the woods. We've got him all right." Anastasie, as we know, was having a belated meal at the time behind locked doors, in the house of the farmer and his daughters. Nor did he venture to return to Sussac until three days later in case the Germans should still be on the look-out.

Staunton, however, got more definite news long before then. Early the next afternoon, two men came in from Limoges to see him. They said they belonged to the Resistance forces there. An English girl, believed to be a secret agent, had been brought in the night before by guards of the Das Reich SS Panzer division. She was lodged in Limoges jail and that morning they had seen her being taken by two guards to be questioned at the Gestapo headquarters. "A pretty girl," they said, "limping badly. But such dignity—and that look of utter contempt for her guards." If any help was required, they said, the Resistance in Limoges, were ready to give it. It might even be possible to effect her rescue. Staunton asked about Anastasie. There was just the girl, they said.

Staunton decided that everything should be done to rescue her. It would have to be planned with the utmost care. The jail would have to be watched. The positioning of the guards, the times of her journey to Gestapo headquarters, for no doubt she would be taken there many times, would also have to be noted exactly. All this, he felt, might be better done by those who were already in Limoges, since new and unfamiliar faces would undoubtedly attract attention.

The men agreed and offered to undertake the work. It would be organised down to the last detail. Obviously it was going to involve a slow and very careful process of observation. Bob Mortier was deputed to keep in close touch with them and to rally such aid as might be required eventually from the outside for the carrying out of the rescue.

The jail at Limoges is a large sombre building with very high walls. It faces on to a wide paved square. Twice each day, at the hours of eleven in the morning and four in the afternoon, a little door, standing between two heavy ones, was opened and Violette was led out by two guards. They marched her, limping, across the the square to the Gestapo headquarters down a street on the far side. This house, three stories high, stood right on the road. It was guarded of course. Violette was kept there for an hour, sometimes more, while the Gestapo colonel questioned her himself. Then she was led back to the jail. Thus there were four journeys in all every day, with only two guards in charge of her, though all around, in the streets and on the square, there were others to be reckoned with—German soldiers, either passing through or assembled for some purpose, or on guard outside certain buildings. The times of their assembly were noted, and checked on subsequent days to discern all possible variations. The hours at which the guards were changed were noted too. The passers-by, the shopkeepers, the residents, most of whom were of course French, but might be collaborators, had also to be taken into account. Patterns were detected in their coming and going. At some moments the streets were busy, at others they were comparatively deserted.

The watch revealed at the end of three days the precise hour at which the rescue could be made. Ten men would be needed, four to deal with the guards, the others to prevent any intervention. They would then seize Violette and place her in a motor-car, which, they felt, could be obtained quite easily: they had got cars before. But they would have to find a good one for this purpose, a car that was large and could travel fast. It was possible they would not be able to make their get-away in it, as all the exits from Limoges were heavily guarded. This, however, was where the men from Sussac could co-operate effectively.

When this report was brought to Staunton, he arranged that Bob should go into Limoges and work with the four men who were to deal with the guards. All would have to take along their Tommy guns in case anything went wrong. From Sussac a second car would be sent in with six armed men to deal with the guards at the town exit the moment they saw the rescue car approaching. Here, it was expected, they would have to fight it out.

The day selected for the rescue was Friday, June 16th—six days after Violette's capture. The hour was to be eleven o'clock in the forenoon. Carefully they went over all the details. Each man in each of the two groups rehearsed the role he was to play. Nothing was left to chance. Nothing could be allowed to go wrong.

Early on the Friday morning Bob went into Limoges with the faked pass of entry the Resistance men there had procured for him. Everything was ready. Just before ten o'clock the car they had earmarked for their purpose was stolen and held in readiness in a little-frequented side street. The four men who were to make the rescue with Bob checked their Tommy guns, saw that the spare magazines were accessible. They looked at their watches and waited.

Just before eleven o'clock they made their way towards the square in the car. They pulled up short of the square at a point from which the small prison gate through which Violette would be brought was fully in view.

The minute hand slowly approached the hour. Then the church clock began to strike eleven. It seemed to be a minute fast. Soon the hour was struck by other clocks in the town, some near, others distant and faintly audible. With their eyes on the jail door they waited. But there was no sign of it being opened.

The minutes passed. Something had apparently gone wrong. It was five past eleven. Then ten past eleven, and still there was no sign of Violette and her guards.

They waited until half past. Bob said: "Let's give it another half-hour. There may be a reason for the delay." But even at midday, as the clocks struck again, there was no sign of her.

It was learned later that Violette had been moved out of Limoges that very morning just before dawn. Where she had been taken nobody yet knew. On the day before she had made her four normal journeys to and from Gestapo headquarters. There had not been the slightest variation when they made their final check through.

Had their plot been discovered—or was it by the merest chance that she had been moved from Limoges at the eleventh hour? The acutest disappointment marked their faces. They escorted Bob to the town's exit, where the men in the second car were waiting and wondering what had happened.

CHAPTER EIGHTEEN

INTO GERMANY

VIOLETTE was taken by road to Fresnes, the vast prison just outside Paris. It was a journey of over 200 miles. From the main entrance on the road a long drive down an avenue of tall and attractive trees takes one past a series of massive buildings on the right, each with large heavy gates. At the third of these the car pulled up. The gates were slowly swung back and, escorted by her armed and uniformed Gestapo guards, she was led through the yard into the section where the women prisoners were kept. There was accommodation in that and the adjacent male block for over 1600 prisoners. In that summer of 1944 the prison was full to overflowing. The men far outnumbered the women and had five or even six prisoners in each cell, whereas the women for the most part had a cell each to themselves. Most of the prisoners were French, but others had been brought in by the Germans from Jersey and Guernsey on various charges and often on no charges at all but merely on suspicion. Many were held as hostages, so that the threat of their death might elicit information from relatives and friends who were in hiding. The number of British prisoners here was small and only a very few of these were secret agents.

What her fate there would be Violette had a fairly shrewd idea. She had already sampled the severities of detention and it was clear to her that her arrest had not been effected merely to prevent her achieving a predesigned purpose, nor yet to punish her for what she might already have accomplished, but to extract from her certain vital information. At the Gestapo headquarters in Limoges, to which she was taken twice each day, the colonel of the Gestapo, seated in his office at his large desk, desired to know the plans in hand for the effective use of the Maquis in preventing the free movement of the German forces through that region. A large map of the area was produced. He wanted her to indicate the points selected for the blowing up of roads and railway lines, and for cutting communications. In view of the difficulties the Germans had already encountered in policing the area, and the added difficulties at this juncture because of the acute shortage of men, it was only by obtaining such information that time could be saved and much could be accomplished. He wanted to know where the vast supplies of arms were stored, what fields had been selected for parachute landings. He wanted to know the identity of the principals in the organisation and where they could be found (the Gestapo were, for example, aware of Anastasie's activities and had for a long time been trying to find him). He asked about the work on which she was herself engaged, the instructions she was carrying, the code used by the wireless operator, for each operator had his own individual code, and, as she had been taught to use the radio, it was felt that the code would be known to her or could be obtained by her. There was also the question of the expected landings in the South of France, in readiness for which ten German divisions had been kept in the south by Hitler. Had these landings been abandoned—or were they to be made now that these divisions were being moved to the north? It was a vital question and the Gestapo were convinced that a secret agent, strategically placed midway between north and south, must be able to supply the answer and they were determined to prise the information out of her if in fact she did possess it.

At first there was a show of affability and friendliness. She was told by her Gestapo inquisitor that it was not their purpose to torture or even to punish her. All they wanted were answers to a few simple questions. She did not deny that she knew some at least of the answers. She merely refused to answer any of the questions. There then followed a protracted process of persuasion. It began quite calmly with an endeavour to prove that the people for whom she worked did not care what became of her, whether she survived or was executed. Their one desire had been to use her and, if she failed, to use in her place someone else. "They will not lift a finger to save you or help you. We, on the other hand, want to—and can." She did not know that at that moment plans were in hand for her rescue, nor would it have mattered if she had. She realised that her work had now taken on a completely new form. It was only by her silence now that she could make her greatest contribution to the cause. No matter what pain and suffering she might be called upon to endure, that silence would have to be maintained and she prayed that she would be strong enough for the ordeal when it came. "I must not show any fear," she said again and again to herself, and in her heart she knew none; for she had been aware all along of the price she might one day be called upon to pay. Her face was composed as she listened to the colonel's soft-voiced expressions of concern for her and his desire to help her. "Of course you Germans always are most considerate and kind to your enemies," she said with a mocking smile.

"Of course."

It was then that she laughed.

This angered the colonel. He instantly ordered the guards to take her back to the jail.

Some hours later she was brought again before him and the persuasion went on.

"It is only a question of time," he said, "before we find out everything—yes, everything we want to know. I want you to save us this loss of time, and in return I will guarantee you your life and the lives of your friends. All those whose names you give me . . ."

She merely exploded with laughter. "What do you take me for? A half-wit?"

A day or two later he appeared to have learned one or two things about her.

"You are really French," he said, "and you should give a thought to the fate of your own people. Your husband, who was also a Frenchman, very foolishly allowed himself to be used by the English. What good did it do him—or France? He lost his life, as you will lose yours if you persist in remaining silent. He could have lived in peace with us. There is peace between Marshal Pétain and ourselves. We arranged a most generous peace. But your husband is dead—just one of many thousands who have been too blind to see things clearly. You have been very, very stupid.

You have a child, I believe—haven't you? What do you think is going to become of your child if we shoot you? Mind you, I don't want to shoot you. I am anxious to help you. I want to see you get back to your home. . . ."

"You do talk a lot of silly rot," she interrupted. "I'll tell you nothing—nothing. Can't you get that into your head? No matter what you do, it won't make any difference. I despise you—I despise the whole lot of you." With the agility of a young animal she took a quick menacing pace towards him, but the two guards sprang forward and seized her to prevent whatever mischief she had in mind.

"Take her away," said the colonel.

She had noticed that he had made no mention at all of her earlier mission to Rouen and Le Havre. It seemed obvious that he did not know of it. She was puzzled how he had learned of her marriage. Was it just a shot in the dark?

The next morning at eleven she was brought in again. And so it went on until in anger he ordered her removal to Fresnes. "We shall see if that will bring you to your senses," he said.

"It isn't my senses you should be concerned about, but your own. In a very short time the tables will be turned. Then you will be standing here and one of our men will be seated in that chair."

That indeed happened much sooner than she anticipated, though not entirely as she foresaw it. She knew, of course, that Anastasie had completed all his plans for harrying and impeding the movement of German troops before they set out together on their fateful journey. These plans had since been put into operation. The messages she was to deliver were taken on by others and the work was thus spread out over the entire Maquis area. Railway lines were torn out. Bridges were destroyed. The road was blown up at many points and as fast as one section was repaired the Maquis speedily blew up another. Ambushes were constantly operated. If the German troops survived one, a little further on they ran into another. The Germans threatened to shoot hostages, but that did not deter the Maquis. "We piled up in a deep cutting two kilometres north of Salon-la-Tour," Staunton states in his report, "two successive passenger trains.

This produced an effective block for six weeks, the Germans being short of heavy cranes." At the same time the Maquis in the Corrèze piled several tons of rock on the line between Uzerche and Brive. As a result of all this the Das Reich SS Panzer division never reached Normandy. The fighting there was over before it could get through.

Of all these operations Jean-Claude Guiet, the American wireless operator attached to Staunton, kept London fully informed and, through him, fresh directions were constantly being received with regard to work that had still to be done.

These developments occurred for the most part while Violette was at Fresnes; they brought about a complete reversal of the position at Gestapo headquarters in Limoges, as will presently be revealed.

With her suitcase left in the car at Salon-la-Tour, she was without any change of clothing and not even her handbag—no comb or toothbrush, not a pair of stockings or a handkerchief. At the jail at Limoges they brought her two coarse garments to wear as underclothes and for the rest she had to make do during the six days she was there with what she had on. On arrival at Fresnes, after her name had been entered in the office off the hall, she was led away by an SS wardress in grey, through a long underground passage, then up an iron staircase off which ran tier upon tier of corridors, caged in with iron bars, until they reached a cell on the fourth floor.

It was a small, dark cell, measuring about twelve feet by eight. The plaster was peeling off the walls, leaving horrible scars. On the wall opposite the door was a dirty window made up of small panes of frosted glass and heavily barred on the outside. The window could not be opened, for the handle had been wrenched off, but fortunately some of the panes had been smashed. The bed, a very rough and rusty iron frame, was folded against the wall. There was a lumpy palliasse to serve as mattress when the bed was let down. A rickety chair was the only other piece of furniture. There was a lavatory seat by the door with a cold-water tap above it.

When she looked at the walls later Violette was able to discern numerous scratches, made with the fingernail or a hairpin. They were mostly dates, a phrase or two from a prayer and a few angry words and curses. She had been brought up to believe that being sent to prison was a disgrace that one would never be able to live down; but here, as at Limoges, she felt a little proud that she could still make her personal contribution to the war. So far the Germans had extracted no information from her. Would she be able to hold out—and for how long, she wondered.

As night began to fall she heard raised voices, mostly the voices of the women in the cells around. In the gathering gloom of the unlighted cells, these voices seemed to bring an unseen companionship; for together, as one led and the rest joined in, some voices delightfully musical, others cracked and tuneless, they sang the old songs of France and of other countries. At intervals, rising above the singing, came harsh, defiant curses and cries of '*Courage, mon vieux*' and '*Vive de Gaulle*' and '*Vive Churchill*'. Curses, vile and bitter curses, were heaped too upon the heads of Laval and Pétain, who were regarded as primarily responsible for the sufferings they were all enduring. Violette, who joined vehemently in these curses, would have derived some comfort had she known that in a very few months both Laval and Pétain would be occupying cells in this very prison.

A trolley trundling on rails along the corridor brought them their food. In the evenings it was cabbage soup with a few beans in it. This was brought in a wooden tub and, as the prison was very crowded and the wardresses did not want to waste time opening doors, they poured the soup through the peep-hole into a small rusty tin bowl on a ledge on the inside. Bread was restricted to 100 grammes a day. Sometimes a piece of cheese was served, usually it was unfit for human consumption. A thin finger of margarine appeared occasionally and even more rarely one got a solitary sausage, made, one found, of meat and bread salvaged from a bombed warehouse with bits of brick still in it. Not much nourishment could be obtained from such a diet and Violette, like the other prisoners there, was always very hungry.

For what purpose she had been brought to Fresnes was revealed a day later when the wardress opened the door and led her away. She was taken along the metalled corridor, down many flights of stairs, through the underground passage again, and out into the front yard. Here a Black Maria was waiting to take her into Paris.

As the van was windowless, save for a small grille in the back door, she caught only fleeting glimpses of the streets through which only a few weeks before she had roamed in freedom. She knew where she was being taken, for they had talked of it in England. It was to the house in the Avenue Foch where the Gestapo did their harsher questioning, aided by the persuasive refinements of torture. So it had come—the ordeal that had been constantly at the back of her mind. Urged by curiosity, and perhaps even awe, she had visited the Avenue Foch when she was last here and, with a swift glance at No 84, she had walked quickly on.

Now, as the Black Maria swept along the Paris streets, she saw people seated in groups at the little round tables of the pavement cafés. The van turned into the Avenue Foch, one of the most attractive streets in all Paris, running from the Arc de Triomphe to the Bois. Gardens flanked it on both sides. The van coursed along an inner track which gave access to the houses and pulled up at No 84. The guards swung back the gate, and she alighted in the sombre covered entrance to the house.

It was not at all like the Gestapo headquarters at Limoges. Once a private residence, it was almost palatial. A wide staircase led to five floors, each with many rooms that were used by the Gestapo for questioning and for torture. Her inquisitor was not in uniform. He was young, good-looking and rather dandified. His manner was calm, polite and assured. He had been carefully selected and trained for the work he was to do, just as she had been for hers. And he was determined to get the information he sought.

At that first interview he was unsuccessful. He was patient on that occasion, but when she was brought before him again the next day, after a bleak and uneasy night in her cell at Fresnes with a short, sharp volley from a firing squad under her window early in the morning (staged possibly for her benefit), she realised that today he meant to get down to business. This was confirmed by the presence in the room of a second man. The moment she sat down the man came up and stood by her chair. As the questioning proceeded and she still proved recalcitrant, implements of torture were produced and each was held up before her. The inquisitor said: "Will you answer now?" and, just as defiantly as when she was a child, she replied: "I won't. I *won't*." The young German then gave the sign. There followed the most atrocious torture.

She winced and bit her lips. Her face was contorted in her horrible agony. But still, though hardly able to move her lips, her eyes unable now to flash their fire, she repeated, almost inaudibly: "I won't. I *won't*."

After a time the man said: "All right, take her away." Then, turning to her, he added: "I have given you your chance. As you won't speak, there seems to be nothing left now but the firing squad."

She refused to be assisted from the room. "Don't touch me," she said as, limping, she walked from the room.

She was in an agony for many days. Tossing amid constant discomfort and pain, her mind groped for precious memories from the past. The soothing hands of Etienne were on her brow, she heard again his whispered words of comfort, and she drew to her breast the warm, tender caresses of her child.

She did not know when she would be taken again to the Avenue Foch, or on which morning it would be her turn to face the firing squad. But, mingled with the dread and the suffering, was a feeling of elation. She had said nothing. By not one word had she betrayed what she knew. Mentally she felt invigorated, and she thanked God that she had been strong.

She wondered if her friends in Sussac knew where she was. They had, of course, heard that she had been taken to Fresnes and they were aware what the Fresnes prisoners had to undergo at the Avenue Bosche, as they called it. But Paris was too far away for any further attempt at rescue. Besides, they had important work in hand, which they had been undertaking with efficiency and dispatch. On June 25th, that is to say a fortnight after her capture and only a few days following her torture, the first parachute drop ever made by daylight during the war was made near Sussac. It was on a formidable scale. A force of 86 Flying Fortresses came over attended by many Lightnings and Mustangs. They dropped 864 containers filled with supplies—weapons, ammunition, hand grenades, explosives, stores, petrol and even money. It took 300 Maquis three days to carry these supplies away. Thirty lorries were used. All the roads on this journey were guarded by Maquis, who even put up road blocks at vital points to prevent the Germans getting in.

The effect of this vast daylight operation was electrifying. Seeing the planes come over in such great numbers, the entire countryside rushed into the fields to witness the unforgettable scene. As the hundreds of parachutes descended in successive waves, cheer upon cheer rose to greet them. There was the wildest jubilation. The people began to sing and sang while they loaded the trucks and took the supplies home. The few hundred Maquis of the Haute Vienne swelled overnight to well over 3000.

Of all this Violette, of course, knew nothing. The Germans did not send for her again. At the Avenue Foch they were anxious and short tempered. Too much was happening in swift and startling succession in every direction. Much of Normandy was in Allied hands by the end of June. The Maquis were rising everywhere as fresh supplies reached them. In July an American assault group, comprising thirty men, all in uniform, was dropped by night in the Sussac area. Bob Mortier, who was in charge of the reception committee, had met some of the parachuted men in London. They included two English officers, Captain Bissett and Captain Ted Fraser, who had been conducting officers for the French Section of SOE. Shortly afterwards, in the next parachuted batch, came Major de Guelis, who had been responsible for recruiting Bob Mortier in North Africa and sending him to Buckmaster in London; and young André Simon, son of the famous wine connoisseur. A third group followed composed entirely of French Special Air Service officers. Together they totalled just on a hundred. Arriving in such numbers, these highly trained officers both strengthened and heartened the Maquis. Staunton and Bob and Guiet unpacked the uniforms they had brought with them and wore them always thereafter. It was sad, they felt, that Violette's uniform had to remain in the suitcase she left behind above the grocer's shop at Sussac.

She spent her birthday in bed in the most acute pain. It was her twenty-third birthday and the last she was to know. Etienne had been dead for two years: it was three years since their last meeting. All through July she remained at Fresnes, the pain easing, her spirits rising, for, despite German efforts to withhold all news of these tremendous developments, some of it inevitably percolated through. Women tapped it out in the Morse code on the walls of their cells to tell their neighbours. In the evenings, as darkness fell, there was a greater lustiness in their singing. Violette led them in the singing of the British National Anthem. But only two voices joined hers, the others apparently did not know the words, but made a valiant effort at *la-la*-ing to give support. It suggested, of course, that there were only two other women from England in the prison at Fresnes.

The Allies landed in the South of France in the middle of August. They did not drive north in the direction of the Maquis of the Haute Vienne, but turned eastward and pursued the Germans up the Rhone Valley into Germany. Staunton and his group made their own swift moves. With what was now quite a large and well-disciplined force they harried the Germans to right and to left, giving them no respite, and on August 20th they entered Limoges. General Gleiniger, commanding the German forces there, refused at first to surrender. On Staunton pointing out that the town was surrounded by a force 20,000 strong, with reinforcements on the way, Gleiniger signed the surrender. His troops laid down their arms and were moved into a former prison camp for Jews.[1]

The next morning, Staunton, Bob and Guiet moved into the Gestapo headquarters. In the room in which Violette was so persistently questioned only two months before, Staunton now sat in the colonel's chair. The Gestapo, shirking the consequences of the altered situation, had already fled. Staunton was not, however, concerned with questioning and threatening. He had a bar set up at one end of the room, gaudily arrayed with bottles of whisky and the gay liqueurs of France. Here, while they planned their next moves, they were able in that blazing summer of 1944 to assuage their thirsts and to drink a toast to the courage, devotion and steadfastness of Violette.

Early in August there was bewilderment and alarm among the

[1] The Supreme Allied Commander, General Eisenhower, has recorded: 'Thanks to the underground movement the liberation of France was accelerated by some six months.'

Germans in Paris, for the Third United States Army, under General Paton, and the Free French Forces led by General Leclerc, were marching steadily on the capital. Nothing the Germans could do could stop them. Each day the panic grew. Orders came suddenly for the removal of certain specially selected prisoners from Fresnes to Germany as the Gestapo did not want them 'to become available' to the advancing Allies.

On the morning of August 8th, that is to say seven and a half weeks after being brought to Fresnes, Violette was taken through the underground passage into the prison yard. There she saw three small coaches waiting. One of them was just moving off with a batch of male prisoners. The second, also containing men, was not yet full. She thought she saw in it someone she knew. He raised his hand in greeting and she realised that it was Harry Peulevé. For months she had been seeking him in London. It was strange that they should have been so near to each other in Fresnes. In the third coach there were fewer than a dozen girls. Harry called to her as his coach drove out. They could not speak, but there was the hope that they might meet if they happened to be travelling by the same train.

Harry was in London when the war broke out. He instantly joined the Territorials, served in France with the British Expeditionary Force and was evacuated at Dunkirk. He was a secret agent when he first met Violette at the Studio Club and had already been to France on a mission. She was working at the aircraft factory in Morden at the time. Etienne had been dead for nearly eight months, but Violette did not yet know it. A few weeks later, on learning the sad news about Etienne, Violette was herself to become a member of Harry's section of SOE and, though the girl who introduced them at the club that night had apparently a hand in getting Violette's name sent to the War Office, it was not until after the war that she revealed this to Harry. This girl, widow of a Battle of Britain pilot, who could not serve herself because she was an Italian by birth, wrote to say of Violette that she was 'an extremely suitable candidate for work in France as a secret agent.' At their next encounter in the Piccadilly underground, Harry saw that Violette had on the uniform of a FANY. They went about a great deal together after that and some thought a romance might be developing. The last time they saw each other was early in 1944. They were with a large party at the Astor Club. Two nights later he left. He was dropped not far from where Violette was herself to come not many months later, for he was with the Maquis in the Corrèze area, only a few miles from Salon-la-Tour. Harry was arrested in March 1944, Violette in June; and both had been for many weeks in adjoining blocks at Fresnes.

As each coach left the prison yard parcels of food, enough to last for two days, were handed to the prisoners by the Red Cross. Those who had suitcases were given them now. Violette had only a bundle containing the few garments given her in the prison at Limoges. No prisoner got back either jewellery or money, even their watches and rings were withheld. Etienne's engagement ring, which Violette had hoped to convert into cash when in a tight corner, she never saw again.

The men handcuffed in pairs, but the girls unfettered, they were taken to the Gare de l'Est and put into the train for Germany. It was not a long train. For the prisoners there was just one coach, which had been tacked on at the end. The other carriages were filled with German wounded. There was also an anti-aircraft gun in case of a raid.

The prisoners' coach had a lavatory and next to it a third-class compartment in which the girls were placed. Beyond that was what looked like two horse-boxes with stout iron doors that worked like lift gates and were kept shut to prevent access to the corridor. They had been formed by removing the seats from two compartments. Guards paraded the corridor and had a small compartment of their own to sit in just beyond the horse-boxes.

The girls were no sooner ushered into their compartment than they were chained by the ankles, in pairs. This was to prevent escape since there was no grille on their door.

After a wait at the station of many hours, during which, despite their efforts, Violette and Harry were unable to get to each other, the train started at last very late in the afternoon. It was obvious that the men would not be able to sleep, for there were nineteen of them in one section and eighteen in the other, with barely enough room to stand. Yeo-Thomas, known now as 'The White Rabbit', who was a director of Molyneux in Paris before the war, took charge, as the senior ranking officer among the prisoners. He arranged that they should take it in turn to lie down during the night, as only two pairs could do this at a time while the rest stood. It was a stiflingly hot August night and the men suffered the acutest discomfort. The women, though crowded closely together, at any rate had seats. Violette met now the two other Englishwomen at Fresnes. They were Denise Bloch and Lillian Rolfe; both had been wireless operators in the French Section of SOE. Lillian, who came from Horsell, near Woking, in Surrey, was tall and dark, with attractive brown eyes. She had a French mother and had been brought up in Brazil. Denise, broad-shouldered and blonde, had escaped from France during the Occupation. These three were to remain together through many ghastly and tragic developments.

In the morning, after a restless and exhausting night, the men were taken to the lavatory in pairs, still handcuffed together. The guard stood by the open door all the time. No further visits were allowed. As the day wore on the heat became increasingly intense. By the afternoon it was unbearable. The water, supplied in bottles by the Red Cross, had all been drunk during the night. The men kept clamouring for something to quench their raging thirst. They begged the guards to bring them just a glassful, but the guards ignored their pleas.

There were recurrent alarms that British planes had been seen overhead and there was a great fear that the train might be attacked. Near Châlons-sur-Marne, having come only eighty miles in twenty-two hours, these fears materialised. Two RAF planes bombed the train. There was a thundering explosion. Many windows were smashed. The train shuddered and came to a halt. In a panic the guards locked the doors of the coach and ran out into the fields where they took refuge in ditches. A machine-gun was mounted on a small mound and trained on the carriage so that none might try to escape. The anti-aircraft gun got into action. Flying very low, the RAF planes dropped more bombs and then opened fire with their machine-guns. The roof of one of the carriages was split open and the prisoners heard the screams of the wounded and the dying.

The women had begun to cheer at the start of the attack, but the men, imprisoned in confined spaces behind the locked grilles, were possessed by the fear that, if an incendiary hit their coach, there could for them be no escape and they would all inevitably be burned to death. There were Belgians and Frenchmen among them and some of them got hysterical. Unable to throw themselves down on the floor, they threw themselves on top of each other. A few were frothing at the mouth. Yeo-Thomas says: "We all felt deeply ashamed when we saw Violette Szabo, while the raid was still on, come crawling along the corridor towards us with a jug of water which she had filled in the lavatory. She handed it to us through the iron bars. With her, crawling too, came the girl to whose ankle she was chained."

This act of mercy made an unforgettable impression on all. She spoke words of comfort, jested, went back with the jug to fill it again and again. "My God, that girl had guts," says Yeo-Thomas. "I shall never forget that moment," says Harry Peulevé, "I felt very proud that I knew her. She looked so pretty, despite her shabby clothes and her lack of make-up—and she was full of good cheer. I have never under any circumstances known her to be depressed or moody."

When the planes departed and the guards returned, it was found that seventeen Germans had been killed. The raid was successful, says Yeo-Thomas. Either the engine or the track must have been damaged, for the train was unable to proceed. After a very long wait the prisoners were led out of their coach by the guards and put into two trucks requisitioned from farmers.

The trucks took them on to Metz, once regarded as a vital sector of the Maginot Line. Here they spent the night in the stables attached to the barracks. Straw had been spread out in the loose boxes. The men, also chained in pairs now, were given the stalls on the right, the women were separated from them by a narrow alleyway along which flowed the stable drain. The guards threatened to shoot if any attempt was made to cross from one side to the other. None the less, as the night advanced, some of the men and women crawled towards each other and talked across the drain until dawn. Peulevé says: "Violette and I talked all through the night. Her voice, as always, was so sweet and soothing, one could listen to it for hours. We spoke of old times and we told each other our experiences in France. Bit by bit everything was unfolded—her life in Fresnes, her interviews at the Avenue Foch. But either through modesty or a sense of delicacy, since some of the tortures were too intimate in their application or perhaps because she did not wish to live again through the pain of it, she spoke hardly at all about the tortures she had been made to suffer. She was in a cheerful mood. Her spirits were high. She was confident of victory and was resolved on escaping no matter where they took her."

Thus, in the darkness, with each chained by the ankle to another and the drain between them, they had their last romantic interchanges, with their hopes and dreams unvoiced but no doubt shared.

The journey to the German frontier took the best part of a week. They were taken from Metz to the Gestapo headquarters at Strasbourg and then northward to Saarbrücken. Here the women were detached from the rest of the party and sent off to Ravensbrück.

CHAPTER NINETEEN

RAVENSBRÜCK

VIOLETTE arrived at Ravensbrück in the last week of August 1944. She had been brought across the greater part of Germany, for Ravensbrück stood on the lakes of Mecklenburg, about fifty miles to the north of Berlin.

It was the largest prison camp in Europe, indeed the largest prison for women the world had ever known. When it was first built on these swampy marshlands in 1939, it was designed to accommodate 7000 women prisoners in groups of huts. But the number of women grew as the war progressed. By the time Violette arrived, there were 40,000 women, crowded together in large huts and sleeping often six in a bunk on straw. In all nearly 120,000 prisoners are known to have entered it. Of these fewer than 12,000 were alive when the Russian advance overshot the camp and gave them their freedom. The Soviet soldiers, tough and hard-bitten, were appalled by the pitiful condition in which they found the survivors.

The place was like a walled town, with electrified barbed wire above the high walls. Inside, around and beyond a central square, were groups of huts, separated by rough rutted roads. The beds were built in double-tiered bunks, with only one blanket for three or four women to share. There were workshops, laundries, large rooms in which the prisoners were made to weave or to sew, and a very small compound for a handful of male prisoners. At one corner, near the crematorium (which was just outside the walls) was the Bunker or *Zellenbau.* Here women, and men too, had to undergo solitary confinement. Few in the Bunker escaped the firing squad or the gas chamber.

The heavy mortality suffered by the prisoners was attributed to

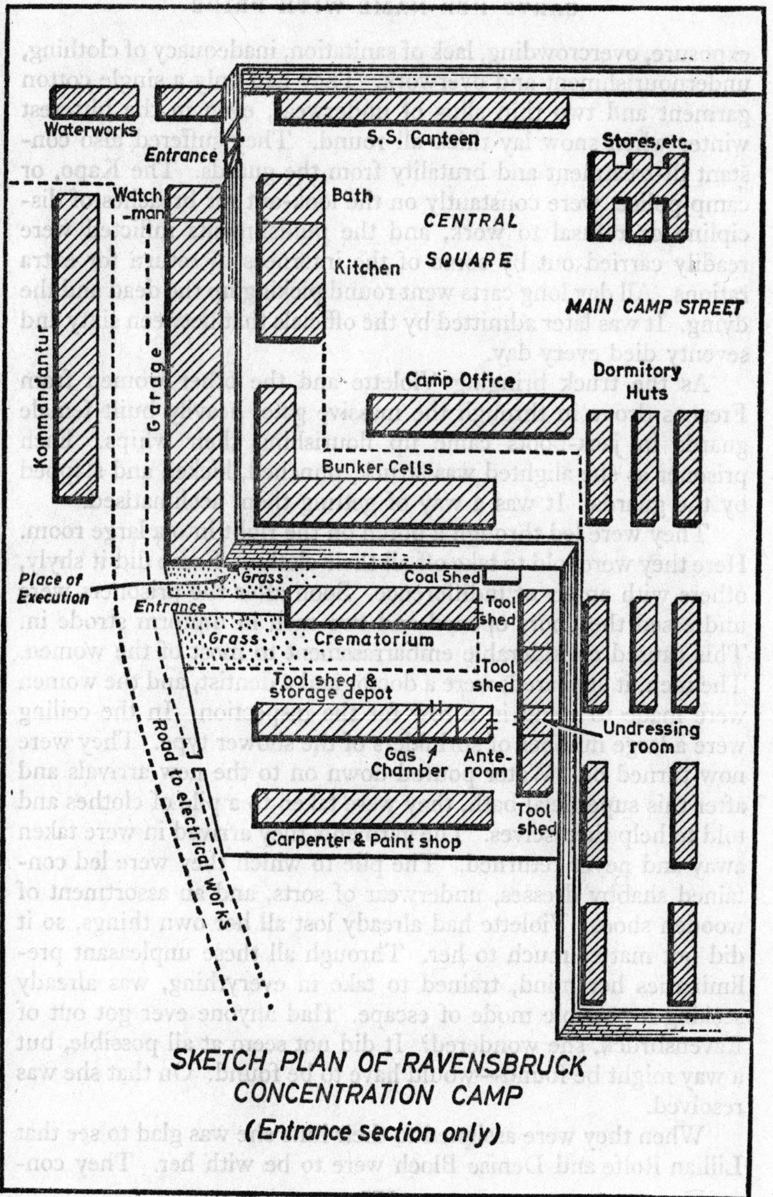

SKETCH PLAN OF RAVENSBRUCK CONCENTRATION CAMP

(Entrance section only)

exposure, overcrowding, lack of sanitation, inadequacy of clothing, undernourishment and overwork. They had only a single cotton garment and two thin slips of underwear, even in the bitterest winter when snow lay thick all round. They suffered also constant ill-treatment and brutality from the guards. The Kapo, or camp police, were constantly on the look-out for breaches of discipline or refusal to work, and the punishments inflicted were readily carried out by some of the internees in return for extra rations. All day long carts went round picking up the dead and the dying. It was later admitted by the officials that between sixty and seventy died every day.

As the truck bringing Violette and the other women from Fresnes drove in through the massive gate, heavily built female guards in jack-boots came up flourishing their whips. Each prisoner as she alighted was struck, punched, kicked and slapped by the guards. It was a way of getting them acclimatised.

They were led through a porch on the right into a large room. Here they were told to take off all their clothes. Some did it shyly, others with an air of indifference. Soon after the prisoners were undressed the doors opened and two men in uniform strode in. This caused considerable embarrassment to most of the women. The men, it appeared, were a doctor and a dentist, and the women were made to stand in a row for the inspection. In the ceiling were a large number of sprinklers of the shower type. They were now turned on. Water poured down on to the new arrivals and after this superficial bath, they were taken to a pile of clothes and told to help themselves. The garments they arrived in were taken away and never returned. The pile to which they were led contained shabby dresses, underwear of sorts, and an assortment of wooden shoes. Violette had already lost all her own things, so it did not matter much to her. Through all these unpleasant preliminaries her mind, trained to take in everything, was already seeking a possible mode of escape. Had anyone ever got out of Ravensbrück, she wondered? It did not seem at all possible, but a way might be found—would have to be found. On that she was resolved.

When they were assigned to their huts she was glad to see that Lillian Rolfe and Denise Bloch were to be with her. They contrived indeed, after much argument with the other women, to share the same bunk with two others.

Of the women in the camp by far the greatest number were Russians and Poles. There were Czechs too and Danes, Norwegians, Belgians, Dutch, French and even Germans. Only twelve were English and fourteen American. They could not all be spies or secret agents. Had they all fallen foul of the Gestapo that they should be confined in a prison under such strict surveillance? The fact is that the bulk of them were there for no crime that they were aware of committing. Most of them, taken away when the German armies invaded their countries, had been placed in work camps and, through insubordination or defiance, or because of malicious tales told against them by their fellow prisoners, had been sent on here. Others had been brought here in order to punish their husbands or lovers or fathers, for it was a way of getting the men to talk, but whether the men did or not the women remained, for there was work to be done here. Every morning they were roused at five o'clock—in the summer it was as early as three-thirty—and assembled in the central square, where a roll-call was taken. This lasted often as long as two hours, the prisoners standing at attention all the time. They were then formed into work-parties and marched away, some to weave, others to spin, others to work in one of the factories for textiles or electrical equipment, or to load and unload lorries, or to make roads. The duties varied from day to day according to their physical fitness. At all these tasks overseers stood by them and urged them on with whips. If their output lagged they received the most cruel punishments. They were kept at work for close on eleven hours and suffered inevitably immense strain on their inadequate diet.

The food, for which they had to queue, consisted of a bowl of artificial coffee in the morning, some soup made of cabbages or potatoes at midday, and the same soup again in the evening. They received in addition a small piece of bread, approximating to about one-tenth of a loaf, which had to last through the day. That was all. From time to time Red Cross parcels arrived for the prisoners, which they were made to sign for, but the parcels were taken away by the camp officials and enjoyed by their families in their own homes. To divert themselves the guards would throw bits of bread that had gone mouldy into the midst of the prisoners for the sheer pleasure of seeing them fight for it like demented animals.

The entire camp was infested by vermin. The smell in many parts, caused through lack of sanitation, was quite unbearable. Savage dogs, trained to attack the prisoners, were set upon them from time to time and there were appalling cases of suffering from dog bites.

Violette realised that her chance of escape was exceedingly slim. Chosen because of her still robust health to work on the roads, she felt that this might provide her with an opportunity. As she trooped out with the gang to the section outside the walls at which they were to work, her active mind sought the best means of breaking away. Each day the plan advanced a stage further and at last she took it. But she did not get far. The guards were too vigilant. She was led before the commandant, the inhuman Fritz Sühren, who ordered her to be beaten cruelly. A few days later she and her two friends were sent to Torgau. Violette had been in Ravensbrück in all only two and a half weeks.

Torgau lies about half-way between Berlin and Leipzig and is close on 120 miles to the south of Ravensbrück. This small town was before the war the centre of the accordion industry. Most of the accordions that the Germans sang to in their beer halls and their homes were made here. But the factories had been taken over for war work and were now making precision tools or serving the needs of the Luftwaffe.

Violette found conditions at Torgau infinitely better than at Ravensbrück. For one thing, where she was lodged it was not so much a prison as a work camp. The huts were less congested and the food a little more palatable. The guards, though numerous and heavily armed, were far less brutal. The work she was set to do was in an aircraft factory and not unlike the work she had been doing at Morden before she became a secret agent.

Here the chances of escape seemed a little easier. She intended this time to plan it with the utmost care and to obtain, if possible, the co-operation of people she could trust. It would of course, she realised, take a great deal of time. Always cheerful, ever ready with a jest, her light-hearted affability won her the regard of many of the other prisoners. Some of the men slipped her some cigarettes and chocolates that they had managed to get smuggled in, and with their aid she contrived to send off, for the first time since her capture at Salon-la-Tour, a brief message to her parents.

Mrs Bushell had been informed of course by Buckmaster that Violette had been arrested by the Gestapo. This news reached her in August when Violette was already on her way to Ravensbrück. Now, at the end of September, Violette managed to send a card. It took many months to reach Brixton. Mr and Mrs Bushell did not in fact get it until January 10th, 1945, that is to say more than seven months after Violette's departure from England on her second mission and five months after they had been told that she was a prisoner. The card did not say much. It was in fact somewhat puzzling. For one thing it did not bear her signature, but was signed with the single word 'Petit', as though it were a masculine surname. It might of course also have meant 'The Little One', but it was not in its feminine form. The card read: "Dear Godfather, I am pleased to say that I am well. It is a long time since I wrote. Glad to hear from you. Happy to say I have met Violette. She is well and wishing for the war to end, as I do—Petit."

At any rate it indicated that their daughter was well and that it was at her direction that the message had been sent. The card bore no address, but just the single word 'Leipzig', which is about fifty miles from Torgau.

Violette, meanwhile, was working ceaselessly on her plan of escape. A man in the precision tools section fashioned most cunningly a key that he claimed would open any door. With it, provided each move was planned with care, she could work her way by swift, successive stages out of the camp without having to negotiate the electrified barbed wire. But each move would have to be studied, times would have to be worked out in order to evade the guards. She worked on it for weeks, aided readily by one or two others. But the moment the plan was completed and about to be put into operation, she was quite unexpectedly searched and the key was found. It seemed as though somebody might have talked.

She was of course taken before the commandant and punished.

Later, after consultation on the telephone with Ravensbrück, it was decided to send her back there and again the other two girls, for reasons that are difficult to fathom, were sent back with her. The burly women wardresses greeted them again, as they alighted, with a vigorous and vicious use of their whips. The three girls were shoved and pummelled through the door to the ceremony of inspection with which they were already familiar. They were then taken before Commandant Sühren and Violette received, as she had expected, the lash of his condemnation for this second attempt at escape. Punishment followed inevitably. It would be, she realised, more severe than for just a breach of discipline or for failing to accomplish the expected quota of work. She was sentenced to ten strokes with a stick and to solitary confinement for a week in the Bunker or *Zellenbau*, the prison within the camp. Here the meagre food ration was reduced to but one hot meal every three days. The cell, one of sixty-eight in a stout concrete building, was on the ground floor and so had a window, which was of course kept shut. It was more modern and far better equipped than the rest of the camp. There was a lavatory with a tap above it, as at Fresnes, a bed to herself, with a thin straw mattress on hard boards, and a heavy iron door. There was also surprisingly central heating in these cells, which the huts had not; but, adjustable for individual cells, it was used on occasion for punishment, being turned on full in summer and off in winter. Odette Churchill (now Mrs Hallowes) was at that time in one of the underground cells here and recalls hearing Violette's voice quite clearly one afternoon, talking to one of the guards stationed outside. Violette said: "How do you like being on duty on a Sunday? It should be your day off, or don't you get one?" The man laughed. He said he didn't mind. "Have you to do much more of it? When do you go off?"—"Oh, another hour," he replied. It seems to suggest that even here her mind was exploring the possibilities of escape, through the co-operation possibly of one of the guards. In the cells around were a number of male prisoners. The former Mayor of Vienna was here and alongside him was a professor from one of the German universities with his wife. They were special prisoners. Their cells were well furnished and their rations were more plentiful. They had been brought here, to this camp for women, in order that there should be no trace of them. It was a convenient way of getting them lost.

At the end of the week Violette was taken again before Sühren, who bellowed fresh dire threats. As always she was scornful, for she has been set down as a difficult prisoner—intractable and quite ungovernable.

Flaming with rage, he had her taken away. She was physically fit still, despite the undernourishment and ill-treatment; and, since the shortage of labour was acute, after some days he assigned her to the harsh and strenuous task of laying out a new airfield at Königsberg, not far from the Russian front, where the retreating German armies were in ever-increasing need of bomber-fighter support. Once again the two English girls who had returned with her from Torgau were made to accompany her.

Königsberg stands on the River Oder at what was then the north-eastern corner of Germany. It is more than 300 miles from Ravensbrück and the journey, which was again made by truck, was a long one through pine-clad country. Violette, together with Lillian Rolfe and Denise Bloch, was made to fell trees and then to clear the ground and level it. Arriving there in the first week of November, they found the weather intensely cold and severe. Winter had already set in. They were lodged in an unheated hut. Their clothes were still what they had worn through the summer. The food was no better and their hard labour had to be sustained despite the ceaseless gnawing of their hunger.

Here, as at Torgau, they were not in a concentration camp, but members of a work-party. Most of the others were men, chiefly Russian and Polish prisoners of war, with a sprinkling of French prisoners among them. The small teams of women were required to undertake the same arduous, back-breaking tasks as the men, and SS guards, using whips, saw that their efforts should be unflagging.

During the three months she was here, the three hardest and bitterest months of a bleak Russian winter, Violette suffered the greatest privations. Often for her insubordination and her attitude of contempt she was beaten and denied her scant rations. Her intention unceasingly was to seek the first chance of escape. But, out in the open though they were all day long, it was by no means easy. Police dogs prowled around them. There were guards with loaded rifles on the watch. Wires encircled the encampment. And if, despite these, she succeeded in breaking away, she would have to embark on a long and difficult journey across the tell-tale snow, into Russia perhaps, or back across Germany to the westward. None the less she was resolved to attempt it.

During December the Allied Armies in the West entered Holland and penetrated into Germany at Karlsrühe. In the East the Russians were sweeping through the Baltic States and in January crossed the German frontier into the great industrial regions of Upper Silesia. To the north, much nearer to Königsberg, they crossed the Vistula on both sides of Warsaw. On January 17th they entered Warsaw.

These mighty sweeps from both sides, destined before long to meet in the very heart of Germany, were the subject of many rumours among the prisoners at Königsberg. Excitement was high at the realisation that their liberation must now be near. A sweep northward from Warsaw soon endangered Königsberg itself, and, though the town was heavily defended, it was obvious that it would before long be completely isolated. Violette's hopes now took a fresh turn. She had often wondered, at Ravensbrück and Torgau, which of the Allies would be responsible for her liberation. It seemed clear now that Königsberg would be the prize of the Russians. That would involve, she foresaw, a journey eastward, possibly right across Russia and the steppes of Siberia into China, which happily was on the side of the Allies. Or, more swiftly perhaps, southward to Odessa and through the Black Sea into the Mediterranean. At any rate freedom was now in sight.

But quite suddenly at the end of January Violette and the two other English girls were sent back to Ravensbrück. Was it to prevent their liberation by the Russians? Or was there something more sinister behind this?

In any case in just over three months the war in Europe was over.

CHAPTER TWENTY

WAITING FOR NEWS

WHEN the war ended in Europe Violette's parents realised that her return home was imminent. It could not now be more than a matter of days or possibly weeks. Mrs Bushell, who had kept in the closest touch with Tania, visiting her at Mill Hill often two and three times a week, was able to bring her to London. She had prepared a room for her at Brixton and also got Violette's room ready for her home-coming.

But the weeks passed. The war in Japan ended too, and the summer of 1945 was nearly spent without any news at all from her or of her. She must have written, of that they felt certain; with the war over there was nothing now to stop her. The only message they received was the one she had sent from Torgau, which reached them in January. Since then—nothing. There was no longer either bombing or torpedoes or the confusion of war to send letters astray. And yet, a month after the war had ended, they read in the newspapers of a postwoman in their area burning letters in her grate. 'A Stockwell postwoman,' the papers said. On June 11th the caretaker of a block of flats found hundreds of letters strewn about the floor of a flat. Some of the letters were intact, others were torn up. There were also fragments of charred paper in the grate. Many of these letters, it was said in court, for the postwoman was found guilty of stealing postal orders, were from members of the Forces serving abroad. It was possible that a letter from Violette might have been among them.

Inquiries were made of Colonel Buckmaster and Vera Atkins, but they had themselves been trying to get some news. Mr Bushell called at the War Office, but no information was available there either. He got in touch with the Red Cross. They at least, with their widespread international branches, should be able to trace her. But there too nothing was known, and after months of seeking nothing was learned. The Bushells went to see the Member of Parliament for Brixton, Colonel Marcus Lipton. He took up the inquiries, pursued them through every available channel, but was unable to elicit any news at all.

Unofficially it was said that Violette had undoubtedly been freed when the Russians reached Ravensbrück in April. With the war still in progress at that time and a large slice of Germany separating the Russians from the Allied lines in the west, Violette would necessarily have to make her way home through Russia. It was believed that she was travelling southward to Odessa. It was a long way round of course and would take time; that was no doubt why she had not got home yet.

Bewildered, anxious, and at times a little fearful, her two parents wandered pathetically through London on their forlorn quest, holding hands to give each other courage and hope. The mother, with her large sad eyes, listened, shaking her puzzled head, while the father, his eyes filling often, was doggedly persistent in his questioning and at times even angry when no one could tell him where he might go to obtain definite news. Months had passed since the ending of the war—and still nobody seemed to know. Couldn't anybody do anything? With some difficulty they traced Staunton and wrote to him in North Africa, but he had no news and was too far away to help: he died not long afterwards quite suddenly at his desk at Casablanca. They went again to the War Office and to the Red Cross, to Colonel Buckmaster and to Vera Atkins. Vera, anxious to locate Violette as well as others who were missing, was about to go to Europe herself in their quest. She was resolved to find out. The news would have to be obtained.

Sadly Mr and Mrs Bushell returned to their home. From time to time they wept and went over their memories of her childhood, tender moments, fiery, defiant moments, lighthearted and gay moments that had filled their days with laughter. And after a while they set out still again—to the War Office, to the Red Cross, to the headquarters of the French Section of SOE. Again they wrote letters to their MP and to the Prime Minister. They wrote also to the newspapers and followed up their letters by calling on the editors.

The Press took it up. PARACHUTE GIRL MISSING said the headlines in the latter weeks of 1945 and shortly afterwards one of the newspapers published an interview with three Englishwomen who had been at Ravensbrück and had only just arrived in Sweden. This gave Mr and Mrs Bushell great hope. Violette must be on her way home too and would no doubt be found before long by some newspaper correspondent in China or India.

One of the women who had arrived in Sweden, Mrs Doreen Verani, of Southport, said she had seen three English girls, including one named Corinne. It was, of course, the name by which Violette was known. "She was small and slim, with dark blue eyes. I don't remember the names of the others. All three were parachutists and had demanded to be treated as officers and war prisoners." She had met them, she said, in September 1944, which would have been shortly after their arrival at Ravensbrück from Fresnes. "They were in the camp for a short time before being transported to work in factories or on the roads."

In March 1946, after ten months of persistent seeking since the end of the war, the Bushells received the following reply from the Red Cross office in Geneva:

> Comité International de la Croix-Rouge, Agence Centrale des Prisonniers de Guerre, Palais du Conseil-General, Genève.
> Charles G. Bushell, Esq., 18 Burnley Road, Stockwell, London, S.W.9. March 29th, 1946.
>
> Dear Sir—We beg to acknowledge receipt of your letter dated 18th inst., concerning:
>
> Violette *SZABO*, taken prisoner in June 1944.
>
> We regret very much to say that we cannot give you any information on your daughter, but, as the inquiries have been taken up by the British Authorities themselves since the cessation of hostilities, we have sent your lines together with the newspaper cutting, to the British Red Cross in London and they shall answer you direct.

Hoping that you shall soon have some news, we beg to remain . . .

That same month some of the newspapers, approached again by the Bushells, published a picture of little Tania, now aged three and a half. She was shown gazing at a photograph of her mother. Under it were these words: 'Wondering, she gazes at a picture of her missing mother'. Her imprisonment at Ravensbrück was then referred to and the caption added: 'Since then nothing has been heard of her, and the War Office thinks the chances of her being still alive are "extremely remote". But her parents, Mr and Mrs C. G. Bushell, of Burnley Road, Stockwell, SW, refuse to give up hope'.

Among those who saw this picture was Mrs Julie Barry, living at Nettlebed in Oxfordshire. She told the *News of the World* that she was in Guernsey when the Germans came and that she had been taken to Germany as a prisoner.

"At Ravensbrück," she said, "I was made a prison policewoman and given the number 39785 and a red band with letters on it to indicate my status.

"I was handed a heavy leather belt with instructions to beat the other women prisoners. It was a hateful task, but in it I saw my only chance to help some of the condemned women."

She claimed to be the last person to see Violette alive, the last person to speak to her.

"It was this camp into which three British parachutists were brought. One was Violette Szabo. They were in rags, their faces black with dirt, and their hair matted. They were starving. They had been tortured in attempts to wrest from them secrets of the invasion, but I am certain they gave nothing away.

"Mrs Szabo told me all about herself—about her dead soldier husband and her child, to whom she was devoted. I think that she and her two companions knew they had been brought to Ravensbrück to die. Even among the thousands of women in the camp these three were outstanding. They were British and the Germans knew it. Nothing could break their spirit.

"One morning came the order for the three of them to go to

the Commandant's office. Mrs Szabo walked unaided. The other two were carried. Many of the inmates wanted to die, but Mrs Szabo and her companions wanted to live to tell the world how they had been treated."

The War Office immediately sent two men to interview Mrs Barry. Mrs Bushell was later asked if she would care to see the woman herself, but she flatly refused to speak to anyone who had been a camp policewoman at Ravensbrück.

Was this statement of hers correct? Mr and Mrs Bushell could not believe that their daughter was dead.

Vera Atkins meanwhile had set out on her personal search for news of those secret agents who were still missing. In the course of her wanderings in Europe she visited the jail at Minden where many who had been in positions of authority at Ravensbrück were awaiting their trial. On April 13th, 1946, she saw Johann Schwarzhuber, the camp Führer. He had been second in command at Ravensbrück, but the Commandant Fritz Sühren had anticipated the coming of the Russians by taking Odette Churchill across to the Allied lines in the hope that he might obtain his own freedom in exchange for her deliverance. He was, however, arrested, but managed to escape.

Schwarzhuber had been interrogated since his arrest, but so far had declined to say anything except that he was not personally responsible for what had happened. He had been acting under orders from his superiors, he said, and quite often his subordinates had acted on their own initiative.

Vera Atkins, after a prolonged attempt at trying to make the man speak, said: "I am greatly concerned about three girls who were in your camp at Ravensbrück. But you are running true to type, Schwarzhuber. Once you were pleased to have your rank and the responsibility it conferred. Today you deny all knowledge of what was done. It amazes me that you should do so.

"I shall leave you now, but in a few hours I shall be back. I want you to think about it, Schwarzhuber. I am not saying 'Try to remember'. You remember all right. You could not possibly forget. I am asking you to think about what I have said."

As she turned to go, he lowered his eyes. He was a dark, squat man, with tired eyes behind his pince-nez.

"All right," he said. "I'll tell you." He thereupon made a statement. It was brief. He said:

I declare that I remember that I had delivered to me towards the end of January 1945, an order from the German Secret Police countersigned by the Camp Commandant Sühren, instructing me to ascertain the location of the following persons —Lillian Rolfe, Danielle Williams [Williams was her code name; her real name was Bloch], Violette Szabo. These were at that time in the dependent camp of Königsberg on the Oder and were recalled by me. When they returned to the Camp they were placed in the punishment block and moved from there into the block of cells.

One evening, towards 1900 hours, they were called out and taken to the cemetery yard by the crematorium. Camp Commandant Sühren made these arrangements. He read out the order for their shooting in the presence of the Chief Camp Doctor, Dr Trommer, SS Sergeant Zappe, SS Lance-Corporal Schult or Schulee [a block leader from the men's camp], SS Corporal Schenk [in command of the crematorium], Dentist Dr Hellinger. I was myself present.

The shooting was done by Schult with a small-calibre gun through the back of the neck. They were brought forward singly by Corporal Schenk. Death was certified by Dr Trommer. The corpses were removed singly by internees who were employed in the crematorium and burnt. The clothes were burnt with the bodies.

I accompanied the three women to the crematorium yard. A female camp overseer was also present and was sent back when we reached the crematorium. Zappe stood guard over them while they were waiting to be shot.

All three were very brave and I was deeply moved. Sühren was also impressed by the bearing of these women. He was annoyed that the Gestapo did not themselves carry out these shootings.

I recognise with certainty the photograph of Danielle Williams and I think I recognise the photograph of Lillian Rolfe. I know that the third had the name of Violette.

I am prepared to make this declaration under oath. Read, found correct and signed of my own free will.

Vera Atkins took it down in German. "You realise," she said, "that this is deeply incriminating."

He said he did. She then signed it too and it was entered as his deposition at the trial.

It will be noticed in this statement that there were some officials as well as some internees and at least one other attendant present. That there was talk of it afterwards in the camp is clear from what Mrs Julie Barry said in the interview published in the newspapers. Schwarzhuber told Vera Atkins in the course of a short talk afterwards that Lillian Rolfe was ill and could not walk. She was suffering apparently from lung trouble and had to be assisted to the place of execution. A sketch showing a part of the camp, the block of cells where the three girls were confined and their place of execution, was made by Vera Atkins with the guidance of Schwarzhuber. It shows that quite a long walk was necessary. They had to go from the cells through the camp, past the kitchen and the wash-room, up to the massive gate leading out of the camp; then on the outer side of the walls a correspondingly long walk had to be undertaken all the way down again to a point opposite the cells in the Bunker. Here, on a grass patch adjoining the crematorium, the girls were executed. Mrs Julie Barry persists that two of the girls had to be carried on stretchers and only Violette was able to walk. "On each face," she adds, "was a look of contempt for the guards."

Violette, they say, was the last to be executed and had to suffer the agony of seeing her friends put to death, aware all the time that the same fate awaited her. She did not flinch. Her spirit was indomitable. Again and again in the past, when all seemed lost, she had fought her way out—with her wits at Rouen, with a gun, despite overwhelming odds, at Salon-la-Tour, where she rose again after her injury and fought even when they came to seize her. Even in captivity she tried repeatedly to break away so that, returning, she could fight on. But now there seemed to be no way out at all. With such power as still remained to them, the Germans, encircling her here with guards, held her at their mercy.

It was her turn now. Lifting her head with haughty scorn, she walked the last few paces to her death.

Schwarzhuber was sentenced to death after his trial at Hamburg and was hanged. Fritz Sühren, a fugitive for some years, was caught eventually, tried and also executed.

CHAPTER TWENTY-ONE

TANIA PUTS ON HER PARTY DRESS

FOLLOWING Vera Atkins' talk with Schwarzhuber, the War Office, able at last to supply facts, wrote instantly to Mr and Mrs Bushell.

> We have now obtained from an eyewitness news of her fate. This witness was the camp overseer who is now under arrest. Mrs Szabo, together with two friends, was executed by shooting one evening by special command of the German Secret Police. The witness has testified that the bearing of the three women was of the highest order and greatly impressed all those that performed or who were present at the execution. Death was instantaneous and the body was immediately cremated.
>
> In giving this news to you, news which I know must be very difficult to bear, I should like to offer on behalf of this Branch my own very sincere sympathies. You must be very proud of the way your daughter maintained her calm dignified courage throughout her ordeal. It is testimony of that courage that she impressed and moved even those responsible for her death.

The news was of course shattering, coming as it did after months of hope, however slender it may often have seemed. They were appalled by the cold-blooded and barbaric manner of her execution and the complete senselessness of it all. Without any pretence at a trial, she had been brought back all the way from Königsberg to Ravensbrück and killed just as the war was about to end, when she was no longer in a position to endanger any plans of the German High Command. Why, they asked themselves again and again, why this deliberate and quite brutal murder? Why were these three English girls singled out for execution from among the thousands of other prisoners in the camp? An intense hate had been fostered by the German hierarchy against the British throughout the long years of war, born no doubt of the realisation that only British stubbornness had denied them their triumph and caused their country to be now in ruins. In part this was responsible for the British prisoners being treated far more harshly than the rest. But not all the British women in Ravensbrück, although a mere handful, were executed. The ones singled out to die were those who had been made to suffer the most atrocious tortures, and that apparently was what the Germans wanted to cover up. Their aim was to obliterate the evidence that these women would be able to give of their vile and brutal behaviour. If they were allowed to live, much would be revealed and many in authority now would undoubtedly be called to account by the victors. Thus, when the tide turned, the order went forth and to it was attached a list of names. The list was scrutinised carefully. The location of those on it had to be ascertained, as Schwarzhuber revealed in his statement. Odette was spared because it was felt that the name of Churchill might be of some value at the eventual reckoning.

And so, during the days and nights of darkness she had to endure in the Bunker—in an underground cell now which was kept in total darkness so that when the light was suddenly switched on, as an eye was applied to the peep-hole, it was quite blinding—Violette must have known that the end was very near. She heard the firing squads at their fell work only a few yards from where she lay, and she breathed in the suffocating smoke from the crematorium on the other side of the wall. Often she heard screams when the crematorium doors were opened, which suggests that some at least of those thrust into it were still alive, despite the assurance given by Schwarzhuber to the court about a doctor examining the bodies after execution.

With the passage of time the parental hurt was assuaged a little and their hearts were filled with a great pride at the courage and the vast capacity of endurance of their daughter. The adventurousness of her spirit in childhood, her unshakeable will, her moments of defiance were illumined now with a new light.

From Colonel Buckmaster, chief of the French Section of

SOE, they received a warm personal letter, in the course of which he said:

> I felt I must write to you at this time, now that more has been learned of Violette's heroic behaviour, to tell you how much we all admired her and how magnificently she upheld the tradition of the French Section, of which we were all very proud.
>
> There are just two facts about Violette's work which you, maybe, do not yet know. The first was her courageous defence of her Headquarters. We know that she fought the Gestapo, armed only with a Sten gun. . . . She went on firing until she was exhausted.
>
> The second incident was in the train which took her, and a large number of other prisoners of both sexes, to Germany. Between Compiégne and Saarbrücken, the RAF bombed and machine-gunned the train. The German guards, in panic, locked the prisoners in and took shelter. Violette managed to get into the corridor of the train, and, together with another girl, took water to the men who were in another carriage at the far end of the train.
>
> This valiant action greatly cheered the prisoners. We were very proud that Violette took this gallant initiative: British prestige was even further enhanced by her action.
>
> I hope these two incidents will help you to regard with great and legitimate pride the magnificent record of your daughter, who was very dear also to us.

Later that year came the posthumous award of honours. On December 17th, 1946, Violette was gazetted for the George Cross—the first British woman ever to receive it. The citation, though written eighteen months after the war had ended, was based apparently on information officially available in London at the time. There is no mention in it of the ambush at Salon-la-Tour and the chase of close on two miles across the countryside, but it refers instead to a house in which she and 'other members (plural) of her group' were surrounded by the Gestapo. The citation states:

Madame Szabo volunteered to undertake a particularly dangerous mission in France. She was parachuted into France in April 1944, and undertook the task with enthusiasm. In her execution of the delicate researches entailed she showed great presence of mind and astuteness She was twice arrested by the German security authorities, but each time managed to get away. Eventually, however, with other members of her group, she was surrounded by the Gestapo in a house in the south-west of France. Resistance appeared hopeless, but Madame Szabo, seizing a Sten gun and as much ammunition as she could carry, barricaded herself in part of the house, and, exchanging shot for shot with the enemy, killed or wounded several of them. By constant movement she avoided being cornered and fought until she dropped exhausted. She was arrested and had to undergo solitary confinement. She was then continuously and atrociously tortured, but never by word or deed gave away any of her acquaintances, or told the enemy anything of value. She was ultimately executed. Madame Szabo gave a magnificent example of courage and steadfastness.

It is by no means unusual for an official citation to need revising in the light of subsequent information. There have indeed been instances when, the fresh facts warranting it, a higher award has been made in place of the one conferred earlier. In the case of Violette Szabo it is felt by those who have examined the new evidence that, in view of the fact that there are many witnesses still alive who saw her heroic battle against the swarming hordes of the Das Reich SS Panzer division at Salon-la-Tour, and also because of her act of mercy to the prisoners in the railway train conveying them to Germany when, under fire, she brought water again and again, manacled though she was, to the suffering prisoners, she ought to be awarded the Victoria Cross. Dame Irene Ward, MP, has been persistently advocating that this award should be made.

The Croix de Guerre was awarded posthumously by the French Government early in 1947.

On January 28th, 1947, Mr and Mrs Bushell and Violette's daughter were invited to Buckingham Palace to receive the George

Cross from the King. For days beforehand Tania, who was four and a half and too young to understand what had happened to her mother, applied herself strenuously to learning how to curtsy—'skirty' she called it. The pretty French frock which her mother had bought for her at the Trois Quartiers in Paris during her first mission was brought out and ironed with immense pride by Mrs Bushell on the kitchen table, while Tania watched, her chin resting on the edge of the table, her eyes wide with wonder. She was about to wear it at her first party.

The King seemed to know every detail of Violette's great heroism. He told her parents about incidents of which they had not yet heard. He then handed the George Cross to Tania. "It is for your mother. Take great care of it," he said.

Turning to Mr and Mrs Bushell he added: "I don't think I would have had the courage to do what your wonderful daughter did. She really had remarkably great courage."

As they emerged from the palace, photographers surrounded little Tania and asked her to show them the George Cross. She opened the box. The cameras clicked. One of the photographers said: "How wonderful! What a great honour."

"It's for Mummy," said Tania. "I'll keep it for her till she comes home."